634:582.475 STE

A3079

WITHDRAWN

THE RESOURCE CENTRE, SPARSHOLT COLLEGE, HAMPSHIRE

ACCESSION No: 011373

CLASS NUMBER: 634 : 582.475 STE

WITHDRAWN

THE NATIVE PINEWOODS
OF SCOTLAND

WITHDRAWN

THE NATIVE PINEWOODS
OF SCOTLAND

BY

H. M. STEVEN
PROFESSOR OF FORESTRY
UNIVERSITY OF ABERDEEN

AND

A. CARLISLE
RESEARCH FELLOW
UNIVERSITY OF ABERDEEN

FIRST PUBLISHED 1959

COPYRIGHT © 1959 H. M. STEVEN AND A. CARLISLE

Printed and bound in Great Britain by Hartnolls Limited, Bodmin, Cornwall

PREFACE

THIS BOOK is about the native and natural pinewoods of Scotland, and discusses them from the historical, the ecological, and the forestry point of view. These woodlands are often called the Caledonian Forest. The evidence presented in this volume shows that the surviving native pinewoods are the lineal descendants of those of early post-glacial times. Their predecessors had been growing for several millennia when Ptolemy first used the name Caledonian Forest early in the second century A.D. The Caledonian Forest of that and later times, however, did not consist of pinewoods only but also of oakwoods, birchwoods, and alderwoods. These associated communities are discussed in this book, but most of it deals with the pinewoods, hence the reason for selecting the more appropriate if less romantic title.

These woodlands are of great interest, and not only to the specialist. Even to walk through the larger of them gives one a better idea of what a primeval forest was like than can be got from any other woodland scene in Britain. The trees range in age up to 300 years in some instances, and there are thus not very many generations between their earliest predecessors about 9000 years ago and those growing today; to stand in them is to feel the past. Moreover, they contain their own distinctive plants and animals, some of which are rarely found elsewhere in Britain. The native pinewoods are also of practical importance to the forester today. He wants the best strains of the different tree species he uses, and the pine in these woodlands have persisted through successive generations, often under adverse conditions, and retained their health and vigour. The different strains in these woodlands are described. Not all are useful from the silvicultural point of view, but some are, and will form part of our future woodlands in other parts of this country and indeed in other countries. They remain important and valuable tree material which should not be contaminated by non-indigenous strains. From every point of view, therefore, these woodlands should be preserved and perpetuated. It is hoped that the publication of this book will create a new interest in them, and that their different owners, public and private, will co-operate in carrying out investigations into the best methods of protecting them and securing their perpetuation.

The aim in this investigation was to include only pinewoods which have been regenerated naturally from ancestors of like origin. A number of criteria of varying validity were used to determine this, and these are stated in Chapter 1.

This volume has been written by Professor H. M. Steven and Dr A. Carlisle in collaboration. It is based on investigations carried out from 1950 to 1956. These were initiated and supervised by Professor Steven, except for the work on the morphological variations of the pine, which was supervised by Dr E. V. Laing, Reader in Forestry in the University of Aberdeen. Dr Carlisle carried out the field and laboratory work, and Chapters 12 to 17 are based on an unpublished thesis, part of the requirements for the Ph.D. degree awarded to him by the University of Aberdeen in 1954.

The investigations could not have been carried out nor the book written without the co-operation and help of a large number of people. We wish to express sincere thanks to all of them. Special mention must first be made of the owners who gave permission for the studies in their woodlands. The name of the owner at the time of the investigation of each individual forest is given in Chapters 4 to 11. In many instances also help was given by their factors, foresters, and gamekeepers. The Forestry Commissioners gave generous financial help to enable the investigation to be carried out. A number of their officers were also helpful. In particular, we wish to mention Mr James Macdonald, c.b.e., Director of Research, for his continued interest in the work, for reading the manuscript, and making a number of valuable suggestions; and Mr James Fraser, o.b.e., Conservator until 1956 of the North Conservancy, in which many of the native pinewoods are located. Dr W. D. Simpson, o.b.e., Librarian, University of Aberdeen, gave much help on the sources of historical information and kindly read the manuscript of pages 39-60. Sir James Fergusson of Kilkerran, Bt., Keeper of the Records of Scotland, and Dr C. T. McInnes, Curator of Historical Records, gave facilities and help in the Scottish Record Office, Edinburgh. Professor T. C. Phemister, Geology Department, University of Aberdeen, kindly read pages 6-19, Dr W. E. Fraser, of the same department, pages 65-66, and Mr S. E. Durno, Macaulay Institute for Soil Research, pages 26-38. Dr C. Gimingham, Botany Department, University of Aberdeen, gave help in the identification of some of the plant material, particularly mosses. Mr James Barnetson prepared the maps and diagrams, which in the cases of Figures 13 to 37 inclusive, are based upon the Ordnance Survey 1″ maps of these areas and are here reproduced with the sanction of the Controller of H.M. Stationery Office, Crown Copyright reserved, and Miss E. M. Robson gave valuable secretarial assistance.

The following works have been followed in the nomenclature of plants and animals, and the authorities for the naming of individual species have, therefore, been omitted from the text: Conifers, Dallimore, W. and Jackson, A. B., *Handbook of the Coniferae*, 4th edn. London 1954; herbs, shrubs, broad-leaved trees, and ferns, Clapham, A. R., Tutin, T. G., and Warburg, E. F., *Flora of the British Isles*, Cambridge 1952; mosses, Richards, P. W. and Wallace, E. C., "An annotated list of British mosses," in *Transactions of the British Bryological Soc.*, 1 (4), Appendix, p. i, Cambridge 1950; liverworts, Watson, E. V., *British Mosses and Liverworts*, Cambridge 1955; lichens, Smith, A. L., *A Monograph of the British Lichens*, London 1918; fungi, Brooks, F. T., *Plant Diseases*, 2nd edn. London, New York and Toronto 1953; mammals, Matthews, L. H., *British Mammals*, London 1952; birds, *Check list of the birds of Great Britain and Ireland*, British Ornithologists' Union, London 1952, with corrections as recommended in *Ibis*, 98 (1956), p. 157; amphibians and reptiles, Smith, M., *The British Amphibians and Reptiles*, London 1951; insects, Kloet, G. S. and Hincks, W. D., *A check list of British insects*, Stockport, 1945.

H. M. STEVEN
A. CARLISLE

Department of Forestry
University of Aberdeen

April 1957

CONTENTS

ILLUSTRATIONS

PLATES

TEXT-FIGURES

KEY TO FIGS. 13 – 37

 Predominantly native and natural Scots pine

 Scots pine of native origin but probably planted

 Scots pine of native origin amongst planted conifers

 Plantations of conifers

 Birchwoods with or without scattered individual trees or groups of native Scots pine

 Oakwoods

Woods of birch and oak

P ◢ Scattered pine

B Scattered birch

O Scattered oak

B/P Scattered birch and pine

B/O Scattered birch and oak

B/O/P Scattered birch, oak, and pine

+ Natural regeneration of Scots pine

CHAPTER 1

THE NATURAL DISTRIBUTION OF SCOTS PINE

General Distribution

SCOTS PINE (*Pinus silvestris*) is the most widely distributed conifer in the world (see Fig. 1). It is found growing naturally from the Atlantic sea-board in the west, across Europe and Asia, to the vicinity of the Pacific Ocean in the east, and from beyond the Arctic Circle in Scandinavia to the Mediterranean. Its altitudinal range is from sea-level to about 8000 ft. (2400 m.), and, while like other widely distributed plants in the northern hemisphere it reaches its highest altitudinal limit towards the southern part of its range, it is found nevertheless up to 3500 ft. (1050 m.) on the Jotunheimen in Norway (Mork, 1954), and goes down to about 670 ft. (200 m.) in northern Italy (Pavari, 1955), the Balkans (Anić, 1954), and Turkey (Irmak, 1954).

Its extreme northern limit is in the coastal districts of Finnmark in Norway at 70° 29′ N. and about 25° E. (Enquist, 1933; Robak, 1954), and it reaches about 70° N. in Sweden (Enquist, 1933; Sylven, 1916) and Finland (Ilvessalo, 1949). Beyond the last pine in Norway, there is a fringe of birch (*Betula pubescens*) before the tundra is reached. In European Russia, the extreme northerly limit is on the Finnish border, north-west of the town of Murmansk, at about 69° 30′ N., and there are extensive forests of pine with spruce (*Picea*) and birch to the west of the White Sea and also eastwards towards the Urals, in places extending beyond the Arctic Circle. In Siberia, Scots pine is also found at about this latitude at Salekhard near the south-west tip of the Gulf of Ob and on the River Taz, near Kureyka, but the species does not form extensive pine forest farther north than about 65° N. (anon., 1937; Kruberg, 1937). The larches, *L. sibirica* in the west and *L. gmelini* in the east, extend to much higher latitudes, being more resistant to winds from the Arctic in winter, and *L. gmelini* reaches the highest latitude of any tree species in the world at 72° 23′ N., 105° E. according to Kimble and Good (1955), but at about 114° E. on the Map of the Forests of the U.S.S.R. (Malev, 1955).

Scots pine reaches its absolute southern limit as a native species in the Sierra Nevada in Spain at about 37° N., where it grows up to 8000 ft. (2400 m.). It is found also on the mountain ranges above Valencia, Barcelona, and the Costa Brava (Rubner, 1953; Schreiner, 1956; Vazquez, 1947). In France, its southern limit is in the Maritime Alps, where it is found up to about 6650 ft. (2000 m.) (Mouillefert, 1892-8). In northern Italy, it is a native species in the Alps, Prealps, and in a few places on the Appenines of Liguria and Emilia, reaching its southern limit in Italy in the latter province at about 44° 30′ N. In the Alps, it is found as a sporadic species almost to the tree line at about 6650 ft. (2000 m.), and forms forest below 5330 ft. (1600 m.), while it mingles with sweet chestnut (*Castanea sativa*) at only 670 ft. (200 m.) in parts of Lombardy and Piedmont (Pavari, 1955; Susmel, 1954). In Yugoslavia, while it is not an important timber tree because it does not form large or pure stands, it is distributed from the Austrian Alps in the north along the Dinaric Massif to the south, although not continuously; the most important region is in the watersheds of the rivers Bosna and Drina (Anić, 1954). Its distribution extends into Macedonia, Bulgaria, and northern Greece, but in the latter country its natural range and extent is small (Kossenakis, 1954). Across the Bosphorus, Scots pine is again found between about 670 ft. (200 m.) and 6650 ft. (2000 m.) as in Italy, for example on the mountains along the north coast of Turkey, and sporadically up to 8000 ft. (2400 m.) in north-east Anatolia (Irmak, 1954); it has been discovered recently in south-east Turkey in the neighbourhood of Pinarbasi, at 38° 34′ N. (Kayacik, 1954). On the north side of the Black Sea, Scots pine comes as far south as about 49° N. in the Ukraine (anon. 1937; Kruberg, 1937); it has been stated to be native on the Crimea (Beissner, 1930), and the species is shown near Yalta on the Map of the Forests of the U.S.S.R. (Malev, 1955). The Scots pine is found also in the Caucasus (Beissner, 1930; Grossheim, 1939; Gulisasvili, 1951), and is probably native in Azerbaijan, while cones of this species are a feature of early Iranian royal sculptures, although it is no longer native in Iran, except perhaps on the Russo-Iranian border to the west of the Caspian Sea. In the Volga region it only reaches about 53° N., and in the Urals 50°, but in the Kazakh Uplands in south-west Siberia it comes a few degrees farther south. The southern limit in Siberia continues easterwards at about 50° N., and there are large pine forests in the uplands of Irkutsk, near Lake Baikal (anon., 1937; Kruberg, 1937). Its south-eastern limit extends along the Soviet border into the north-eastern provinces of China. There are definite records of this species in the lowlands of the Amur River valley at about 53° N., in the foothills of the Great Khingan Mountains at 45° N. around Lake Khanka, and in the Ern Tao Ho valley; in the Khingan Mountains Scots pine woodlands adjoin the Mongolian grasslands (Wang, 1954).

The extreme western limit of Scots pine is in some doubt. It is said to be spontaneous in the Sierra do Gerez in northern Portugal (Eliseu, 1942), but whether truly indigenous or sub-spontaneous is not known. It is native, however, at about 7° W. in the Cantabrian Mountains in the north-west of Spain (Rubner, 1953; Vazquez, 1947). The next most westerly limit is in Scotland at Shieldaig in Wester Ross, 5° 37′ W.

There is also some doubt about the absolute eastern limit of Scots pine. In a number of older works (Loudon, 1838; Watson, 1832), and repeated recently (Clapham, 1952), it is stated to be in Kamchatka on the Pacific at about 160° E. It was not found in this region, however, during a botanical expedition in 1927, although *Pinus pumila* was listed (Hulten, 1927), nor is it shown on the Map of the Forests of the U.S.S.R. (Malev, 1955). The species has been recorded at Okhotsk on the Okhotsk Sea at 143° E. and there may be outlying stations on that coast (Kruberg, 1937), but the Scots pine forests do not extend much beyond 138° E.

Within these limits Scots pine is widely, but by no means continuously, distributed. It occurs throughout the Scandinavian countries, except Denmark where it is not now native. Elsewhere in western Europe it is largely confined to the higher elevations, for example in the Vosges, Auvergne, Pyrenees, and Spanish Sierras, but it is an important native species from Middle Europe eastwards through Poland to Russia. In the latter country and in Siberia, while there are many extensive areas where Scots pine is the principal dominant, these are discontinuous and often separated by long distances (anon., 1937; Malev, 1955; Rubner, 1953).

Within that enormous area there are the most diverse climates, and Scots pine is clearly one of the most adaptable of tree species. In Scotland and western Norway the climate is oceanic, with rainfalls often exceeding 70 in. (1780 mm.), while in Siberia there are extreme continental climates, and towards the north-easterly limit of its distribution rainfalls below 8 in. (200 mm.) have been recorded (Kruberg, 1937). The species can survive very low winter temperatures, for example – 83° F. (– 64° C.) in the region of the Verkhoyansk Mountains in Eastern Siberia, the so-called "cold pole" of the world, and it grows where the subsoil is permanently frozen (Kruberg, 1937), but it persists also at relatively low altitudes in Mediterranean lands. Its distribution as a whole indicates that it is a tree of continental climates, and its phenology, with early cessation of shoot elongation in summer, suggests that it evolved under such a climate. Its associated species may show a like contrast, ranging from pubescent birch and Siberian larch at or beyond the Arctic Circle to sweet chestnut in Italy. Some of its associates, however, have a like adaptability to contrasting conditions. It is curious that *Prunus padus* should be in some of the Scottish native pinewoods and be recorded with Scots pine in north China (Wang, 1954). *Vaccinium myrtillus* and *V. vitis-idaea* may be equally typical plants in the field layer of Scottish and Scandinavian pinewoods and those of Siberia (Kruberg, 1937).

DISTRIBUTION IN SCOTLAND

While some ecologists, for example Godwin (1956), have expressed the view that a few Scots pine in England, on sites such as bogs, may be relics of the pinewoods of earlier post-glacial time and hence truly indigenous, and the same view may be postulated for Ireland, the only truly native and natural pinewoods in Britain are in Scotland, in the region north of the Firths of Forth and Clyde (see Fig. 2). Moreover, it is probable that this has been so during most, if not all, of historic time.

All the pinewoods and groups of trees which have been considered native and natural at various times have been investigated. It has not always been easy to determine whether a pinewood is genuinely native, that is, descended from one generation to another by natural means, because it is known from the *Black Book of Taymouth* that Scots pine was planted on some scale in the region of its present natural distribution in Scotland from at least about 1600. A number of criteria have been used to determine the status of the woodlands. First, in many instances there are historical records going back to the eighteenth, and sometimes the seventeenth and sixteenth centuries; if there were old and reputedly natural pine-woods at that time, it is almost certain that they and their predecessors were not planted. Secondly, the age structure of the present woodlands provides some evidence, because the native pinewoods of any size are to some extent uneven-aged. The associated field layer communities may be a little help, but are not in themselves conclusive, because some of the plantations may be on the sites of earlier native pinewoods. The range of morphological variations in the Scots pine is an important criterion, because it has been found that the trees in the native pinewoods show greater individual variation than trees in plantations, no doubt because during the collection of seed to raise plants for the latter some selection was made. Finally, in some very inaccessible places, it is almost certain that no one would have planted woods. Taking all these criteria together, it has been possible to come to a definite conclusion in almost all instances, and where there has been doubt, such pinewoods have been excluded. In a few instances, groups or scattered trees have been considered native, but the number of trees was too small to constitute a community, and they have not been described in detail or listed below; but they are mentioned in Chapters 4 to 11 where all the evidence is given.

The native pinewoods have been put into eight geographical groups (see Fig. 2).

The latitudinal distribution of the existing native pinewoods in Scotland is from Glen Einig (No. 30) in Ross and Cromarty, 57° 57′ N., to Glen Falloch (No. 35) in Perthshire, 56° 22′ N. The most easterly native pinewood wood is Glentanar (No. 1), Aberdeenshire, 2° 53′ W., and the most westerly Shieldaig (No. 27) in Ross and Cromarty, 5° 38′ W.

The highest living Scots pine found was a stunted tree, about a foot (30·5 cm.) in height, at 2800 ft. (840 m.) on Sron Riach on the south-eastern shoulder of Ben Macdhui in the Cairngorm Mountains and north-west of Mar (No. 3). The highest pine community, however, is much lower, at 2050 ft. (615 m.) on Craig Fhiaclach in Rothiemurchus (No. 5). At the other extreme there are native pine-woods growing at practically sea-level at Shieldaig (No. 27) and Barisdale (No. 15), and the upper limit there is only 1000 ft. (300 m.). In Deeside and Speyside, where the tree line reaches its highest limit under the shelter of the Cairngorm Mountains, the pinewoods are upland communities, while in the other groups, and particularly the more westerly and northerly, pinewoods are at much lower altitudes. This depression in altitudinal limit in the more oceanic climate of the west is shared by other species, and mountain plants may be found almost at sea-level.

CHAPTER 2

THE HISTORY OF THE NATIVE PINEWOODS AND OTHER FOREST COMMUNITIES IN SCOTLAND

Although what we know now as Scotland had a long forest history before the glaciations during the Pleistocene or Quaternary period, our present-day natural forest communities have only taken form since that time.

The Pleistocene Glaciations

In order to understand the history of the post-glacial immigration and development of our tree communities, it is necessary to outline what is known about the glaciations during the Pleistocene period, not only as it affected Britain but in Europe and elsewhere.

The study of glacial geology in Scotland began with Jamieson's classic paper published in 1862, and two British geologists, James Geikie (1894) and W. B. Wright (1937) have summarised the knowledge available in their time. Recently Charlesworth (1957) has dealt exhaustively with the Quaternary era. From the beginning of such studies, the Pleistocene glaciations have been viewed in their relationship to the development of man and his cultures. The increase in the tempo of archaeological research in recent years has thus stimulated study, particularly of the correlation of the phases in the different regions and in the dating of these phases. Such trends are clearly shown, for example, in recent books by Movius (1942), Zeuner (1952) and Lacaille (1954).

It has been accepted by most glacial geologists that during the Pleistocene epoch in Europe and elsewhere there were not one but several glaciations, separated by interglacial periods of varying duration, when the climate was favourable for at least the present-day tree flora. It is relevant, however, to consider first of all the maximum extent of glaciation during the whole period, because although it may not have taken place everywhere at the same time, it indicates the possible refuges where the tree flora survived, and from whence it emigrated both in interglacial and post-glacial times.

In Europe, the principal accumulation of ice was centred in the northern part of the Gulf of Finland, and the ice-sheets spread outwards into the Atlantic Ocean in the west, the Arctic Ocean in the north, and for greater distances southwards and eastwards (Charlesworth, 1957). There were also centres of accumulation in the British Isles, and the ice from them met the Scandinavian ice in the eastern coastal regions of Britain during more than one epoch. During the period of maximum glaciation, the southern limit of the ice in Britain was roughly the Thames-Severn line (see Fig. 3). Most of what is now Holland and the north German plain was covered, and the northern ice reached almost to the barrier of the Riesen Gebirge, the Tatra Mountains, and the Carpathians. In European Russia, the ice sheet extended below lat. 50°, and occupied the valleys of the Dnieper and the Don, but there was a large unglaciated region between them; the line then passed near Gorki to the River Kama. The northern part of the Urals formed a separate centre of dispersion (Flint, 1957; Wills, 1951). Beyond the Urals, the Siberian Ice Sheet occupied a large area in the north-west of Siberia, and, during maximum glaciation, this ice-sheet extended south of lat. 60° between the Urals and the Yenisei River, but farther east it turned northwards round the Puturan Mountains, reaching the Arctic Ocean a little west of long. 120° E. A second centre of glaciation was on the higher land of the Central Siberian Plateau at about the latitude of the Arctic Circle, but it was neither extensive nor continuous with the other glaciated regions. The third centre was in the mountainous region in north-east Siberia, the limits being approximately the Lena River in the west, a region east of the Bering Strait in the east, the Arctic Ocean in the north, and the Sea of Okhotsk at about lat. 60° in the south (Flint, 1957).

The conditions that caused the glacial phase in northern lands also led to intensified glaciations in the mountain regions farther south. The principal of these was in the Alps, which is classic ground in the study of the Pleistocene glaciations. Here Penck and Brückner (1909) differentiated four glaciations, Günz, Mindel, Riss, and Würm, separated by interglacial periods. These were not all single advances of the glaciers; the Würm, for example, was divided into three sub-stages, separated by interstadial periods. During the period of maximum glaciation in the Alps, the snow line was almost 4330 ft. (1300 m.) lower than at present. At one time the glaciers almost reached the Danube in places and there is evidence that, to the north but not to the south of the glaciers, there were extensive areas of tundra and loess steppe. There were also relatively minor extensions of the glaciers in the Pyrenees, the Caucasus, and other mountain regions (Charlesworth, 1957; Flint, 1957; Wright, 1937; Zeuner, 1952).

It has been calculated that at the maximum of the Pleistocene glaciation, about

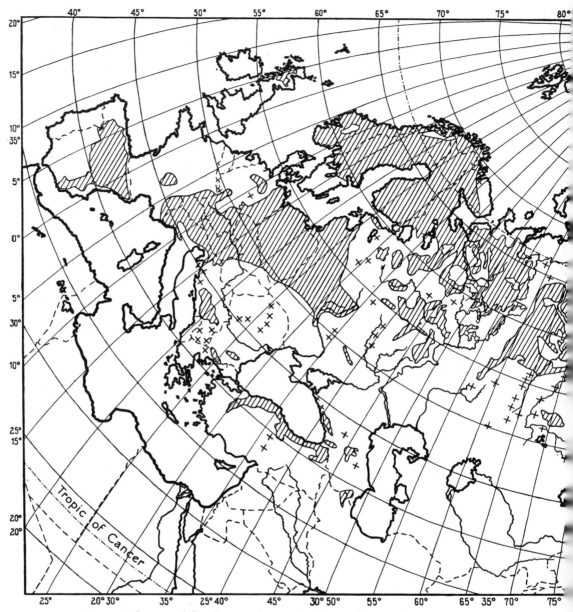

FIG. 1.   The natural distribution of Scots pine (*Pinus silvestris* L.) in Europe and Asia, based on the authorities given in Chapter 1. The hatched areas are the major regions of natural distribution and the crosses (+) the minor.

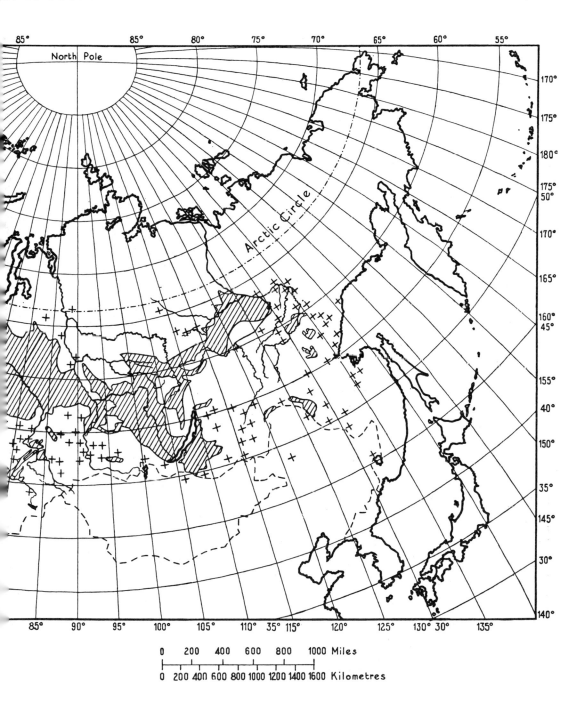

North Pole

Arctic Circle

0   200   400   600   800   1000 Miles

0   200 400 600 800 1000 1200 1400 1600   Kilometres

32 per cent. of the land surface of the world was covered with ice, compared with about 10 per cent. today. Moreover, there were extensive regions of outwash sedimentation and tundra beyond the ice sheets. On the other hand, the locking up of immense volumes of water in the ice-sheets led to a fall in the sea-level during glacial phases, which exposed areas of the continental shelves estimated to have added two to three per cent. to the land area of the world at the period of maximum glaciation (Flint, 1957).

During later Tertiary and Quaternary times in Europe the earlier rich tree flora became progressively impoverished, some of the Chinese and North American genera that disappeared being *Liriodendron, Ginkgo, Sciadopitys, Sequoia,* and *Taxodium* (Charlesworth, 1957). At the period of maximum glaciation, the surviving tree species, including Scots pine, must have found their principal refuges in Europe in south-west France and the Iberian peninsula in the west, and in the southern Balkans in the east. Charlesworth (1957) has discussed the available evidence. The southern distribution of Scots pine today in Spain, the Balkans, and Asia Minor no doubt dates from this migration southwards. In Siberia the limit of glaciation was farther north, and so is the present-day distribution of Scots pine (see Fig. 1). One possible method of adding to the evidence about the Pleistocene migrations of tree species would be to study the pattern of morphological variations in different species throughout their natural habitat. Evidence of such variations in Scots pine in the native woods in Scotland is presented in Chapters 13 to 17 and compared with the pattern in Sweden, the only other region where similar detailed studies have been made.

GLACIATIONS IN BRITAIN

The general pattern of the successive advances and retreats of the ice-sheets in Britain has been known since the time of James Geikie (1894), and much detail has been added by the work of glacial geologists since that time, but knowledge of the Pleistocene period is still very incomplete.

In the regions of Britain which have been covered with ice, the deposits laid down can be classified broadly into the Older, the Newer, and the Youngest Drifts. The first are to be found in the Midlands of England, the southern boulder clays, denuded and dissected deeply by river valleys. These are the result not of one advance of the ice, but of at least two. They may be correlated with the North German stages, Elster, Saale and Warthe, and the Alpine stages up to Würm I (see Table I). The southern limit of the Newer Drifts is the so-called York Line which in the east probably stopped on the Yorkshire coast (Farrington, 1951), but on the west covered most of Wales. The Youngest Drifts are to be

TABLE I

THE PLEISTOCENE GLACIATIONS IN EUROPE WITH TENTATIVE CORRELATIONS

The following sources have been consulted: Charlesworth (1956, 1957); Lacaille (1954); Movius (1942); Wills (1951); and Zeuner (1952)

Zeuner's Nomenclature	Britain	Fenno-Scandia and North Germany	Alps
	Beginning of post-glacial time	Ragunda stage	
	Moraine or Valley in Scotland	Fenno-Scandian moraines	
	Retreat (Allerød period)	Allerød period	
	Scottish or Highland	Baltic moraines	
	Retreat	Retreat	
Last Glaciation (L. Gl.)	North British including Scottish Readvance	Pomeranian moraines	Würm III
	Retreat	Retreat	
	York Line in England and Strathmore drift in Scotland	Weichsel Brandenburg moraines	Würm II
	Interstadial (Temperate flora in Scotland)	Interstadial	Interstadial
	Early Scottish glaciation and Upper Chalky Boulder-clay in England	Warthe?	Würm I
Last Interglacial (L. Igl.)	Interglacial	Interglacial	Interglacial
Penultimate Glaciation (P. Gl.)	Great Chalky Boulder-clay	Saale	Riss
Penultimate Interglacial (P. Igl.)	Interglacial	Interglacial	Great Interglacial
Ante-penultimate Glaciation (Ap. Gl.)	North Sea Drift	Elster	Mindel
Ante-penultimate Interglacial (Ap. Igl.)	Cromer Forest Bed	Interglacial	Interglacial
Early Glaciation (E. Gl.)	Late Crags	Elbe?	Gunz

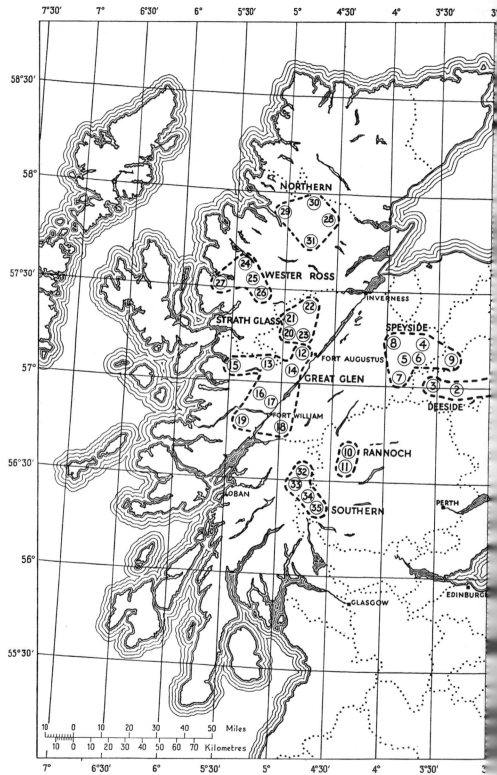

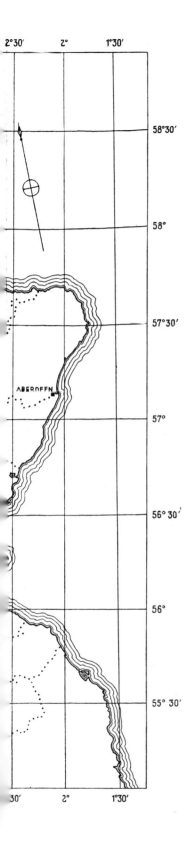

FIG. 2. The natural distribution of Scots pine in Scotland

Deeside
1. Glentanar
2. Ballochbuie
3. Mar

Speyside
4. Abernethy
5. Rothiemurchus
6. Glenmore
7. Glen Feshie
8. Dulnan
9. Glen Avon

Rannoch
10. Black Wood of Rannoch
11. Old Wood of Meggernie, Glen Lyon

Great Glen
12. Glen Moriston
13. Glen Loyne
14. Glengarry
15. Barisdale
16. Loch Arkaig and Glen Mallie
17. Glen Loy
18. Glen Nevis
19. Ardgour

Strath Glass
20. Glen Affric
21. Glen Cannich
22. Glen Strathfarrar
23. Guisachan and Cougie

Wester Ross
24. Loch Maree
25. Coulin
26. Achnashellach
27. Shieldaig

Northern
28. Amat
29. Rhidorroch
30. Glen Einig
31. Strath Vaich

Southern
32. Black Mount
33. Glen Orchy
34. Tyndrum
35. Glen Falloch

found in the Highlands of Scotland, the western Southern Uplands of that country, and in the hills of the Lake District and North Wales. Wills (1951) has recently published maps of the principal epochs based on available information, and Charlesworth (1957) has reviewed the evidence. He (1956) has described and illustrated the closing stages of the last glaciation in Scotland. Fig. 3 gives the approximate areas covered in Britain, based in the main on his views.

In Scotland, the first glaciation for which there is definite evidence has been called the Early Scottish Glaciation. This great ice-sheet moved from its principal centre of distribution in the western Highlands in a general south-easterly direction. It came into contact with the Scandinavian ice on our east coast, and this barrier caused it to divide in the Moray Firth, one stream flowing north and another south (Bremner, 1934 *a* and *b*, 1936). This glaciation, which formed the basal, grey boulder clay in Scotland, is believed to have extended into the Midlands of England, East Anglia and Wales. Although the earliest glaciation of Scotland of which there is as yet definite evidence, it is considered to have come comparatively late in Pleistocene times, being phase one of the Last Glaciation in Zeuner's (1952) terminology; it may be that it is correlated with Würm I in the Alps and Warthe in North Germany (Lacaille, 1954; Movius, 1942) (see Table I). If this view is correct, this glaciation must have swept away the deposits of any earlier glaciations in Scotland.

This ice-sheet then retreated northwards. In Scotland it is probable that the ice did not disappear from the western Highlands, but a polleniferous peat bed has been found in the Burn of Benholm, Kincardineshire, between the grey boulder clay and the succeeding Strathmore drift. Pine pollen was dominant in the lower layers and birch in the upper, and there was some oak and alder pollen throughout (Campbell, 1934). In peat at Cowdon Burn, Ayrshire, and elsewhere in the Midland Valley of Scotland, pine, birch, and hazel have been found in what is believed to be a similar horizon (Lacaille, 1954). In the period after this Early Scottish glaciation, some of the elements of our post-glacial tree flora, therefore, appear not only to have existed in Britain but to have spread to the north-east of Scotland.

Then followed a renewal of glacial conditions. The ice flowed from the Highlands and again met the Scandinavian ice; the Scottish ice was therefore in part deflected northwards to form the Strathmore drift, the characteristic red drift in Angus (Bremner, 1934*b*). In England, the drift laid down by this glaciation reached the York Line already mentioned, but a large area in the Midlands and the south of England was not glaciated at this time. There is no evidence that pine and other tree species survived from the previous interstadial period, and the

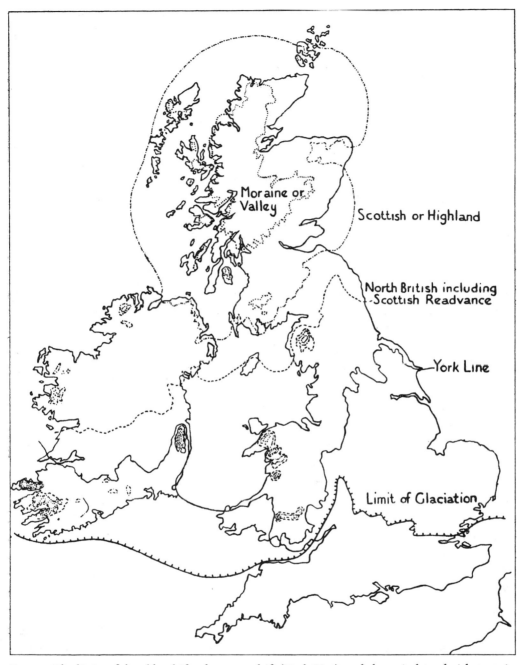

Moraine or Valley

Scottish or Highland

North British including Scottish Readvance

York Line

Limit of Glaciation

FIG. 3. The limits of the older drifts, the newer drift (York Line), and the main late-glacial stages in the British Isles, based on Charlesworth (1956), with a modification of the eastern end of the York Line according to Farringdon (1951).

present view is that the region south of the York Line, including the area of the continental shelf exposed to the south and east of England through the eustatic fall in the sea-level, and indeed most of France, were tundra during this glacial phase (Charlesworth, 1957; Woldstedt, 1954).

As the Pleistocene period has been studied with increasing intensity, it has become clear that the ice-sheets advanced and retreated with greater or less amplitude. There were all gradations from major interglacial periods separating successive advances, such as the so-called Great Inter-glacial between the Mindel and Riss glaciations in the Alps, estimated by Ebers and also Köppen and Wegener to have lasted 193,000 years (Charlesworth, 1957), to minor oscillations which indeed are to be seen in present-day glaciers; most of these are retreating, but a few are advancing (Ahlmann, 1953).

The period following the Newer Drift Glaciation, marked by the York Line, was one mainly of deglaciation; but there was a series of local advances of the ice-sheets, and these are not yet fully investigated. After the maximum of the Newer Drift Glaciation, the ice gradually retreated from the north of England in a northerly and westerly direction, and some of the eastern seaboard of Scotland may have been free from ice. Then followed a further advance from the Highlands and Southern Uplands of Scotland which reached Cumberland and the Isle of Man. This is the glaciation called the Scottish Readvance by some authorities, and the North British Glaciation by others, for example Charlesworth (1956, 1957). After a period of retreat, there was a pause or another advance, and on this occasion the ice flowed in a general easterly direction, most of Scotland being glaciated at that time, except for the south-east and a region in Buchan in the north-east. This is termed the Scottish stage by Charlesworth (1957); it may include the Perth Readvance of Simpson (1933), and the Aberdeen Readvance of Synge (1956). The glaciers then retreated into the mountain regions, but there was a minor advance, termed the Moraine or Valley Glaciation. The ice margin then was at or near the sea on the west coast, but in the east only near Dinnet in Deeside and Boat of Garten in the Spey Valley (Charlesworth, 1956) (see Fig. 3). As the glaciers retreated up the valleys in the final retreat, much of the characteristic topography in the Highland region was formed, the moraines in the upper valleys, and the deposits from ice-dammed lakes and dead lobes of ice. It is the newest land form in Britain, and bears a strong resemblance to similar regions in Fenno-Scandia and Canada. Charlesworth (1956) considers that the retreating ice made it possible for plants and animals to re-enter the Highlands, first along the west coast, and later along the route of the present Perth-Inverness road. It is in this region that many of the native pinewoods in Scotland have persisted to the

PLATE I

General view of Rothemurchus with Glenmore and the
Kincardine Hills in the background

present day. This association between pinewoods and recently glaciated terrain, both in Scotland and Fenno-Scandia, is not altogether chance; for example, the sands and gravels of the moraines and fluvio-glacial deposits are favourable sites for Scots pine, and it tends to persist on them.

CORRELATIONS BETWEEN BRITAIN AND THE CONTINENT

In recent years attempts have been made to correlate the glacial stages in the Alps, North Germany and Scandinavia, and Britain (Charlesworth, 1957; Flint, 1957; Lacaille, 1954; Movius, 1942; Wills, 1951; Zeuner, 1952), but there are still many uncertainties. Table I gives tentative correlations based on information from different sources. It has been mentioned already that all the glaciations described for Scotland are believed to be substages of the Last Glaciation in Zeuner's (1952) sense. If so they correspond with the different substages of the Würm Glaciation in the Alps. The correlations with the Scandinavian ice-sheets in North Germany are less certain. It is generally considered that the Newer Drift or York Line Glaciation corresponds with the Weichsel Glaciation. As the ice-sheets retreated northwards, the next evidence of a readvance is the so-called Pomeranian Moraine south of the Baltic, which runs from north-east Denmark through Lithuania to the Valdai Hills. This may be the equivalent of the North British stage. Following a further retreat, there was another pause or advance marked by moraines in the region of the Baltic. This may be the equivalent of the Scottish or Highland Glaciation. The stage marked by the moraines in the coastal districts of Fenno-Scandia may be correlated with the Moraine or Valley Glaciation. The next retreat freed most of Scandinavia, and the ice-sheet finally split at Ragunda in Sweden.

A system of absolute chronology based on varve analysis of clays, laid down in lakes or other stretches of quiet waters, has been elaborated by de Geer and his collaborators in Sweden, by Sauramo in Finland, and others (Zeuner, 1952). De Geer's dating has been widely accepted, but there is some doubt, particularly about the earlier phases. There is general agreement, however, for a date about 6800 B.C. for the Ragunda stage, and 7900 B.C. for the Fenno-Scandian End Moraines. The application of radio-carbon methods to organic material (Libby, 1952), and the study of the *Foraminifera* in deep-sea cores (Emiliani, 1956; Suess, 1956) are helping to elucidate the chronology of the different stages.

THE RELATIVE DISTRIBUTION OF LAND AND SEA

It has been mentioned already that, during glacial periods, the sea is at a lower level because of the locking up of water in ice-sheets, while when the ice melts there is a rise in the sea-level. Superimposed on this eustatic effect, there is the isostatic reaction of the land depressed by the weight of the ice-sheets – the slow recoil of the earth's crust as the ice melts. The eustatic rise and fall of the sea-level is worldwide, but the isostatic effect is greatest at the centres of the accumulation of ice, and decreases outwards. Thus the beaches marking previous sea-levels – the result of the interplay of these two effects – although horizontal at the time they were formed, are now warped. It is possible to map the isobases, therefore, and elucidate the land movements relative to the sea. The eustatic rise in sea-level along retreating ice margins towards the end of the glaciations was greater than the isostatic recovery, but the latter became dominant for a period thereafter.

In Scotland, there is a series of high-level "beaches" marking the sea-levels during the closing stages of the last glaciation. The maximum level is about 150 ft. (45 m.) near Doune in the Forth basin, where there is a beach nearest to the maximum subsequent recoil of the land. The isobases of the lower beach levels form a series of ellipses. There are beaches at about both 100 ft. (30 m.) and 50 ft. (15 m.) in the coastal regions of north, south, east and west Scotland. The name Late-glacial Sea is given (Lacaille, 1954; Movius, 1942) to the waters of this marine transgression which flooded the coastal fringes, and, by extending the Forth and Clyde estuaries, almost separated the Lowlands from the Highland region. Such beaches are absent from the heads of some Highland sea lochs, as James Geikie first pointed out, and this must mean that there were valley glaciers down to sea-level at or subsequent to this time. This and other evidence, which has been reviewed recently by Lacaille (1954), suggests that the Late-glacial Sea dates from the retreat of the ice of the Scottish or Highland Glaciation until the end of the Moraine or Valley Glaciation and the beginning of post-glacial time, the date of which is generally agreed to be about 8000 B.C.

Attempts have been made to correlate the changes in sea-level round our coasts with those in the Baltic associated with the retreat of the Fenno-Scandian ice-sheet. The changes in the Baltic have been worked out in detail, and have been discussed and illustrated by various authors, for example Charlesworth (1957) and Zeuner (1952). The melting of the ice of this great ice-sheet produced a much greater volume of water and a greater isostatic recovery of the earth's crust than in Britain. The maximum recoil on the west coast of the Gulf of Bothnia was about 830 ft. (250 m.), and the southerly zero-isobase runs from Lake Ladoga in Finland to south Sweden. As the ice retreated northwards from the Baltic moraines, the melt water formed a lake, called the Baltic Ice Lake, which was not connected with the sea except by an overflow. This is believed to correspond with the Late-glacial Sea round our coasts (Movius, 1942). By the time that the ice had retreated beyond the line of the Fenno-Scandian moraines, the Billiger gap was freed and salt water came in from the sea. The name given to this change in the Baltic is the Yoldia Sea. The corresponding period in Scotland is probably the retreat after the Moraine or Valley Glaciation (Lacaille, 1954; Zeuner, 1952). During this period, both in Britain and in Fenno-Scandia, the isostatic rise of the land was gaining rapidly on the eustatic rise of the sea-level, and a period of land emergence followed, which extended far beyond the ice centres. The actual amount of the fall in sea-level relative to the land is not known with accuracy, but it is believed on available evidence to be at least 20 fathoms. This emergence of the land not only added to the land area in the coastal fringes and estuaries, but the shallow southern part of the North Sea became land, forming a bridge from the east of England to the Low Countries and Denmark, over which animals, including man, and plants could migrate. In Britain, the land thus gained from the sea was colonised by forest. In the Baltic region, the Yoldia Sea became the fresh-water Ancylus Lake, with an outlet along the Svea River in Sweden, probably about 7000 B.C. (Lacaille, 1954; Zeuner, 1952). A slowing in the isostatic rise of the land relative to the sea then led to another period of gradual submergence. In Scotland and the north of England, the maximum of this submergence is repre-sented by the so-called 25-ft. beach which has provided sites for so many of our coastal towns and villages. It is not always at this level, being again higher in the upper estuaries, for example above Stirling in the Forth; Movius (1942) has summarised the available evidence. Various authors have suggested alternative names for this beach, the most recent being Early Post-glacial raised beach (Lacaille, 1954). The estuaries were again extended and the waist-line in the Forth-Clyde region reduced. At this period the carse clays in the Forth, Tay, and other estuaries were laid down, in part burying the coastal forests. The corres-ponding stage in the Baltic region was the salt water Litorina Sea with a connexion to the ocean through the Danish Sound. The period when the sea-level was rising lasted for several millennia; the date of the level of the beach of the Early Post-glacial Sea appears to be about 5000 B.C., but this is not certain. Then followed a period of slow emergence of the land to the present coast-lines, although there is evidence of relatively minor fluctuations, at least in southern England – for ex-ample a minor marine transgression about the beginning of our era (Godwin, 1945, 1956). If, therefore, birch and pine at least did not persist in southern England during the Newer Drift Glaciation, these and other species could have migrated from the Continent during the subsequent retreat of the ice, before the rise in sea-level marked by beaches of the Late-glacial Sea, and again during the subsequent period when the southern part of the North Sea was land, before the Early Post-glacial Sea submerged this bridge about 5000 B.C.

The Late-glacial and Post-glacial tree flora in Britain

EARLIER OBSERVATIONS AND INVESTIGATIONS

For centuries, there has been some knowledge of the forests of past ages in Scotland from their remains entombed in peat bogs. Peat is still the domestic fuel in the remoter parts of the Highlands and Islands, to say nothing of its use in the distillation of whisky, but the first *Statistical Account* shows that it was used as a fuel throughout Scotland until the beginning of the last century. More of our present-day agricultural land has been won from the bogs than is generally realised. The Rev. James Peter, writing as late as 1875 in his paper *The Peat Mosses of Buchan*, stated: "Of the 11,475 acres of Peat Moss existing 30 years ago, 3132 have been added to the arable land, yielding an annual rent of £2382." Such work disclosed the remains of trees in the bogs, and the species were identified, partly as a matter of interest, and partly because pine roots were used not only for fuel but for light. The species most commonly mentioned in the first *Statistical Account* were oak (*Quercus*) and pine, and less frequently birch (*Betula*), hazel (*Corylus*), alder (*Alnus*), mountain ash (*Sorbus aucuparia*), willow (*Salix*), and juniper(*Juniperus*). Some observers noted also that oak predominated in the lowland bogs and pine in the upland (Geikie, 1866). In many instances only root systems had survived, and these were rooted either in the soil underlying the peat or in the peat itself. There were numerous references, however, to whole trunks both of oak and pine, and often of large size. From at least the eighteenth century, there was speculation about the causes of destruction of these forests. It was noted that the trunks often lay in a north-easterly direction, suggesting windthrow by south-westerly gales, and it was thought that this had blocked natural drainage and encouraged the growth of peat. The parish ministers who wrote in the first *Statistical Account* and others naturally turned to the Roman authors, and made much of the few references they found to the felling of forests in Scotland at that time. There was some evidence of axe marks on the trees and even the finding of Roman remains in the peat to support this view. As early as 1866, however, James Geikie postulated climatic changes for the succession of trees and peat plants in the bogs, and he developed this view in successive editions of his book *The Great Ice Age* (1894). He differentiated, from the base upwards, an arctic phase, a lower buried forest, a peat zone with the carse clays above it, an upper buried forest, with peat to the present surface. He endeavoured to correlate this evidence of changing climatic conditions with variations in the sea-level in post-glacial times. Blytt (1876) put forward similar views for Norway; and with Sernander, who had investigated bog sequence in Sweden, he devised the terminology for the different post-glacial periods which are still in use: Sub-arctic or latpre-bial, ore-glaceal, boreal, atlantic, sub-boreal and sub-atlantic.

In the early years of this century, James Geikie's work in Scotland was followed up by Lewis (1905-11). He studied the peat stratigraphy in a large number of sections in the Southern Uplands, the Highlands, and Islands, and identified the plant remains, including tree species, usually on macroscopic remains, but with an occasional reference to pollen grains. While there were differences in the sections, his general summary of the sequence from the base upwards was:

1. A zone resting on glacial material, consisting of an arctic-alpine vegetation such as *Salix herbacea*, *S. reticulata*, *Betula nana*, and *Empetrum*, and sometimes marsh plants indicating pools in the tundra. This is the First Arctic Bed. It was not always present, presumably because the bogs had begun to form at a later period.
2. A zone of birch and often hazel remains – the Lower Forestian.
3. Then followed a zone of bog plants, mainly *Sphagnum* and *Trichophorum* (*Scirpus*) *caespitosum*. Within this zone he often found a second arctic-alpine zone both at the higher elevations in the Southern Uplands and at almost sea-level in the Shetlands. He considered that this indicated a recurrence of glacial conditions and that the forest zone below it represented an interglacial period. The whole of this zone was the Lower Turbarian in the Geikie-Lewis terminology.
4. The next zone consisted of tree species, usually pine but sometimes birch and some hazel. In the Highlands, the pine roots might be at two levels. This was his Upper Forestian.
5. Finally there was a layer of peat consisting of moorland plants – the Upper Turbarian.

This sequence, suggesting climatic fluctuations, confirmed the work of James Geikie.

Before the publication of Lewis's last paper, Samuelsson (1910), a Swedish investigator, visited Scotland and studied the bogs, including some of the sections described by Lewis. He, like Lewis, relied mainly on macroscopic remains, but he made considerable use of pollen grains, both of trees and ericaceous species, which were identified by Lagerheim, who a short time afterwards helped L. von Post to lay the foundations of modern pollen analysis. These identifications, although not expressed as percentages, are of interest because they showed the presence of tree pollen in zones consisting only of macroscopic bog plants, and also the presence of pine pollen in the Lower Forestian of Geikie and Lewis, although macroscopic remains of that species had not been found there. Samuelsson agreed with the general sequence established by Lewis, but he did not accept the interpretation of a second Arctic phase which did not accord with the sequence in Scandinavia. The correlation between Lewis's zones and the Blytt-Sernander sequence suggested by Samuelsson (1910), and later by Erdtman (1924, 1928,

1929) was: First Arctic Bed – Pre-boreal, Lower Forestian – Boreal, Lower Turbarian – Atlantic, Upper Forestian – Sub-boreal, and Upper Turbarian – Sub-
atlantic. Such modern pollen analysis work as has been done since has not given
support to the arctic zone in the Lower Turbarian, but Movius (1942) has suggested the possibility that the Lower Forestian may be the so-called Allerød period
or Late-glacial Zone II of more recent workers and not the Boreal Zones on the
Blytt-Sernander terminology as Samuelsson and later workers thought. The
necessary re-examination of Lewis's sites by modern methods has not yet been
made.

POLLEN ANALYSIS

Our present-day knowledge of past forest history has come principally from the
use of pollen analysis. As we have seen, Lewis and to a greater extent Samuelsson
used fossil pollen identifications in the earlier peat investigations in Scotland. A
significant advance was made, however, when Lennart von Post, then State
Geologist in Sweden, developed the method with Lagerheim, and in particular
expressed the proportion of pollen of different tree species on a percentage basis
at successive horizons in peat bogs. This was in 1916, and the method was later
refined and standardised into a reliable technique. The method, its uses, and its
limitations have been discussed by Faegri and Iverson (1950), Godwin (1934, 1951,
1956) and others.

It is remarkable that a pollen grain, a not only microscopic but apparently
ephemeral plant organ, should be preserved almost indefinitely under anaerobic
conditions in lake sediments and peat bogs. It is the outer layer or exine which
exhibits this remarkable resistance to decay, and it has a great variety of structural
and sculpturing patterns that enable generic, and in some instances, specific,
identifications to be made. The amount of pollen liberated into the air is immense,
particularly in the case of wind pollinated species, which include most of the
European trees, grasses and sedges; but even insect pollinated species such as *Salix*,
Tilia, and *Calluna* produce so much pollen that in this respect they behave as
anemophilous species. Moreover, owing to wind and cloud, and the slow rate of
fall of pollen, there is general dispersion from the vegetation of a region. During
the flowering season, a rain of pollen falls on land and water surfaces, and some of
it is preserved under anaerobic conditions in lake sediments and peat bogs. The
question is, how far are the results given by pollen analysis applied to such sites a
reliable quantitative index of the vegetation of the district as a whole? Different
aspects of this question have been investigated by various workers (Faegri, 1950;
Godwin, 1956; Jonassen, 1950; Leibundgut, 1953). The principal results may be
summarised briefly as follows:

1. *The distance to which pollen is dispersed*

Investigations both on land and sea have shown that tree pollen can be transported for long distances, the absolute limit being placed at over 1200 miles (2000 km.) (Scamoni, 1955), and indeed pollen from America has been found in mid-Atlantic. In a wooded region such distant pollen is an insignificant part of the whole, but in treeless areas its presence may, of course, lead to an erroneous conclusion. It is now customary to determine non-tree as well as tree pollen as an aid to the elucidation of the true position, because the former is low in closed woodland but high in open woodland or treeless areas. Even thus, there may still be difficulties in interpretation.

2. *Production of pollen by different species and under varying conditions*

There are important differences between tree species in the age when flowering begins, in the amount of pollen produced in a season, and in the interval between seasons of heavy production. Pine, birch, and alder begin flowering early and are heavy pollen producers relative to say oak and beech. They also produce considerable amounts of pollen annually.

The ecological conditions also influence pollen production. It is much reduced in dense stands and is only high in margins and on isolated trees. There is also a negative correlation between vegetative vigour and flowering, and it is often observed that scattered, stunted pine, on say bogs, may produce vast quantities of pollen. Investigations have been made into the relationship between the composition of existing forests and the deposition of recent and sub-recent pollen. Different methods have been used, and the results have not always been consistent, but certain conclusions can be drawn (Faegri, 1950; Jonassen, 1950; Leibundgut, 1953). Pine and birch are very large pollen producers relative to most other species, and their pollen is widely dispersed. Alder is also a large pollen producer, but its diffusion is less extensive. These species, therefore, tend to be over-represented in deposits. The production of oak, beech, and lime pollen is relatively much less, and these species tend to be under-represented. Hazel flowers freely, but its pollen only appears in quantity in deposits when the species is a dominant, for example in groves, and not when it is an underwood. These considerations led Faegri and Iverson (1950) to propose that tree species be classified into three groups: A. the heavy producers – pine, birch, alder (*Alnus*) and hazel; B. the moderate producers – oak, ash (*Fraxinus*), beech (*Fagus*), etc.; and C. *Ilex*, *Hedera*, and other species whose pollen is scarce. In the construction of diagrams, they suggested that the number of pollen grains per species in group A be divided, by say four, before being added to those in group B to make the pollen sum. While this suggestion has not been followed in general, it is important to keep the relative representation in mind in interpreting pollen diagrams. If only the pollen of the large producers are present in a deposit, the percentages are likely to represent more closely the composition of the woodlands.

3. *Other factors*

There are other possible sources of error such as the differential rate of destruction of pollen of different species, over-representation due to the presence of a heavy pollen producer on the site at the time of deposition – this, of course, does not apply to lake sediments, and also the difficulty in differentiating the pollen of certain genera and species, for example hazel and *Myrica*.

The general consensus of opinion, however, is that, if due precautions are taken, pollen analysis gives at least an approximate picture of the composition of the forest that it purports to represent. Because it tends to give a picture of the surrounding vegetation as a whole, it is more trustworthy than the use of macroscopic fossils alone, but the latter often help to elucidate the true position, for example whether a species represented only by a few grains was actually growing near the site or no.

Workers in different countries have found it desirable to zone the succession of changes in the vegetation as depicted by pollen spectra, because this enables pollen diagrams of different sites to be synchronised and compared. Several different systems of zoning have been devised in different countries (Zeuner, 1946, 1952). Godwin (1940, 1956) has designed one, based initially on his work in East Anglia, which is now generally followed in this country, and Jessen (1949) has modified his Danish system, as applied in Ireland, to accord with it. The zones are differentiated by so-called "rational borders" of the principal tree species, the rational border being the level at which there is an abrupt change in the frequency of the pollen of a species. The following is a brief definition of the zones with the approximate Blytt-Sernander periods, based largely on Godwin (1956), and for England.

Late-Glacial Time

ZONE I: *Lower Dryas clay or* Salix herbacea *period*

As shown by the high values for non-tree pollen, the vegetation consisted of grass-sedge tundra with *Betula nana* and willow, and probably clumps of *B. pubescens*, and perhaps *B. verrucosa*.

ZONE II: *The Late-glacial birch or Allerød period*

In this zone the tree birches appeared to have formed woodland. Pine pollen has been found in this zone in Ireland and England (Godwin, 1956), but whether there was pine in the woodlands is still uncertain.

ZONE III: *Upper Dryas clay or younger* Salix herbacea *period*

There was a return to tundra conditions, but the tree birches continued to survive, and pine was probably present in southern England and perhaps in Ireland.

Post-Glacial Time

PRE-BOREAL TIME

ZONE IV: *The birch period*

There was a rise to dominance of tree birches, with a decline in the non-tree pollen. Pine may have been present but was not yet important.

BOREAL TIME

ZONE V: *The hazel-birch-pine period*

The rise in the curve of hazel pollen marks the boundary of this zone. In south-east England pine predominates over birch, but in the north and west birch retains its dominance. There may be small amounts of oak and elm (*Ulmus*) pollen. The amount of non-tree pollen continues to fall.

ZONE VI: *The hazel-pine period*

At the beginning of this zone there is a rise in the pine pollen relative to birch, and a rise in the oak and elm percentages. Hazel may reach values several times the figure for all other tree pollen.

The zone may be sub-divided into three sub-zones.

(*a*) marked by a rise in elm which is more important than oak, with high values for hazel.

(*b*) where oak generally exceeds elm, and the values for hazel may be falling.

(*c*) oak and elm continue at about the same level, pine and hazel continue to fall, but alder may be consistently present.

ATLANTIC AND SUB-BOREAL TIME

ZONE VII: *The alder-mixed oak forest period*

The beginning of this zone is marked by a rapid rise in the percentage of alder pollen at the expense of birch and pine. Oak may continue at previous levels or may increase. Lime may become more important, for example, in southern England.

The zone may be sub-divided:

(*a*) no decrease in elm.

(*b*) a decrease in elm.

SUB-ATLANTIC TIME

ZONE VIII: *The alder-birch-oak period*

This zone is marked by a rise in birch accompanied by a fall in pine and alder. Beech, and, to a lesser extent, hornbeam (*Carpinus*) pollen may be present in small amounts even in the north of England and north-east Scotland.

AN OUTLINE OF THE FOREST HISTORY OF BRITAIN WITH
SPECIAL REFERENCE TO SCOTLAND

Although, as we have seen, early investigators of post-glacial forest history in Britain devoted their attention largely to Scotland, most of the work done since pollen analysis was developed has been in England and Ireland, and the history of the flora of these countries is thus much better known. Godwin (1956, with extensive bibliography), his collaborators, and other workers have carried out numerous investigations in England and Wales, and the Dane, Jessen (1949), his Irish collaborators and others in Ireland. The first pollen diagrams for Scotland were published by Erdtman (1924, 1928, 1929) about thirty years ago. A little later G. K. Fraser studied samples from two Scottish bogs under the direction of von Post; the results have only been published recently in collaboration with H. Godwin (1955). There have also been papers by Blackburn (1946), Mitchell (1948, 1952), Knox (1954), and Donner (1957). In the last few years, S. E. Durno (1956, 1957), working at the Macaulay Institute, Aberdeen, first under the direction of G. K. Fraser, has investigated a number of sites, and he has summarised his results to date in Figs. 4, 5, 6, 7, 8, and 9. The account that follows is based on these sources. There is as yet no final conclusion for the dating of the zones, and those given can only be considered approximate. In most instances the dates are those adopted by Godwin (1956).

Late-glacial time. It has been seen already that three late-glacial zones have been differentiated: Zone I, from about 13000 to 10000 B.C.; Zone II, 10000 to 9000 B.C.; and Zone III, 9000 to about 8000 B.C. It is considered (Pennington, 1947; Godwin, 1956) that Zone I in Britain may fall into the glacial phase already referred to as the North British including the Scottish Readvance, Zone II the warmer phase that followed, called the Allerød period, and Zone III the subsequent Moraine or Valley Glaciation in the Scottish Highlands and on the higher hills elsewhere in Britain, the end of which marks the beginning of post-glacial time (see Table I). Charlesworth (1956) considers that the well-known caves at Inchnadamph, Sutherlandshire, to be referred to later, were occupied during Zone II and were closed by the ice during the Moraine or Valley Glaciation – his stage M. The information for late-glacial sites in Scotland is that of Mitchell (1948, 1952) for Berwickshire and near Glasgow, and of Donner (1957) for Drymen and near Keith. The latter concludes that even in Zone II it is likely that there were wide areas of *Empetrum Calluna* and *Empetrum Vaccinium* heaths with a vegetation also rich in grasses and herbs. The deposits referred to Zones I and III were poor in pollen and the vegetation appears to have been open and patchy.

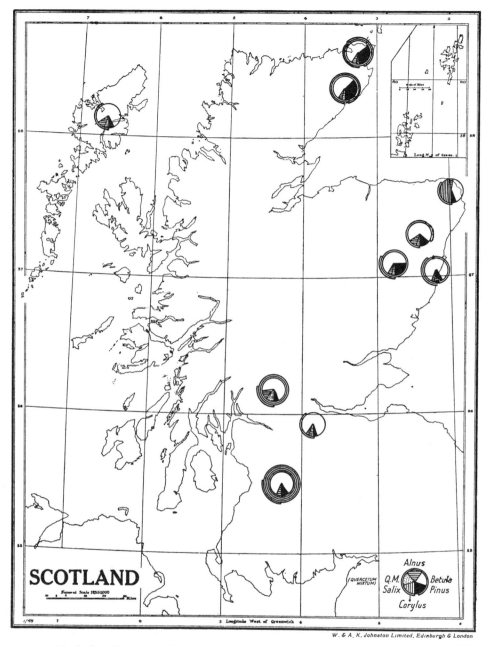

W. & A. K. Johnston Limited, Edinburgh & London

FIG. 4. Clock-face diagrams of Zone V, the first part of the Boreal period, prepared by S. E. Durno, Macaulay Institute for Soil Research, Aberdeen, from his own and other available profiles. The size of each sector of the circles is proportional to the percentage of the tree pollen which it represents. In this zone birch was the principal species in the woodlands, but pine was already well established, particularly in the north and east. There was already some mixed-oak forest and alderwood on lowland sites, and considerable amounts of hazel, particularly in the south-west.

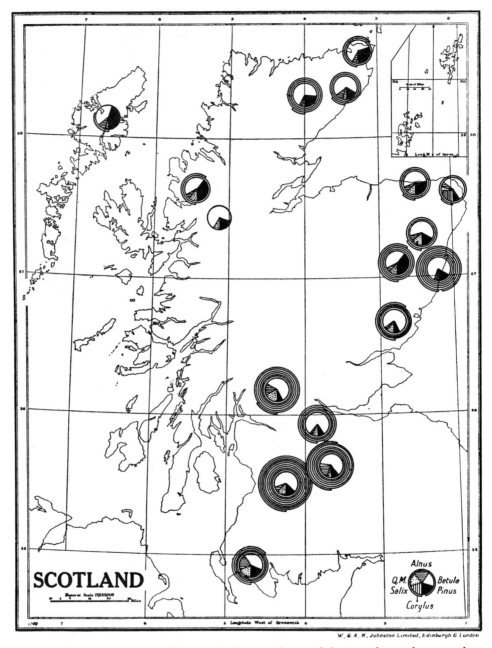

FIG. 5. Clock-face diagrams of Zone VI, the second part of the Boreal period, prepared as in Fig. 4. In this period birch remained the principal species, but pine was increasing, particularly in the north-west. Mixed-oak wood was spreading, and hazel reached its greatest abundance in post-glacial times.

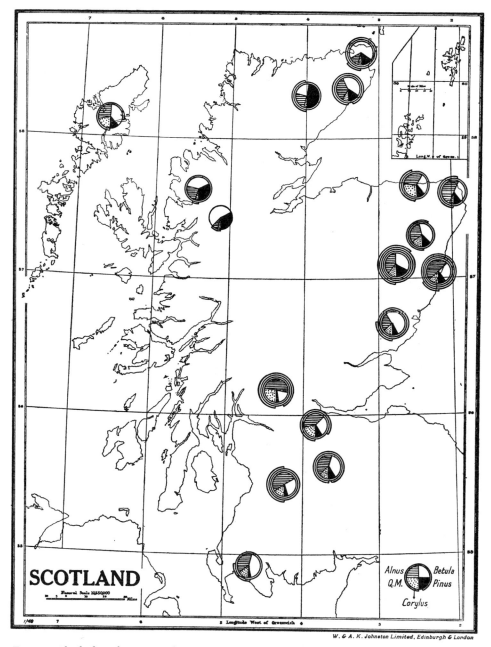

FIG. 6. Clock-face diagrams of Zone VII*a*, approximately the Atlantic period, prepared as in Fig 4. The most important change in this period was the expansion of alder at the expense principally of birch, which, however, continued to be an important species. Pine retained its Boreal status in the north and west, and mixed-oakwood was spreading.

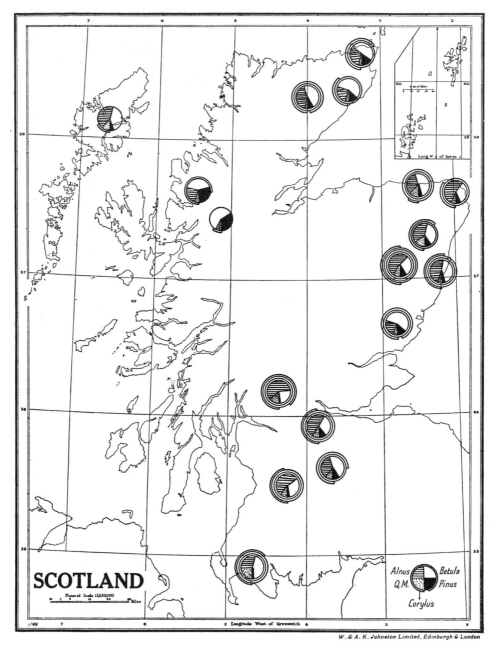

FIG. 7. Clock-face diagrams of Zone VII*b*, approximately the Sub-boreal period, prepared as in Fig. 4. The pollen analyses do not show any marked change compared with Zone VII*a*. There is a slight decrease in the amount of pine.

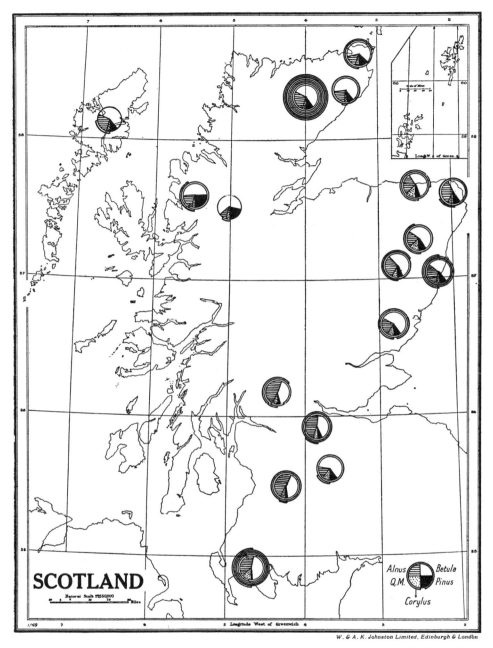

FIG. 8.   Clock-face diagrams of Zone VIII, the Sub-atlantic period, prepared as in Fig. 4. The amount of birch is greater, and that of alder less. The ratio of non-tree (not shown) to tree pollen increased during this zone, indicating a contraction of the woodland area. The high values for hazel in two diagrams may be due to inclusion of pollen of *Myrica*.

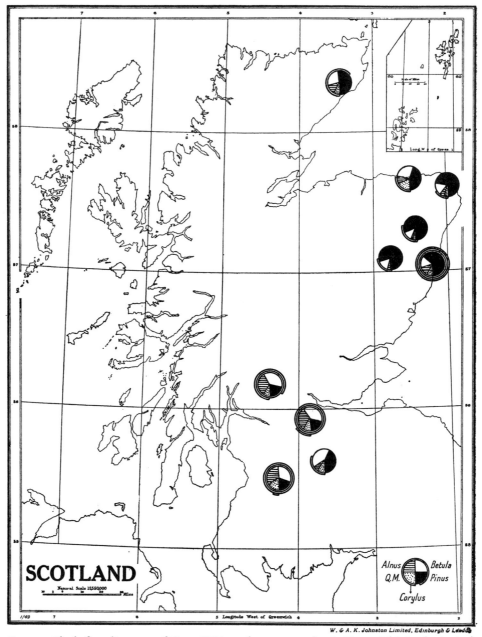

W. & A. K. Johnston Limited, Edinburgh & London

FIG. 9.   Clock-face diagrams of Zone VIII, modern, prepared as in Fig. 4. This is of principal interest in showing the marked rise of the amount of pine, reflecting the effect of the extensive planting of this species during the past two centuries.

PLATE II

THE EASTERN END OF THE BLACK WOOD OF RANNOCH ON
THE SOUTHERN SHORE OF LOCH RANNOCH

Betula nana and willows such as *S. herbacea* were present, and in Zone II also tree birches, probably *B. pubescens*, in southern Scotland. While pine pollen has been found in Scottish deposits believed to be of this period, it is uncertain whether pine had reached Scotland by this time.

Post-glacial time. As already mentioned, the southern half of what is now the North Sea was land during the earlier part of post-glacial time, and tree species that had not yet reached Britain could immigrate without meeting physical barriers. Further, when the glaciers finally disappeared in the Scottish Highlands, the climate would first improve in the south of Britain. Hence there is a general sequence in the stages in development of woodland communities from southern and eastern England to the north-west of Scotland. This is paralleled on the European mainland, where there is a similar gradient from Middle Europe to the north-west of Germany (Firbas, 1949).

Pre-boreal period
Zone IV, 8000 to 6800 B.C.

At the beginning of post-glacial time, the tree birches spread over the tundra and formed woodlands, as is shown by the fall in the ratio of non-tree to tree pollen. In England, there were both *Betula pubescens* and *B. verrucosa* although the former was probably the principal species, and aspen (*Populus tremula*) and rowan (*Sorbus aucuparia*) were already constituents of the woodlands. In the south and east there was some pine and even a little oak, elm, and hazel. There is as yet limited Scottish evidence for this zone, but it indicates that also in Scotland woodland, principally of birch with some pine, spread over the tundra at this time. In Middle Europe, the forests were predominantly of pine, but to the north birch still predominated, and on the north-west plains of Germany pine was a subsidiary species, although there was a little more to the east along the Yoldia Sea (Firbas, 1949).

Boreal period
Zone V, 6800–6000 B.C.; Zone VI, 6000–5000 B.C.

During the first part of this period, pine displaced birch as the principal species in the woodlands in the south and east of England, and as yet there was only a little oak and elm. It would appear that only at this time, and in this region, did pinewoods predominate in Britain. In the north and west of England, however, birchwoods continued to predominate though pine was increasing. Throughout England, and particularly in the west, hazel was spreading. In Scotland, birch remained the principal species, but pine was well established and in the north and

D

east was becoming important. On the more favourable lowland sites, there was already a little oak, elm, and alder, and considerable amounts of hazel, particularly in the south-west (see Fig. 4).

As the Boreal period continued into Zone VI, pine continued to be an important species in England, particularly south and east of the Humber-Severn line, but the mixed woods of oak, elm, and a little lime were becoming more extensive, elm being the most important of these three species at the beginning of this zone. In the north and west of England and in Scotland, birch remained the principal species; but during this period pine was steadily displacing birch, and in Scotland, particularly in the north-west, it reached its post-glacial maximum at or about this time, as it did in Ireland. Mixed-oakwood was spreading. The most striking change, however, in the woodlands in Zone VI was the spread of hazel. This took place throughout western Europe, but the highest pollen values have been recorded in the British Isles, and above all in Ireland and in Scotland (see Fig. 5). Today, hazel is an underwood shrub in the moist facies of oakwood and in woods managed under the Coppice-with-standards System. In Zone VI, however, the woodlands where some of the highest hazel values have been recorded were principally of birch and pine. Godwin (1956) has suggested that the hazel might have been associated with aspen – whose pollen is not preserved – or have formed an understory to open pine. But it has been mentioned already that hazel pollen is only deposited in quantity when it is growing in the open; hence the forest trees must have been sparse or there were extensive groves of hazel on the margins of the woods.

During most of Boreal times, England was still connected with the Continent, and the greater extent of land would tend to make the climate more continental. There is evidence, particularly in eastern England, that the water tables fell during this period; in Scotland the drier conditions were probably less marked, because bogs began to grow during this period, the principal peat-forming plants being sedges and reeds. The waters of the Early Post-glacial Sea, however, were steadily rising and, towards the end of Boreal time, Britain became an island, and further natural immigration of tree flora was unlikely.

Atlantic and Sub-boreal periods

Zone VII.*a*, 5000 to about 3000 B.C.; Zone VII.*b*, 3000 to 500 B.C.

The beginning of Atlantic time was marked by a great expansion of alder in the woods, principally at the expense of birch and pine. High pollen percentages have been recorded for most of England and southern and eastern Scotland, but in northern Scotland alder, while increasing, was less important until later in the period, and pine maintained its late Boreal prominence (see Fig. 6). The spread of alder was no doubt due principally to the rising water tables in coastal lands and in the lower reaches of the river valleys. Alder must have spread far inland at this time, however, and there are still relict alder communities along the rivers in the native pinewoods in the Central Highlands; hence the climate must have become more humid or warmer as Godwin has pointed out (1956). In England, the mixed broadleaved woodlands of oak and elm with increasing amounts of lime, particularly in the south, established the dominance which they have maintained throughout historical times, but in the north and west birch was still an important species. Partly on the frequency of lime, Godwin (1956) has concluded that the summer temperatures reached their post-glacial maximum in England in Atlantic times. The estimates of the increase in summer temperatures for different parts of Europe, while variable, are about 4·5° F. (2·5° C.) (Charlesworth, 1957). In Scotland, while oak and elm woods show some expansion, these species were much less important than in England, then as now. There was a general decline in the amount of hazel throughout the British Isles. There is abundant macroscopic evidence in Scotland that woodlands were giving way to ombrogenous bog which had begun to grow at the end of Boreal times. It is probable, therefore, that in Scotland the area of forest was decreasing. During Atlantic times the sea-level began to fall.

From earlier work in Scandinavia, it was believed that in Sub-boreal times, approximately Zone VII.b, the climate was drier and more continental and this was thought to apply to north-western Europe generally. In the light of more recent evidence, Godwin (1956) considers that the dryness and also the warmth may have been overestimated so far as England is concerned. On the other hand, Jessen (1949) believes that the highest summer temperatures during post-glacial times in Ireland were reached during this period. There is abundant evidence in Scotland and elsewhere that pine spread on to the bogs at this time. If Lewis's Upper Forestian is Sub-boreal in age, as is generally believed, his results and diagrams show this clearly. Moreover, anyone who knows the country between Upper Deeside and the Spey Valley will have seen the stumps, principally of pine, in horizons probably dating from this time; these show that the native pinewoods surviving in this region were then more extensive, although many of the trees were of small size and diameter growth was slow. The evidence of pollen analysis for Scotland and elsewhere, however, does not show any expansion of pine at this time, and it has been deduced by Godwin (1956) that this spread of pine on to the bogs was local, and that the forests of the country as a whole did not change appreciably.

In Scotland, the evidence from pollen analysis indicates that birch continued to be the most important species; but the alder woods were still extensive, although there was some contraction towards the end of the period. The amount of pine tended to decrease and not increase, but this was less marked in the north-west, where high pollen values have been recorded for Zone VII.*b* (see Fig. 7). Oak remained a much less important species than in England, elm was decreasing as elsewhere, but hazel was still widespread. A few grains of beech and hornbeam have been recorded from Zone VII.*b* in a profile at Strichen in north-east Aberdeenshire (Fraser, 1955). The Scottish woods, as is to be expected, thus resembled those in northern rather than southern England, but there was less oak and more pine.

Sub-Atlantic and historical period
Zone VIII, 500 B.C. onwards

The bogs, that in Sub-boreal times had tended to dry out and become covered with *Calluna* and trees, began to grow again, the peat-forming plants being *Sphagnum*, cotton grasses (*Eriophorum*) and *Trichophorum* (*Scirpus*). There is often a definite recurrence horizon at the Sub-boreal/Sub-Atlantic boundary. The growth of blanket as well as basin bogs was renewed, and the trees in the woodlands on upland slopes, such as those already described, must have been gradually killed during this period. The climate, therefore, became more oceanic with greater humidities and lower summer temperatures, and these conditions have continued with minor fluctuations until the present day. There were also changes in the composition of the woodlands, but as man's influence on them was increasing, it is not clear whether these changes were due mainly to climate. In north-west Europe generally birch increased, and in Scotland as in England it was principally at the expense of alder. Oak and to a greater extent elm tended to fall to still lower percentages, and the trend in hazel while variable was generally downwards (see Fig. 8). The fall in the amount of lime in England has been taken by Godwin (1956) to be the best indicator of less favourable climatic conditions. It was during this period that there was an expansion of beech and to a lesser extent hornbeam in England south of a line from the Wash to the Severn (Godwin, 1956). The presence of a few grains of these species in Zone VII.*b* in a deposit in north-east Aberdeenshire has already been mentioned; Zone VIII shows slightly higher frequencies. Godwin (1956) considers that there might have been small stands on favourable sites there as in the north of England. This, however, will remain uncertain until macroscopic remains are found, because the pollen might have been carried by the easterly winds of early summer from the north-west German plains where the species was already established in Sub-boreal times (Firbas, 1949). As the period continued, the ratio of non-tree – particularly ericoid – to tree pollen increased. Durno (1957) has shown that tree pollen in selected profiles in the north-east of Scotland remained between 75 and 50 per cent. of the total pollen (arboreal and non-arboreal) from Zone V to Zone VII.*b*, and then fell sharply in Zone VIII, particularly in the coastal plains where man was already active. This indicates perhaps not less closed woodland but less woodland compared with bog and heath which has characterised Scotland in historical times. Fig. 9, which depicts the proportion of species as determined by pollen analysis for the modern part of Zone VIII, is of principal interest in showing the influence of afforestation during the last two centuries. In some instances, for example, pine reaches its highest percentage in post-glacial times, particularly in the north-east where Scots pine has been so widely planted. While the total area of woodland in Scotland today is much less than in Boreal times, the percentage of Scots pine woodland, planted and natural, is probably as high as it has ever been.

The forest history of Scotland during post-glacial times thus follows the pattern of north-west Europe as a whole, but with some differences. Spruce never reached the British Isles, as it did in earlier interglacial periods (Godwin, 1956). The spruce timber discovered during the excavation of a Neolithic site at Stanydale, in Shetland, was probably driftwood from North America (Calder, 1952; Graham, 1952); and the spruce charcoal discovered in a Broch settlement at Jarlshof in Shetland (Hamilton, 1956) may also be from driftwood. Spruce might not have reached Fenno-Scandia where it is now so characteristic if it had not spread from the east through Finland; even today it is not a native species in south-west Norway west of the neighbourhood of Voss. Similarly silver fir (*Abies* sp.) is not a native species in Britain, although it also was present at least in England and Ireland during one or more interglacial periods (Godwin, 1956). The native status of beech and hornbeam in southern England is now well established. As we have seen, they may have been native in Scotland also in Sub-boreal and Sub-Atlantic times, but if so, there is no definite evidence that they persisted as native species into historical times. Beech has been planted on a considerable scale in Scotland, particularly during the past two hundred years, and the pollen diagram for Strichen already referred to (Fraser, 1955) shows a rise in the beech pollen percentage for the modern period. It is also of interest that beech can produce large crops of seed in Scotland, for example in 1956, and that it reproduces itself naturally to some extent, for example as far north as the coastal lowlands of the Moray Firth. The principal native species in Scotland during post-glacial times have been the birches. Although definite evidence is not yet available, it is probable that the birchwoods consisted both of *Betula pubescens* and *B. verrucosa* since early post-glacial times, and it is not surprising, therefore, that there are many intermediate or hybrid forms in the woods today, which will be mentioned in more detail later. In the latter half of Boreal times, Zone VI, the predominance of birch was challenged by Scots pine, later than in southern England and less successfully. Particularly in the north-west of Scotland, the Boreal pine phase continued longer and into Atlantic times. In Atlantic times, there was a great increase of alder as elsewhere, principally at the expense of birch. During that time, the percentages of oak and elm as well as lime pollen are much lower than in England. The preponderance in Scottish woodlands of large pollen producers, such as birch, alder, and, to some extent, pine at that time may have depressed the oak and elm percentages, and oak stumps and trees have often been found in the past in lowland bogs (Peter, 1876; Sinclair, 1791-9), undated but probably of Atlantic age. Thus while the mixed oakwoods were probably more extensive than the pollen percentages indicate, nevertheless it is certain that they were much less extensive than in England in Atlantic as in historical times. It is not yet possible to separate the pollen of the pedunculate oak (*Quercus robur*) from the sessile (*Q. petraea*); the elm was likely to be *Ulmus glabra*, and the lime *Tilia cordata*. Ash (*Fraxinus excelsior*) has not been mentioned because published records are few, but it has probably been a native species in Scotland since late Boreal times. S. E. Durno, in a personal communication, has supplied data on this species from his profiles. There was an occasional grain in Zone VI in the north-east of Scotland, and from VII.*a* in other sites, including the north and west of Scotland. As in other western regions, the area of bog increased in Atlantic times at the expense of woodland. In Sub-boreal times, pine spread on to the drying bogs, but the pollen diagrams do not show a resurgence of pine, and this extension of pine was probably local and not in the woodlands as a whole. The growth of bogs was again resumed in Sub-Atlantic times. Birch regained its dominance, but pine remained a more important species than elsewhere in Britain, and it is certain that the surviving natural pinewoods are truly native. At the beginning of historical times, mixed woodlands of oak, elm, alder, birch, and other broadleaved species probably occupied the more fertile lowland and valley sites, but there may have been some pine in them on the less fertile soils. On the less favourable upland sites, birch and pine were probably the dominants in the woodlands as they are today. The pollen diagrams show a marked rise in the pollen percentage of pine in recent times, indicative of the widespread use of this species as a planted tree during the past two centuries.

The Impact of Man on the Forests of Scotland
in Prehistoric Times

As already mentioned, man may have been in Scotland in Late-glacial times. In a limestone cave near Inchnadamph, Sutherlandshire, evidence has been found of the presence of man and such fauna as the cave-bear, arctic fox, and reindeer (Callendar, 1927; Peach and Horne, 1917). Charlesworth (1956) considers that this was in the Late-glacial Allerød period (Zone II), and that the occupation was brought to an end by the Valley or Moraine Glaciation, his substage M. Thereafter, as far as present evidence goes, man did not reach this north-west outpost of Europe until relatively late in post-glacial times, after the Palaeolithic period had come to an end. Lacaille (1954) has recently brought together the available information about these immigrants, their origins and cultures.

THE MESOLITHIC PEOPLES

In post-glacial times, man reached Scotland before the peak of the rise of the sea marked by the beaches of the Early Post-glacial Sea, that is towards the end of the Boreal period (Zones VI-VII) and probably about 5000 B.C. Thus, the forests of earlier post-glacial times spread and developed without human interference. Man came at a critical time in forest history when the rising sea-level was raising the water-levels in the valleys, and alder was spreading on these wetter soils and to some extent displacing birch and pine. The first inhabitants in this period were probably from the north-east of Ireland, where a culture called Larnian had been developed (Lacaille, 1954; Movius, 1942). They appear to have been descended from Upper Palaeolithic Cresswellians who had survived the New Drift Glaciation in the Midlands of England, whence they had slowly spread north-westwards, changing their mode of life from inland hunters to dwellers by the sea shore. Other descendants of the Cresswellians appear to have moved northwards to the east of the Pennines during Boreal times, and on the way to have mingled with new immigrants from north-east France, the Tardenoisians; by the time they reached the Tweed valley, probably in early Atlantic times, they had implements characteristic of that culture. In the Tweed valley and round the estuary of the Forth there is also evidence of another cultural group, the Maglemosians from the Baltic. During late Pre-boreal and Boreal times, when the southern part of the North Sea was land, it is known that these people had reached England (Clark, 1952, 1954; Godwin, 1951; Lacaille, 1954). A late Pre-boreal site, occupied by people with Maglemosian affinities, at Star Carr in the Vale of Pickering, Yorkshire, has recently been investigated in great detail. There is evidence of the felling of birch, 14 in. (35·6 cm.) thick with a crude adze or axe as early as 7538±

350 years B.C. according to radio-carbon dating (Clark, 1954; Clark in Bruce-Mitford, 1956). During the millennia of the Atlantic period, these different groups spread in Scotland, and there is evidence of their intermingling (Lacaille, 1954). Two Mesolithic sites are of interest from the point of view of the forests, one at Oban and its vicinity on the western side of the Highlands, and the other at Banchory on the River Dee on the east. Both may be at least late Atlantic in time, because there is general agreement that the food gathering peoples persisted late in Scotland, particularly on coastal strands, and into the time when food producing cultures had been established elsewhere in Britain. The affinities of the Obanians have been the subject of controversy. Many archaeologists thought that some of their tools showed Azilian characteristics, a culture that originated in the region of the Pyrenees (Childe, 1946; Clark, 1932). Lacaille (1954) considers that the balance of probability is against this view, but Clark (1958) in a recent paper has marshalled the evidence in favour of it. Whatever their ancestry, they lived by fishing, fowling, and hunting in the forests, and their middens contained remains of red deer of large size, roe deer, wild pig, wild ox, badger, and cat (Anderson, 1895; Turner, 1895). On the River Dee, about seventeen miles from Aberdeen, microlithic flints have been found showing Tardenoisian affinities and similarities to those in the Tweed valley (Lacaille, 1954; Simpson, 1944). The valley woodlands on the edges of which these early Deeside people lived probably consisted of the more exacting broadleaved species; indeed oak charcoal was found in an occupation layer, but native pinewood has persisted to the present day at Glentanar, less than twenty miles away.

The changing forests of the early part of Atlantic times in Scotland were thus influenced by man little, if at all. Although the Mesolithic people were the only inhabitants of the country for almost 3000 years, their numbers must have been small, and they appear to have kept to the coastal fringes and the river valleys. Their hunting expeditions may have led them deeper into the forest, but they could have had little effect on it, even if they used fire to round up game. Indeed limited burning might stimulate natural regeneration of pine, and they had no flocks of domestic animals to browse it. Their needs for timber, whether for huts or fuel, must have been small. The early Mesolithic people in Scotland may have used trees to make dug-out canoes. One found in the second alluvial terrace at Friarton, Perth, was studied *in situ* by James Geikie (1879). It was found resting above a seam of peat which consisted principally of reed fragments, but also contained stumps of pine which Geikie thought had drifted into the site; the canoe was overlaid with clay and silt. This canoe, therefore, is likely to be of early Atlantic age. It is of interest that it had been made from a pine log, thought to be

4 ft. (1·2 m.) or more in diameter, and hollowed out by charring and scraping. Clark (1952) has recently discussed the way of life of these and other prehistoric peoples in Europe. He depicts their place in the landscape thus: "If one could have flown over northern Europe during Mesolithic times, it is doubtful whether more than an occasional wisp of smoke from some camp fire, or maybe a small cluster of huts or shelters by a river bank or old lake bed, would have advertised the presence of man: in all essentials the forest would have stretched unbroken, save only by mountain, swamp and water, to the margins of the sea."

THE NEOLITHIC PEOPLES

The forests first came under the threat of destruction when man turned from fishing and hunting to the growing of crops and the domestication of grazing animals. The Neolithic peoples who were responsible for this revolutionary change reached Britain probably a little after 2500 B.C., and in early Sub-boreal times (Zone VII.*b*), but the date is still uncertain (Fox, 1938; Godwin, 1956; Piggott, 1954). They came both across the Channel and up the western sea approaches from western France or Iberia. Stuart Piggott (1954) has recently reviewed the available evidence about the western Neolithic people in Britain. They came, not only with stone axes better able to deal with forest trees, but also with seed corn and domesticated grazing animals such as oxen, sheep or goats, and pigs. Iverson (1941) in Denmark first gave convincing evidence from pollen analysis of the clearance of forest by Neolithic peoples using axe and fire, and Godwin (1944*b*, 1951, 1956) has presented a similar picture for the Brecklands in Norfolk by his studies at Hockham Mere. Many of the Neolithic settlements in England are on chalk downlands, and there has been controversy whether or no they were occupied because they were relatively treeless at this period (Piggott, 1954; Tansley, 1949). While the Neolithic farmers sought the lighter soils (Clark, 1945, 1952), there is evidence that they were able to clear forest with their equipment. Cereals were grown; there is evidence of the use of barley in Orkney (Childe, 1946; Piggott, 1954), but in Neolithic Europe as a whole wheat, principally Emmer (*Triticum dicoccum*), was the main cereal (Clark, 1952). They probably practised a form of shifting cultivation, moving on when the fertility of the soil became exhausted. From sites as far apart as Windmill Hill, in north Wiltshire, and Skara Brae in Orkney, there are deposits of animal bones. In the former, cattle and particularly immature animals predominate suggesting autumn slaughtering because of limitation in forage, with the pig second in importance, but at the latter, sheep appear to be relatively important, perhaps because the grazings were already more or less treeless (Childe, 1946; Clark, 1947; Piggott,

1949). The grazing of these animals would tend to reduce natural regeneration in the woodlands and probably had a greater effect than the cutting down of the trees for temporary cultivation. Remains of red and roe deer show that this people also hunted in the woods, and they used red deer antlers for picks – particularly in their flint mines, for example at Grimes Graves in Norfolk – and for making other tools (Piggott, 1954).

The principal evidence of settlement left by the Neolithic peoples is their monumental tombs, used as a rule for collective burial by inhumation or sometimes after cremation – the long earthen barrows or stone-built chambered tombs of different types. In Scotland, they are to be found mainly in the west and in the north; in the Firth of Clyde and the south-west of Scotland; in the Outer Hebrides and also on the adjoining mainland as far south as the Firth of Lorne; the Shetlands; a distinctive group in the Orkneys and down the coast from Caithness towards Inverness; and the so-called Clava group on the south side of the Moray Firth, the north end of the Great Glen and in Strathspey; and there may be an outlier on the Tap o' Noth in Aberdeenshire. There is also a group of long cairns of uncertain affinities on the eastern side of the country from the Borders to Kincardineshire, Aberdeenshire and Banffshire (Childe, 1947; Piggott, 1954; Simpson, 1944).

There is so far little evidence, archaeological or from pollen analysis, to throw light on the influence of Neolithic farmers on the forests of Scotland. They established themselves principally in the north and west, including the outer islands, and in the valleys of the Dee and Spey, in the Great Glen, and at Loch Earn. They probably settled on the better soils carrying oak and other broad-leaved species as they did in southern Norway (Clark, 1952), rather than pine, and they must have begun the slow process of woodland destruction in the places where they settled. The Neolithic period in Scotland was short, however, probably about 500 years, and the influence of this people was small relative to that of later inhabitants and probably less than in other parts of Europe.

BRONZE AGE PEOPLES

The so-called Beaker people invaded Britain before the middle of the second millennium B.C., thus in Sub-boreal time and in the later part of Zone VII.*b*. They came from the Low Countries and the Rhineland, and on this occasion the immigrants settled on the eastern side of the country, for example in Scotland from the Lothians northwards and particularly in the lowlands between the Dee and the Spey, but some penetrated to the west and the north (Childe, 1946; Fox, 1938; Simpson, 1944). They thus settled on the more fertile land at the lower altitudes which, as we have seen, was probably covered with mixed deciduous forest of oak, elm, alder, and birch, with little if any pine. They did not come armed with metal tools, and they used flint for making larger implements as did the Neolithic peoples, but in due course they imported bronze equipment, probably from Ireland, one of the routes being along the Great Glen, up which some of the Neolithic peoples may also have come. These early Bronze Age people usually buried their dead in a crouched position in a short stone cist, with a distinctive piece of pottery, the beaker. A few such burials have been found in Neolithic chambered tombs, which suggests an intermingling of the two peoples (Childe, 1946).

The middle stage of the Bronze Age is characterised by food vessel burials; this may not mean a new immigration, however, but a further intermingling with Neolithic people and renewed contacts with Ireland (Childe, 1946). During this period the Beaker people continued to predominate in the north-east of Scotland, where there appears to have been close settlement; and the population appears to have increased, because there was penetration into the heart of the Highlands, for example Glen Lyon (Childe, 1946). At this time, cremation began to replace inhumation, and it has been suggested that the wood needed for the funeral pyres was a further drain on the forest (Piggott, 1949), but this is not likely to have been serious. The working of wood progressed with the improvement in tools; a wooden cist made from slabs of split oak has been found in Aberdeenshire, while burial in coffins hollowed out of oak logs may date from this period (Childe, 1946, 1947).

In late Bronze Age times, cremated remains were interred either in cinerary urns or unurned. The distribution of those found is still principally in the Borders and the east coastal plains (Childe, 1946). There was an increase in bronze equipment but this was rather in implements of war than in tools to clear forests for further settlement.

During Bronze Age times the people still remained peasant farmers, although the latter working in bronze was no doubt a specialised industry, the artificers probably coming from Ireland. The evidence suggests that the agriculture was principally pastoral, but cereals and particularly barley were cultivated with the use of a hoe, and many querns for the grinding of corn have been found on sites dating from this period. During this period of about 1500 years settlements spread in all the better lowland areas. While in Europe generally, the appreciable destruction of forests dates from the Neolithic period, in these parts of Scotland there was probably little destruction until Bronze Age times, when the population was larger and the period longer. It must have been the mixed deciduous forests in the lowlands and valleys rather than the pinewoods that suffered from clearance and grazing. Before the end of the Bronze Age, the climate was becoming cooler and wetter, and the decline in the forests as shown by the fall in tree pollen relative to non-tree pollen (Durno, 1957; Fraser, 1955) in these regions was probably the combined effect of human and climatic agencies.

THE IRON AGE PEOPLES

The displacement of bronze by iron for making cutting tools marked an important advance, because iron ores, albeit poor, were widely distributed and more abundant than copper, and durable equipment became available for tree felling and other purposes. Knowledge of the working of iron came late to Scotland, probably only in the last centuries before our era, and perhaps as late as 100 B.C. (Childe, 1947; Piggott, 1949). It is not clear who brought this skill, but there appears to be an indication of Middle European Halstatt influence, while ornaments indicative of the La Tène culture of the Continent have been found. Bloomeries believed to date from this period have been located in different parts of Scotland from the Lothians to Aberdeenshire and in the Outer Isles (Childe, 1946; Simpson, 1944). Some striking structures may have been built about this time, such as the crannogs in lochs, the brochs particularly in the north, the earth houses, and above all the so-called Gallic and vitrified forts (Childe, 1946, 1947), but the forts may have been constructed in Roman times or even later. The Gallic forts, often on the tops of hills are both numerous and widely distributed, both in the east and the west (listed in Childe, 1946). Particularly in the west they are often small, but the construction of the large ones made important new demands on the woodlands. They were built of roughly dressed blocks of stone, with timber lacings in a manner similar to that of the *murus gallicus* described by Caesar, but they may have been of a more ramshackle construction (Wainwright, 1955). Childe (1946) has estimated that the Finavon fort in Angus required 100,000 cu. ft. of timber and twice that amount of stone. Thus, while timber had been used in the construction of houses and tombs from Neolithic times, this was a demand of quite a new magnitude, even if the estimates mentioned are too large. It was the destruction of these forts by fire, either accidentally or in war, that resulted in vitrified forts when the stone was fusible, as has been shown experimentally by Childe and Thorneycroft (1938).

Reviewing the 5000 years to the end of the prehistoric period during which man was an inhabitant of Scotland, one can state certain general conclusions, although the evidence is so scanty. First, man had no influence on the development of the forests in Boreal times nor on the change in the type of forest at the beginning of Atlantic times. Secondly, the Mesolithic peoples had little if any influence on the forests. Thirdly, while Neolithic farmers, principally through their pastoral activities, began the destruction of the woodlands, particularly in the north and on the islands, it was during Bronze Age times that this became more important, partly by progressive clearance for tillage, and partly by the browsing of tree regeneration by flocks. During a period of a century such effects would probably be small, but over fifteen centuries it would be appreciable. When in Iron Age times large quantities of timber were used for constructional purposes, the forest would definitely shrink, because the cleared areas would be near the places of settlement where the timber was to be used, and it would be there also that grazing would be most intensive. During the 500 years before the beginning of our era, the deteriorating climate would accentuate the destructive effects of man's activities in lowland woodlands of mixed deciduous species. The interval between heavy seed years in some species may have tended to lengthen, making natural regeneration less prolific, and some cleared woodlands may have become heath; pollen analysis has shown that ericoid pollen increased markedly during Sub-Atlantic times. The shrinkage of upland woodlands of pine and birch was due, as we have seen already, to the renewed growth of the bogs, an effect of climate and not of man.

THE IMPACT OF MAN ON THE FORESTS OF SCOTLAND IN HISTORIC TIMES

IN ROMAN TIMES

The influence of the Romans on Scotland came later than south of the border, it was not so continuous, and a large part of the country, including the mountainous Highland region and the north and west, was never occupied. Julius Caesar's two incursions into south-eastern Britain in 55 and 54 B.C. had, of course, no effect on the north. It took almost forty years after the Claudian invasion in A.D. 43 for the Romans to establish themselves sufficiently securely in southern Britain, after many setbacks, to enable an advance into Scotland to be made under Agricola, then Governor of Britain. It was fortunate that his son-in-law, Tacitus, was a writer, because although scholars have deplored the lack of geographical detail in the *Agricola*, something is thus known about Agricola's campaigns. In A.D. 79 or 80 Agricola advanced from York to an estuary named Tanaus. There has been difference of opinion as to whether this was the Tay or a river farther south (Anderson, J. G. C., 1922; Mattingly, 1948), but Richmond (1944) considers that it was the Tay and that this advance was in the nature of a reconnaissance. In the following year Agricola established a number of stockaded forts on the Forth-

Clyde line and explored his western flank (Richmond, 1944). Recent air re-connaissance and archaeological investigations have added to the knowledge of Roman remains of this period in south-western Scotland (St Joseph, 1951; Miller, 1952; Richmond, 1955b). During the same year, Agricola may have explored the west coast and the islands with his fleet, partly perhaps in an effort to find a way of outflanking the Highland region. If so, his failure to find such a route may have dictated his plans in the following year when he advanced northwards through Stirling and Strathallan to the Tay. As it was essential to protect his left flank, he built a series of forts to block the exits of the Highland glens, the principal one being the legionary fort at Inchtuthil, on the north bank of the Tay, ten miles north of Perth, which controlled the exit from the Tay and its tributary valleys (Crawford, 1949; St Joseph, 1951, 1955; Macdonald, 1919). Roman sea power was used in this and the next campaign to support the advance and reduce supply difficulties. Agricola's plan appears to have been to draw all the Highland tribes to the east by a bold and threatening advance along the eastern coastal plains north of the Tay from which they probably drew some of their supplies, and to bring them to a decisive battle. This he did in A.D. 84. A number of Roman marching camps are known in Angus, Kincardineshire, and Aberdeenshire, such as Oathlaw, Keithock, Kair House, Raedykes, Normandykes, Kintore, Glen-mailen and possibly Auchenhove in Banffshire, but the more northerly may not date from this time (anon., 1956a; Crawford, 1949; St Joseph, 1951; Simpson, 1944). The site of the battle of Mons Graupius between the Romans and a league of the northern tribes is not known; Tacitus' vivid account does not give this information. Crawford (1949) has pressed the claims of Raedykes, near Stone-haven, which was investigated earlier by General Roy (1793) and Sir George Macdonald (1916). It may yet be proved, however, that this battle was fought farther north and in sight of the Moray Firth. Wherever it was, it was decisive. In spite of Calgacus' impassioned speech before the battle, the native tribes lost 10,000 men out of a force of 30,000 and the Romans only 360, if Tacitus is to be believed. Agricola then withdrew after sending his fleet to encircle Scotland. He was recalled the next year. At this time the Romans held the region south of the Forth and Clyde and the eastern lowlands up to the Tay. Their forts blocked the exits from the Highland home of the Caledonians, but they had not penetrated into the Highland region, except no doubt to survey the landscape before planning their defences. This state of affairs did not last for long, however, either because of further attacks by the Caledonians or the necessity of withdrawing troops for use elsewhere. Some of the forts were evacuated shortly afterwards, and recent investigations have indicated that even Inchtuthil was abandoned about A.D. 90

(Richmond, 1955b). In due course the control of the Lowlands was centred on the important fort at Newstead in the Tweed valley, and by about A.D. 100 all the forts north of the Cheviots had been given up (Richmond, 1955a). About twenty years later, Hadrian's Wall between the Tyne and the Solway was constructed, and Scotland was cut off from the Roman world, but not for long. There was another advance when the Antonine Wall, or more correctly a *vallum* with a string of forts, was built about A.D. 142 between the Forth and Clyde by Lollicus Urbicus, then Governor of Britain. The Romans held this line for a period of about forty years, although the tribes to the north of it continued to harass them; the defences were temporarily evacuated about A.D. 155, and there was again damage to them about A.D. 180. The Antonine Wall and probably the forts south thereof except Birrens, about ten miles north of Carlisle, were again abandoned about A.D. 185 (Macdonald, 1934; Richmond, 1955a). Some ten years later southern Scotland, Hadrian's Wall, and the fortresses as far south as York were overrun by the Maeatae, a tribe from Strathmore and Strathearn. This led to a further campaign into Scotland in A.D. 209, led on this occasion by the Emperor Severus. He probably transported his army by sea to the Firth of Forth and his base was at Cramond (Miller, 1952). He first attacked the Caledonians and beat them into unconditional surrender, but further trouble arose both with them and the Maeatae. Severus died in 211, and Caracalla, after a further campaign, endeavoured to secure that these tribes would not attack their neighbours south of the Forth. Thereafter the Lowlands appeared to have been controlled for a period by patrols from outposts of Hadrian's Wall, and became later something in the nature of Roman protectorates (Macdonald, 1934; Richmond, 1955a). The tribes north of the Forth continued to raid the north of England, and the only Roman penetration into Scotland was to drive them back, for example by the expedition of Constantius, the father of Constantine the Great, about A.D. 305. Later, there were sea raids by the northern tribes, joined by the Scots from northern Ireland, and by the Saxons on the English coasts (Macdonald, 1934; Richmond, 1955a). Thus direct Roman influence on what is now Scotland began later and finished more than a century earlier than in England.

In the second quarter of the second century A.D., Ptolemy in Alexandria prepared tables of the latitudes and longitudes of a sufficient number of places to enable maps to be drawn of the then known world, including the British Isles. A map of Britain made by joining these points is included in the Ordnance Survey Map of Roman Britain (anon., 1956a) and also in an article by Bradley (1885). Blaeu's (1654) stylised version of Ptolemy's data is reproduced in Fig. 10. Ptolemy's data were based on information collected by early Greek travellers, such as

Pytheas of Marseilles who circumnavigated Britain about 325 B.C., and by the Romans (Müller, 1883; Rylands, 1893). Unfortunately Ptolemy's data make the northern part of Britain point east and not north, but apart from this distortion it is reasonably accurate. Its principal interest from the point of view of woodlands is that it gives the first reference to the Caledonian Forest as such. This is shown on the western (northern in Ptolemy) side of the Highlands from about Loch Long to about the Beauly Firth, but too much weight should not be placed on the actual location. As we have already seen the forests at this time consisted of oak, elm and alder woodlands and birchwoods, as well as pinewoods.

FIG. 10. A stylised map of Scotland, based on Ptolemy's data, as published in Blaeu's *Atlas*, 1654

The outline of Roman activities already given and the records of discovered Roman remains, as shown for example on the Ordnance Survey Map of Roman Britain (anon., 1956a), bring out clearly that Roman influence on Scotland, including its forests, was much less than in southern Britain. Moreover the forests that may have been affected were those on the lowlands dominated by oak, elm, and alder. The only Romans who may have seen the pinewoods in the uplands of the Highlands were those who penetrated up the valleys to spy out the land. Nevertheless, the Roman campaigns and settlements must have had some effect. In order to ensure that approaching enemies were seen, the forests adjoining roads, forts, and other defences were no doubt cleared, whether or no the timber was

LOCH MAREE WITH PART OF THE WOOD OF GLAS-LEITIRE IN THE FOREGROUND
AND SɪOCH IN THE BACKGROUND

There is a mixture of pine and birch characteristic of many western woods. The pine is mainly var.
horizontalis Don (see PL. XIII.*a*), but there is a typical tree of f. *condensata* Fries (see PL. XIII.*d*) in the lower
left-hand corner.

needed for constructional purposes, to form tracks through the marshes, or other-wise. Large amounts of timber were used in the construction of forts. This is shown, for example, by the excavations made at the Agricolan fort at Fendoch at the mouth of the Sma' Glen in Perthshire, designed to accommodate an infantry cohort – the fort at Inchtuthil was much larger. At Fendoch, Richmond and McIntyre (1939) were able by meticulous excavation to deduce the plan and construction of the numerous timber buildings. These included the parapets on the ramparts, gateway towers, headquarters building, commandant's house, hos-pital, barracks, granaries, and other structures. The posts of the gateway towers were deduced to be about 30 ft. (9 m.) high and 12 in. (30·5 cm.) square. The method of construction of the interior buildings was to place timber sills in trenches, and to insert the upright posts into them. In their original paper the authors stated that the timber framing was clad with weather boarding, but Richmond later postulated wattle and daub (1944). It was considered that the posts in the gateway towers were probably oak and the sills elm. A turf sample gave only hazel, alder and grass pollen, and from this it was deduced that there were no large forest trees in the neighbourhood, though it is almost certain that there would be trees of oak and elm of the required size nearby at this time. The authors pointed out that the plans of the buildings show standardisation in the sizes of the timber, and they considered that the material might have been pre-pared elsewhere in advance and seasoned. When the fort was evacuated all the timber was removed, no doubt for later use. This probably indicates a shortage of skilled carpenters rather than a lack of timber. In addition to that required for construction, timber would be needed for fuel and other purposes. While the consumption of timber per head of the Roman army was no doubt many times that of the native population, the number of people was much smaller. It would be a mistake, therefore, to overemphasise, as has been done by some earlier authors, the influence of the Romans on the forests of Scotland either in obtaining timber for use or in cutting and burning for purely military reasons. The direct influence would also be on the lowlands which had already been populated, albeit sparsely, for almost two thousand years, and where the forests were probably thinning out at that time. Moreover, the evidence of Roman authors, such as Tacitus and Dio Cassius (quoted Macdonald, 1934), suggests that marsh and not woodland covered much of the lowlands. During the Roman period, the native population must have continued to influence the woodlands in much the same way as hitherto. They were still pastoral people, and this is illustrated by Strabo's well-known reference to the Britons: "Forests are their cities: for having enclosed an ample space with felled trees, they make themselves huts therein, and lodge

E

their cattle, though not for any long continuance." Clark (1952) has suggested that this may indicate something in the nature of a Norwegian *sœtter*. The Romans may have had some indirect influence on the woodlands of the Highland region. As we have seen, the native tribes were driven periodically from the lowlands and the eastern coastal plains where the best land was, and this may have led to the extension of cultivation and grazing in the Highland region which hitherto appears to have been sparsely populated.

DURING THE DARK AGES

The limited impact of Roman power, particularly north of the Forth and Clyde, meant that there was no sudden change when Roman influence declined, and indeed the northern tribes were on the attack before the Romans left Britain at the beginning of the fifth century. At that time, there were several British kingdoms south of the Forth and Clyde. From the end of the fifth century, however, the immigrant Angles of Northumbria were thrusting northwards, and the only British kingdom to survive was that of Strathclyde in the south-west. In the fifth century also, there were new settlers in the west, the Scots from northern Ireland, who were later to give their name to the whole country. They formed the small kingdom of Dalriada in Argyll and the adjoining islands, including Iona, and they were later to draw part of their influence from the fame of St Columba. In the rest of the country, there were people whom the Romans called Picts from as early as the end of the third century. There has been long and continuing controversy about this people – for example, whether or no they were the descendants of the earlier tribes such as the Caledonians, what language they spoke, whether the descent of their kings was truly matrilinear or not, and what was their culture. Skene (1867, 1876) dealt with this subject in the last century, and there have been recent books on it by Chadwick (1949), Lethbridge (1954) and Wainwright (1955). To begin with there may have been several Pictish kingdoms, but in due course there was one with seven provinces. About 843, Kenneth MacAlpin, the King of the Scots, became also King of the Picts, uniting the region north of the Forth and Clyde. Before that time, however, the Northumbrian Angles had secured a temporary overlordship of the northern kingdoms and had liquidated the British kingdom of Strathclyde. After the fall of Northumbria in the second half of the ninth century, the frontier of Scotland was advanced from the Forth and Clyde to the Tweed-Solway line.

There are a considerable number of contemporary documents dealing with this period, such as the *Chronicles of the Picts and Scots* and various Irish chronicles, as well as religious works such as Bede's *Ecclesiastical History*. These are available or are discussed in Skene's works (1867, 1876), and in A. O. Anderson's *Early Sources of Scottish History* (1922), as well as in the recent books already mentioned. Unfortunately neither the literary nor the available archaeological evidence throws much light on the way of life of the people, and in particular its effect on the woodlands. The times were disturbed, but the country gradually developed towards an organised unity. During the period, homesteads probably grew into villages, at least in the more closely settled areas in the lowlands, and hoe cultivation gave way to the plough (Piggott in Wainwright, 1955). The woodlands would not only be the source of considerable amounts of timber needed both for constructional purposes and fuel, but would also be the grazing grounds. Graham (1953) has studied the Dark-Age texts from the archaeological point of view. There are some references to the use of timber for building purposes. Timber framing with wattle appears to have continued to be the common method of construction of houses. St Ninian, the first Christian missionary to Scotland, erected a stone church about 400 at Whithorn, but many later churches were of timber construction.

From the end of the eighth century for a period of over four hundred years, the northern and western regions of Scotland suffered from raids and in due course settlement by the Norsemen. This was part of their widespread emigration; they also ranged westwards to Iceland, Greenland and North America, and southwards to England, Ireland, France and Mediterranean lands. In the early part of the period, they were principally bent on pillage, and as much of the wealth – and all the learning – was centred in the monasteries, these suffered severely; for example irreparable damage was done at Iona and other religious houses at the beginning of the ninth century. Later a period of settlement followed, and by 1034 the Norse dominions in Scotland reached their widest extent, and included Orkney, Shetland, the Outer and Inner Hebrides, the Isle of Man, and, on the mainland, the extreme northern and western coasts, and Galloway (Bremner, 1923). The native inhabitants continued to challenge the Norsemen, particularly on the mainland. Following the Battle of Largs in 1263, and the death of King Haakon of Norway at Kirkwall shortly afterwards, there were negotiations between the two countries, and in 1266 Norway ceded Man and the Hebrides to King Alexander III of Scotland for a payment of 4000 merks sterling and a yearly payment of 100 merks. Orkney and Shetland remained in Norwegian hands until 1471, after the marriage of James III with Margaret, daughter of the Norwegian king, Christian I.

Brøgger (1929) suggested that one of the many reasons why the Norsemen were attracted to Scotland was its timber wealth. He appears to have overestimated the extent of the woodlands, but it must have been considerable in the Norse period. There was probably little woodland in Orkney and Shetland by this time, but the evidence of recent pollen analysis in Lewis is consistent with the existence of woods of birch and pine, and oak, elm and alder there during later Sub-Atlantic times. Some of the Inner Hebrides and the western mainland were almost certainly well wooded at this time, and there would be supplies of oak and pine for shipbuilding within easy reach of the sea. The archaeological evidence already mentioned suggests that the extreme north of Scotland was relatively treeless at a much earlier period, but pollen analysis and later historical records show that there was some woodland there. There is little evidence in contemporary documents, such as the Icelandic Sagas, about the woodlands in Scotland, but in the Saga of Haakon Haakonsson written about 1265 (Bremner, 1923) it is recorded that when King Haakon was returning from the Battle of Largs, he put into Loch Eriboll in Sutherland, and, when some of the men went ashore for water, they were attacked by some of the Scots; more Norsemen landed, and the Scots fled into the woods. This region could not have been treeless, therefore, at that time. The Norse emigrations depended on their magnificent ships, and they particularly needed oak planking (Brøgger, 1929) and pine for masts. During their settlement in Scotland, they may have been partly responsible for deforestation on the islands and elsewhere. In a report by an unknown author in the last decades of the sixteenth century (Skene, 1890, Appendix III) it is mentioned that at that time there were no woods on Lewis, Harris, and Raasay, but there were woods on Skye, principally birch and alder, and also on Mull and Jura.

IN FEUDAL TIMES

As we have seen already, the Celtic inhabitants of Scotland were grouped into tribes. Skene (1876) has discussed their organisation and the changes that took place, first under Saxon and later under Norman influence. The system of land tenure in Celtic times remains obscure, but it appears that the tribe held at least part of the tribal land in common, although the head, called the toisech, no doubt had his own holding, and others may have enjoyed individual ownership. Several tribes might be united under a minor king or mormaer. When Scotland first approached political unity, it consisted of several different peoples of diverse origins and customs. The Celtic system of tribal organisation was influenced when the Lothians and its Anglian people became part of Scotland, and this influence was reinforced when Malcolm Canmore – who had carried the unification a stage further – married the Saxon Princess Margaret about 1070, and they welcomed Saxon refugees from the Normans. About this time the Celtic names of mormaer and toisech were replaced by earl and thane. The feudalisation of Scotland did not take place in earnest until David, the youngest son of Malcolm Canmore and Queen Margaret, succeeded to the southern part of the country, with the title of earl, and, on the death of his brother Alexander in 1124, to the whole kingdom as David I. When a youth he had spent much of his time at the English court of Henry I, and had been educated there in feudal ways with young Norman nobles. In the words of Skene (1876), "David founded a dynasty of feudal monarchs of Celtic descent in the paternal line, and in the maternal representing the old Saxon royal family, but governing the country as feudal superiors, and introducing feudal institutions." Ritchie (1954) in his book entitled *The Normans in Scotland* has discussed the history of Scotland under Malcolm Canmore and his sons, and Barrow (1956) has recently presented a picture of Britain, including Scotland, during the period from 1066 to 1314.

The feudal system implied that the king was feudal superior of all the land as far as his authority ran. He made grants to feudal lords, some of whom, from at least the time of David I, were Normans who had come from England. They were vassals of the Crown, holding their land on some form of contractual agreement which might be a feu-holding, that is based on an annual payment to the Crown, or might involve service, military or otherwise. The authority of the king was greatest in the southern and eastern parts of the country, and it was there that this feudal system of land ownership developed first. The kings, and in particular David I, also made grants of land for the foundation of monasteries belonging to a number of orders. Some of the charters have survived and have been edited and published. All the land not granted away remained in the hands of the king. It was in two categories; his demesne which was cultivated, and the other or waste. Those who cultivated the land were of different classes: first, the freeholders who held their land as a rule in return for service; secondly, free farmers who sometimes had a steelbow tenancy, receiving stock and equipment at the beginning of the tenancy and returning an equivalent amount at its end, with rent according to the value of the steelbow goods; and lastly, serfs (Skene, 1876; *Exchequer Rolls of Scotland*, VOL. I, Preface). The serf class appears to have continued as such for a shorter time in Scotland than in other feudal countries, for example only until the end of the fourteenth century in Mar (Simpson, 1944). The feudal lords worked their land in a similar way, and they also made grants of different kinds to the Church and others. The waste land was called forest. In the medieval sense, therefore, the term forest did not necessarily mean woodland, and when it was used during the succeeding centuries in charters, etc., one cannot assume that the land in question carried trees, unless there is other evidence to indicate this. This land was used primarily for hunting and it was protected in various ways to this end. The terms of a grant of forest rights in Eskdale by Roger Avenel to Melrose Abbey at the beginning of the thirteenth century is a good illustration of this interest in hunting in the forest: "The same Roger and his heirs shall have only hart and hind, wild boar and sow, buck and roe, also eyrie of falcons and sparrowhawks, so that the monks do not maliciously hinder them from nesting in the place in which they do nest as long as they have the custom of nesting there. Neither may they take the nests of falcons or of sparrowhawks within the said bounds. Neither may the trees in which they build in one year be cut down until it be examined in the year next following whether they wish to build in these trees or not; and if they do not then make their eyries, the monks shall lawfully take their use of these trees in any way they please" (anon., 1837, 1868). Thus, while the noble owners of the forests may have been interested only in sport, the monks and no doubt others valued the timber. While forest remained in the hands of the king, it was royal forest, and during the centuries there are records of the appointment of persons as foresters. From time to time, however, the king made grants of tracts of forest, and it then passed into private ownership. In the Highlands the progress of feudalisation was slower, and there the clan organisation developed out of the Celtic system.

In the early parliamentary records of Scotland, there are a number of laws relating to the forest which were brought together as *Leges Forestarum* in the *Acts of the Parliament of Scotland* (VOL. I, p. 687). The date of these laws is uncertain, but the editor, Cosmo Innes, considered that, on manuscript evidence, they were not earlier than the fourteenth century. He also thought that they were derived from earlier Norman laws in England but with less drastic penalties. Some of the forest laws were directly concerned with trees, such as the penalty for cutting an oak, but most were concerned with pannage, that is acorns and other food for swine, and the restriction of grazing. No one was permitted to enter the forest with their animals during the time of pannage without a licence under a penalty of eight cows. In another law, swine were specifically excluded. These references to oak and pannage support the conclusion that oak was an important species in the lowland woods. The foresters of these days disliked goats as much as do their present-day successors in this and many other countries. When goats were found in the forest one of them was to be hung up on a tree by the horns for the first three trespasses, and the fourth time one was to be slain and the bowels left. There was also a prohibition of taking fire into the forest.

A glimpse of the woodlands in the mountainous Highland region is got from a description by John of Fordun in his *Chronicle of the Scottish Nation*, written in the closing decades of the fourteenth century (Skene, 1872): "Scotland is a country strong by nature and toilsome of access. In some parts, it towers into mountains; in others it sinks down into plains. For lofty mountains stretch through the midst of it, from end to end, as do the tall Alps through Europe; and these mountains formerly separated the Scots from the Picts, and their kingdoms from each other. . . . Along the foot of these mountains are vast woods, full of stags, roe-deer, and other wild animals and beasts of various kinds; and these forests oftentimes afford a strong and safe protection to the cattle of the inhabitants against the depredations of their enemies; for the herds of these parts, they say, are accustomed, from use, whenever they hear the shouts of men or women, and if suddenly attacked by dogs, to flock hastily into the woods."

The developments that took place in feudal Scotland had an influence at least on the lowland woodlands. Timber was needed in increasing amounts for the building of the castles of the feudal lords and for the numerous new churches and monasteries. There is contemporary evidence of grants of timber on the founding of monasteries, for example, by David I. In the Great Charter of Holyrood it is stated: "I charge, moreover, all my servants and foresters of Stirlingshire and Clackmanan, that the Abbot and convent have free power in all my woods and forests, of taking as much timber as they please and wish for the building of their church and of their houses, and for any other purpose of theirs." And again in the Great Charter of Melrose is included: "Know, moreover, that I have given to all the aforesaid monks and by this charter confirmed, in my lands and forests, to wit Selkirk and Traquair, all their easements, to wit pasture for their beasts, and logs and timber, and pannage everywhere for their own use as I myself have best for my own use, and namely between Gala and Leader" (anon., 1868). There is also evidence of more intensive agriculture and particularly pastoral agriculture, probably led by the monks. The Abbey of Melrose appears to have derived a large part of its revenues from the pasturage of sheep and cattle. Grants from feudal lords to the Abbey show that the monks had large flocks of sheep from the twelfth century (anon., 1837). The woodlands were probably already sparse in the Borders, and later evidence shows that they had become progressively fewer. From about the same time, the eastern Highlands also began to be influenced by religious houses, for example, by the Abbey of Coupar Angus, as is shown both by its charters (Easson, 1947) and its Rental Book (Rogers, 1879), and by the Abbey of Inchaffray, near Crieff (Lindsay et al., 1903). Both had extensive properties in Perthshire. During the Wars of Independence before the Battle of Bannockburn in 1314, there was much destruction which in due course meant the need for more timber. It is of interest that in 1292 forty seasoned oaks were taken from

Darnaway Forest for the fabric of the cathedral church of Caithness (anon., 1814).

A shortage of accessible timber had led to some importation as early as the end of the thirteenth century. Richardson (1921) has noted that Estland or Baltic boards were used during Edward I's campaigns against Scotland. The earliest record found of such timber being purchased in Scotland is in an account rendered at Scone, dated 1329, and recorded in the *Exchequer Rolls of Scotland* (VOL. I, p. 215). Thereafter there is an increasing number of entries of Estland or Baltic boards or timber from Prussia for building and repair work at the castles at Edinburgh, Stirling, Roxburgh, Inverness, and Darnaway, and for other purposes. This was probably all pine timber, because there is an occasional reference to oak as such. In the sixteenth century, the importation of oak was sufficiently important to justify Parliament in 1563 to decide to send an ambassador to Denmark to obtain the removal of a prohibition of its sale to Scottish merchants (*Acts of Parliament*, VOL. II, p. 544).

While there is earlier evidence of efforts, legislative and other, to conserve timber by endeavouring to prevent the unlawful cutting and burning of trees, the first legislation to encourage planting was passed in 1457, in the reign of James II. Freeholders, temporal and spiritual, were to ordain that their tenants plant woodlands and trees, make hedges, and sow broom (*Acts of Parliament*, VOL. II, p. 51). Some at least did so, because it is recorded in the Rental Book of the Abbey of Coupar Angus (Rogers, 1879, 1880) that the monks enjoined their tenants to plant ash trees, osiers and saughs, and that they did so themselves in the Abbey gardens. There is also a reference to the growing of broom, partly for shelter and partly for fuel for the hearths and ovens of the abbey – an indication of the need for tree planting. The effect of this early legislative encouragement of forestry could not have been appreciable, because in 1503 it was stated, no doubt with exaggeration, that the woodlands of Scotland were utterly destroyed. The penalty for burning trees (green wood) was raised to five pounds Scots, and landowners were to plant at least one acre of woodland where there was no great woodland or forest (*Acts of Parliament*, VOL. II, pp. 242, 243, 251). In 1535 (VOL. II, p. 343), and again in 1555 (VOL. II, p. 499), Acts were passed to enforce and sharpen the earlier legislation, and Murray (1935) has quoted from these. There is a record in 1535-36 of the bringing of oak by ship from Lochaber for use at Holyrood (Paton, 1957). These actions could only mean that the woodlands then accessible were rapidly becoming exhausted, and this view is reinforced by an Act passed in 1563 in which the export of salt – an important export commodity – was prohibited except to strangers from Norway and other eastern parts who brought in timber. All the evidence leads to the conclusion, therefore, that by the sixteenth century the timber reserves outwith the Highland region were almost exhausted, and indeed woodlands must have been few in the previous century if Aeneas Sylvius, afterwards Pope Pius II, is to be believed. He stated after a visit to Scotland in the reign of James I that the country he saw was destitute of timber and commented on the use of coal (Brown, 1891).

IN THE HIGHLAND WOODLANDS

The history of the individual native pinewoods and other woodland communities is discussed in Chapters 4 to 11, and only the principal trends in their history will be considered in this chapter.

We have seen already that there were settlements at least in parts of the Highland region from Mesolithic times, and that man began to influence the woodlands from the Neolithic period. While this influence must have increased steadily with each millennium, the population was much smaller than on the better land in the Lowlands, the eastern coastal plains, and on some of the islands. Partly because of their inaccessibility, the Highland woods do not appear to have been exploited to any extent for use outwith the region until 1600. Until then they had to meet only local needs, and, while in some instances these might be considerable, in most they were much less than elsewhere in Scotland. Moreover, the flocks and herds in the Highlands were small up to that time compared with those in the Lowlands, and damage to natural regeneration must have been much less.

The king and the people of the Lowlands do not appear to have had much knowledge about the timber resources in the Highlands until the closing decades of the sixteenth century, when early travellers, such as Timothy Pont, described the countryside in that region (Macfarlane, 1908), and this information was used later to make the maps in Blaeu's *Atlas* (1654). As we have seen, the acute shortage of timber in lowland Scotland was already causing concern, and it is not surprising that this information attracted the attention of James VI and his Scottish Parliament. An Act passed in 1609 (*Acts of Parliament*, VOL. IV, p. 408) throws some light on the Highland woodlands at that time: "Forasmuch as it has pleased God to discover certain veins of rich metal within this kingdom, as also certain woods in the Highlands, which woods by reason of the savageness of the inhabitants thereabout were either unknown or at least unprofitable and unused, and now the Estates presently convened being informed that some persons . . . would erect iron mills in some parts to the utter wasting and consuming of the said woods, which might be reserved for many better uses and upon more choice and profitable metals . . . therefore the Estates statue and ordain and therewith commands, charges and inhibits all and sundry his Majesty's lieges and subjects that none of them presume nor take on hand to work and make any iron with wood or timber under the pain of confiscation of the whole iron that shall be made with the said timber to his Majesty's use. . . ." At that time, while peat was used to some extent in smelting, timber was commonly used, and, notwithstanding this Act, we find the same king granting a licence in 1612 to Sir George Hay of Netherless to make iron and glass within the whole bounds of Scotland (*Acts of Parliament*, VOL. IV, p. 515). Hay appears to have been already engaged in the manufacture of iron in the Loch Maree district of Wester Ross, and this work was greatly expanded and is discussed in Chapter 9. Although this appears to have been the earliest large-scale use of Highland timber for the smelting and working of iron, it was not the only instance; a number of sites where iron smelting was done in Strath Naver, Sutherlandshire, are shown on a map in Blaeu's *Atlas* (1654).

The discovery of the Highland woodlands about 1600 also led to their exploitation for naval purposes. About that time Crown surveyors reported on the presence of very large pine trees, suitable for masts, at Loch Arkaig, in western Inverness-shire, and pine was being floated down the short rivers in Ardgour, Argyllshire, to the sea where timber and masts were loaded on to ships (see Chapter 7).

The Highland woodlands might have disappeared quickly but for extraction difficulties. Transport by land was difficult, if not impossible, and indeed some of the woodlands are inaccessible today from an economic point of view. It is not surprising, therefore, that water transport was used, and that floating was practised first on the short and relatively easy rivers in the west. The exploitation of the large pine forests in central Scotland, for example in the upper valleys of the Spey and Dee, came later. In the seventeenth century efforts were made to exploit the timber resources of Upper Speyside, and some timber was transported by land to Inverness, but efforts at that time to float timber down the Spey were not successful. It is of interest that the first method was to use a coracle or small boat to precede the small raft. These coracles were oval in shape, with a wickerwork frame, and covered with hide; one is preserved in the Elgin Museum (Clark, 1952; Hornell, 1946). It was not until the beginning of the next century that the floating problems were solved and extensive exploitation of the pine forests in this district began. It reached its peak at the end of the eighteenth century and the beginning of the next, when the revenue from Rothiemurchus Forest alone was between £10,000 and £20,000 per annum (see Chapter 5). In Upper Deeside, the pine forests mainly served local needs until the eighteenth century, when the River Dee was used for floating. There was also heavy exploitation at the beginning of the last century when floating was again used (see Chapter 4). Some of the Highland woodlands were already showing signs of devastation by the middle of the eighteenth century, and some repair work was done after the rising in 1745 on estates which were under the management of the Commissioners of the Forfeited Estates, for example at Barisdale, Arkaig, and Rannoch. Grazing animals were excluded by ditch and dyke, pine seed was sown, and young trees planted. Some evidence of this work is to be seen today (see Chapters 6 and 7).

The major exploitation in many Highland woodlands had almost come to an end by the middle of the last century. In some of them there were large flocks of sheep, and, at a later date, many of the woodlands were included in deer forests and the population of red deer increased. Both these developments led to increasing damage to natural regeneration. There was felling on a considerable scale in some of the woodlands during the 1914-18 War, and to a less extent in the last war (see Chapters 4 to 11).

From a forestry point of view the native pinewoods were not only a source of timber but also of seed of Scots pine of the distinctive native strains. In 1621, James VI and I asked the Earl of Mar to send pine seed from Mar Forest in Upper Deeside for use in England. A little later, John Evelyn states in *Sylva* (1664) that he had received seed from the Marquis of Argyll of "a most beautiful sort of fir growing upon the mountains". He sowed the seed with tolerable success. In Hunter's edition of *Sylva* (1776) there is a reference to pine near Loch Broom in Wester Ross; this information is probably not original but derived from a communication to the Royal Society by the Earl of Cromarty (1710). From the beginning of the seventeenth century, the sowing and planting of Scots pine spread also in Scotland. It is known that Sir Duncan Campbell of Glenorchy was doing so on that estate and on his other properties as early as 1613 (anon., 1855), and his son, Sir Colin, sent pine cones about 1637 to Scottish landowners, including the Earl of Lauderdale and Lord Lindsay (Murray, 1935).

While native pine seed was being distributed and used in the seventeenth century, therefore, it was not until the beginning of the next century that relatively large scale planting began, and principally in Scotland. According to the then Earl of Haddington (1765), there was a regular trade in the export of pine seed from the Highlands. He described how he opened the cones by spreading them in the sun. He goes on to say: "The Highlanders are too lazy to be at so much trouble; for after they have gathered the cones, they lay them upon a kiln; this opens them quickly, tho' it often over-dries the seed that it cannot grow." Some of the eighteenth-century Scots pine plantations, almost certainly of native seed origin, were still growing earlier in this century. Very fine plantations at

Langlee, Birkenside, and Mellerstain in the Scottish Borders were felled during the 1914-18 War. A sample plot at Langlee (P.140) gave a mean height of 90 ft. (27 m.) and a volume of 8600 cu. ft., hoppus, underbark, per acre (829 m.³ per ha.) at 141 years (anon., 1928; Steven, 1927). One such plantation at Castle Grant in Speyside still survives, and particulars of it are given in Chapter 5. These early plantations showed the potentiality of growth possessed by the native Scots pine when grown on relatively favourable sites. Already in the eighteenth century, there was a lively controversy about the quality of the timber in Scots pine plantations compared with that in the native forests, and in particular whether the difference was due to site or strain; this is discussed in Chapter 12.

CHAPTER 3

THE GENERAL ECOLOGY OF THE NATIVE PINEWOODS AND ASSOCIATED COMMUNITIES IN SCOTLAND

I<small>N THIS</small> chapter there is a general discussion of the native pinewoods, their habitat factors, flora, fauna, structure, and natural regeneration. There is a similar discussion for each individual wood in Chapters 4 to 11.

CLIMATE

The essential information about the climate of the British Isles is available from a number of sources (anon., 1919; anon., 1949; anon., 1952b; anon., 1953-5; Bilham, 1938; Manley, 1952), and Tansley (1949) has discussed its relationship with plant growth. Anderson and Fairbairn (1955) have recently subdivided Scotland into climatic regions. Only the principal characteristics of the climate within the region of Scotland where the native pinewoods are to be found will be considered. Throughout this region the climate is cool, humid, and oceanic compared with that in other parts of the geographical range of Scots pine, with the exception of western Norway.

RAINFALL

The average rainfall is controlled by the configuration of the land and the distance from the Atlantic, being high to the west of the great land masses and low to the east. Everywhere it increases with altitude. Fig. 11 illustrates the marked differences between easterly and westerly districts at comparable altitudes, Crathes with 34 in. (864 mm.) rainfall and 199 rain days per annum being typical of the eastern native pinewoods, and Fort William with 78 in. (1980 mm.) rainfall and 240 rain days of the western. The rainfall is relatively well distributed, but most falls in the winter months, the growing season from May to August inclusive only receiving 9·8 in. (249 mm.) or 29 per cent. of the annual rainfall at Crathes, and 18·4 in. (467 mm.) or 23·5 per cent. at Fort William. There is no difference in rainfall north to south when the east to west gradient is eliminated. The relative humidity percentage varies in May and June from 60 in the eastern woods to 75 in the extreme westerly and northerly, and in winter it is about 80 in all the regions (anon., 1952*b*).

The incidence of snow may be expressed in different ways, but "snow lying", defined as half the surrounding country covered with snow at the time of the

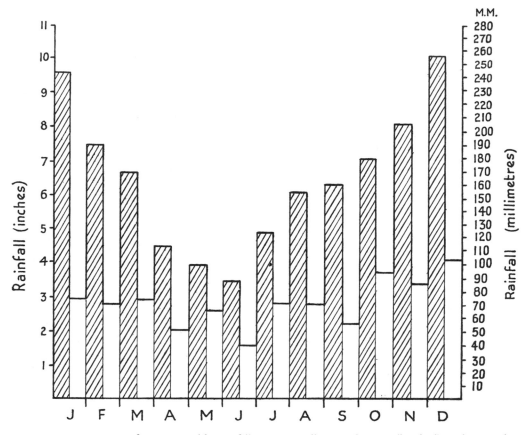

FIG. II. A comparison of mean monthly rainfalls at Fort William in the west (hatched), and at Crathes in the east (unhatched). Fort William, 56° 49′ N.; 5° 7′ W., 171 ft. (51·3 m.) above sea-level, with a mean annual rainfall of 77·84 in. (1977 mm.), and 240 rain-days per annum. Crathes, 57° 3′ N.; 2° 25′ W., 140 ft. (42 m.) above sea-level, with a mean annual rainfall of 33·9 in. (861 mm.), and 199 rain-days per annum. Data taken from *The book of normals, 1881–1915* (anon., 1919).

morning observation, is probably the best record for the purposes of the present study. The duration of the snow covering depends principally on altitude, but the influence of the Atlantic reduces the duration in the west. Thus, the average number of mornings per annum with snow lying is about 10 at the lower altitudes in the western Highlands, 30 in the eastern, while at Braemar at 1111 ft. (333 m.) it is 68 (anon., 1952*b*), and in 1919 it was 122 (Manley, 1952).

TEMPERATURE

The monthly variations in temperature east to west, and including Braemar which is typical of the higher altitudes in the eastern Highlands, and the north and south differences are illustrated in Fig. 12. It can be seen that the temperatures at the different stations vary much less than rainfall, but there is a discernable pattern. The temperatures in the west are higher than in the east at about the same altitude, except in July when they are similar. The higher altitude at Braemar is reflected in lower mean temperatures throughout the year. At the northern limit of the pinewoods, the summer is cooler by about two to three degrees Fahrenheit (1·1 to 1·7° C.) than at the southern, but the winter means are unexpectedly a little higher in the north. The absolute lowest temperatures are reached in the higher valleys of the eastern Highlands, for example − 17° F. (− 27·2° C.) at Braemar, and − 11° F. (− 23·9° C.) at Aviemore, both on 8 February 1895, while high summer temperatures, over 80° F. (26·7° C.) are sometimes experienced in these districts. The native pinewoods in the eastern Highlands are growing, therefore, under less oceanic conditions than elsewhere. Even there, however, it should be noted that the mean temperature for January at all the stations quoted is more than two degrees Fahrenheit above freezing point (1·1° C.) and at Fort William it is seven degrees (3·9° C.). This contrasts with the influence of temperature on the natural distribution of Scots pine in Germany, where there is some correlation with the 32° F. (0° C.) January isotherm (Firbas, 1949; Knoch, 1937).

Enquist (1933) has correlated the number of "frost" days with the distribution of Scots pine and other species in Scandinavia, and the figure for pine is 90 per annum. The average number of days with a maximum temperature of 32° F. (0° C.) is only 62 at Fort William and only over 90 at the higher altitudes in the eastern Highlands.

WIND

South, south-west, and west winds constitute about half the winds, except during the period from March to June when dry easterly winds are common. The latter may influence tree growth in eastern coastal districts, but have less effect in the inland areas where the pinewoods are situated. The annual mean wind speed declines from the west to the east, being just under 15 miles per hour (24 km. per hour) at the westerly limit of the native pinewoods and 10 m.p.h. (16 k.p.h.) at the easterly. The pattern of the distribution of winds of gale force, over 39 m.p.h. (63 k.p.h.), is similar, an average of 20 to 30 days per annum in the west, and 10 in the east (anon., 1952b; Andersen, 1954).

Where the pinewoods reach their highest altitudinal limit, exposure to wind

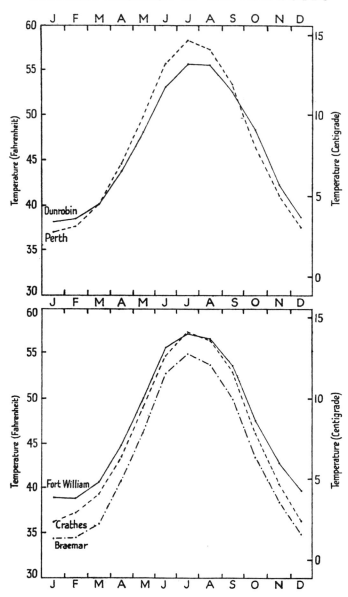

FIG. 12.   Mean monthly temperatures at Fort William in the west, Crathes in the east, Dunrobin in the north, Perth in the south, and Braemar in the mountainous central region of Scotland. Fort William, 56° 49′ N., 5° 7′ W., 171 ft. (51·3 m.) above sea-level, with a mean annual temperature of 47·2°F. (8·4 °C.). Crathes, 57° 3′ N., 2° 25′ W., 140 ft. (42 m.) above sea-level, with a mean annual temperature of 45·8°F. (7·7°C.). Dunrobin, 57° 59′ N., 3° 56′ W., 12 ft. (3·6 m.) above sea-level, with a mean annual temperature of 46·2°F. (7·9°C.). Perth, 56° 24′ N., 3° 27′ W., 76 ft. (22·8 m.) above sea-level, with a mean annual temperature of 46·6°F. (8·1°C.). Braemar, 57° 0′ N., 3° 24′ W., 1120 ft. (336 m.) above sea-level, with a mean annual temperature of 43·3°F. (6·3°C.). Data taken from *The Book of Normals, 1881–1915* (anon., 1919).

PLATE IV

A map by John Leslie, 1758, of part of the Black Wood of Rannoch showing forest, agricultural land (lined), and sawmill with sluice and log pond. (Reproduced by permission from the Forfeited Estates Papers preserved in H.M. General Register House, Edinburgh.)

tends to prevent their upward spread, but in most instances periodic burning of heather, grazing by red deer and sheep, and the presence of bog, rock and scree are more important factors.

No doubt the native pinewoods have suffered some damage by windthrow during the exceptional gales that have affected the forests of Scotland during the centuries. There are actual records of damage at Rannoch in 1771 and 1779, at Ballochbuie, Mar and Glen Lyon in 1879, and at Ballochbuie and Glentanar on 31 January 1953. There is, however, no historical evidence of catastrophic damage by wind in the native woods.

DAY LENGTH

This may be important when comparing different latitudinal strains. The following data in hours per day refer to Fort William, 56° 48′ N. (anon., 1919):

Jan.	Feb.	March	April	May	June	
7·43	9·40	11·74	14·17	16·37	17·62	

July	Aug.	Sept.	Oct.	Nov.	Dec.	Year
17·06	15·11	12·76	10·35	8·10	6·79	12·25

SUNSHINE

The average means of the daily duration of bright sunshine varies seasonally from about one hour in January to about 5·5 in June. There are no marked variations regionally, but the most easterly woods have slightly higher values (anon., 1952b).

GEOLOGY AND SOILS

The native pinewoods in Scotland are all located north of the Highland Boundary Fault running north-eastwards from the Firth of Clyde to Stonehaven in the east. In this part of the country, the geological formations outside the agricultural areas are principally the ancient Moine rocks, Dalradian schists and gneisses, and the intrusive granites. The whole region was heavily glaciated, as we have seen, and the pinewoods are growing on glacial deposits of various kinds. The rocks have determined the form of the land masses and are the source of the material constituting the glacial drifts, but the local topography and the parent material of the soil is largely the result of glacial and water action.

GEOLOGY

Glentanar and Ballochbuie forests in the Deeside Group are mainly on granite, but most of the others are on Moine rocks or their counterpart east of the Great Glen Fault, the Central Highland Granulites. These are gneisses and schists derived

F

from Pre-Cambrian sediments in which felspathic sandstones predominated. They consist mainly of quartz, felspar, and micas in varying proportions, and range from massive and flaggy rocks to finely laminated schists. The proportion of other minerals to quartz determines the nutrient levels of the resulting soils. The granites are of similar mineralogical composition. In a few of the pinewoods, there are minor basic intrusions and occasional thin bands of limestone which are of local importance in soil development.

The native pinewoods have persisted in Scotland in a region, on the one hand of the most ancient rocks, and on the other of the most recent deposits – those laid down in the closing phases of the Ice Age. At that time, as we have seen, the glaciers were restricted to the valleys, and moraines were deposited even in the smallest of them. As the glaciers slowly retreated up the valleys, the melt water in the summer laid down many fluvio-glacial deposits, usually of sand and gravel. Lobes of dead ice became small lakes, and some of the peat bogs in the pinewoods may have developed on such sites. Periglacial action influenced the soil parent material beyond the glaciers. Erosion during and since that period has modified the glacial topography, cutting through moraines and redepositing the material, and there is thus a medley of soil parent material produced partly by ice and partly by water action, and ranging in texture from boulder clays, perhaps dating from earlier glacial phases, to the coarsest gravels of the most recent. Most of the material in the glacial deposits is of local origin, but it contains some from neighbouring formations.

SOILS

The cool humid climate, the nature of the parent material which is usually siliceous and acidic, and the pine with its associated vegetation resulting in a relatively deep litter and raw humus layer, have produced a varying degree of podsolisation in the soils. It is most marked on the freely drained sands and gravels derived from both granitic and siliceous rocks. In these podsolic soils, there may be pockets of iron deposition, but no examples of continuous iron pan have been seen, except in one or two instances where there were only scattered pine growing amongst a heath vegetation. Where the material has been derived from the better schistose rocks, there is on the whole less leaching, while on or near basic rocks there may be brown forest soils, and on such birch and other broadleaves communities are growing. In many of the pinewoods there are banks of alluvium along the streams, usually of coarse gravel, and the pine often regenerates on it, because its intrinsic poverty in nutrients reduces competition from field layer communities. Peat soils are to be found locally in the eastern pinewoods and they are more general and extensive in the western regions of high rainfall. The depth of the peat varies from one to several feet.

THE PINEWOODS, BIRCHWOODS, AND OAKWOODS

The relationship between these communities in past times in Scotland has been outlined in the previous chapter in the discussion of the forest history during post-glacial times. Some fifty years ago, Marcel Hardy (1905) carried out pioneer studies of these communities and more recently Tansley (1949) has described them in some detail. In the last few years Fraser Darling (1947) has written on this subject and the Nature Conservancy (anon., 1955) is carrying out investigations on the relationship between the communities. The present detailed study has thrown some light on this subject.

The oakwoods are part of one of the climatic forest formations of Europe, the Deciduous Summer Forest, while the natural pinewoods and birchwoods are communities of the Northern Coniferous Forest (Tansley, 1949).

The pinewoods in the Highlands of Scotland are similar to those in south-western Norway beyond the natural western limit of spruce (*Picea abies*), which is near Voss at about long. 6° 20′ E.

The birchwoods are by far the most extensive of the three natural communities in the Highlands of Scotland, and, as the birches have rarely been planted, their origin is not in doubt. Both oak and pine have been planted in Scotland from at least the beginning of the seventeenth century, but the pinewoods described in this volume are considered to be natural for reasons given in Chapter 1, although it is known that there was planting or sowing of pine of local origin in some of the native pinewoods as early as the eighteenth century.

The relationship between pine and birch communities is complex and appears to depend partly on habitat factors and partly on historical causes. Birch and pine can form both almost pure woodlands and mixed stands. Considering the influence of habitat factors first, the remaining pinewoods are principally on the north facing aspects, for example at Glentanar, Ballochbuie, Glenmore, Rannoch, Glen Moriston, Arkaig, Ardgour, Cannich, Strathfarrar, Achnashellach, Rhidorroch, the Black Mount Woods, and Tyndrum. The less favourable climatic conditions imposed by that aspect appear to have increased the competitive power of pine against birch and other tree dominants. The effect of altitude on pine and birch is not clear. The absolute altitudinal limit of each in the Highlands is about the same, but as a rule pine is at the tree limit, either in almost pure stands as in eastern woodlands, or with birch as in western, although in a few instances birchwoods are found above the pine, for example at Crannach in the Black Mount and in

Glen Affric. There may also be small clumps of birch on steep cliffs well above the pine. The almost pure pinewoods are to be found principally in Deeside and Speyside where the climate is less oceanic (PL. I). On the whole, therefore, pine predominates under the less favourable and more continental climatic conditions. On somewhat more favourable sites, birchwoods and sometimes oakwoods are to be found (PL. VIII), and, as already mentioned in the previous section, pine gives way to birch on the better soils. The woodlands in which pine and birch are mixed together are to be found mainly in the westerly groups, where the more oceanic climate may favour the birch against the pine (PL. III). The past history of the woodlands may partly explain their present pattern. There is evidence, both in the past and more recently, that birch and other broadleaved species have invaded heavily exploited pinewoods to form birchwoods with scattered pine in them. In some instances these reverted later to pinewood, where the intrinsic conditions, already mentioned, enabled the pine to compete successfully, perhaps when the birch died out. Historical instances of such alternation of pinewood – birchwood – pinewood are known for Glenmore and Rannoch.

Communities dominated by oak are to be found on the better soils under the more favourable climatic conditions. In the eastern coastal plain and lower river valleys, these broadleaved woodlands were almost all destroyed many centuries ago, as we have already seen, and only a few semi-natural woods survive. In Deeside, there is one which throws some light on the tension zone between oak-wood and birchwood. It is at Craigendarroch, Ballater, on a southerly aspect at an elevation between 800 and 1000 ft. (240 and 300 m.). Over a century ago, it was stated to be natural by a reliable observer, and some of the trees were then of large size (Dickie, 1843). The present wood is its coppice-grown successor and has been described by Tansley (1949). There are no historical records of any oakwoods farther up this valley and this wood is surrounded by natural birch and sub-spontaneous pine. In the region west of the Great Glen, there are a number of valleys running more or less east and west where the inter-relationship between oakwood, birchwood, and pinewood can be studied with the aid of available historical records, for example in Glen Moriston, Glengarry, Loch Arkaig, Ard-gour, and some of the valleys tributary to Strath Glass. The general pattern in the past, with relict communities in the present, is oakwood at the lower altitudes on the south-facing slopes, giving way to birchwood as one proceeds up the valley, and on the north-facing slopes birchwoods and farther up pinewoods. Where the gradient of the valley is low and the soil on the north side is more fertile than on the south, oakwoods may face pinewoods as at Loch Arkaig. In the west, where the pine comes down to lower altitudes than in the east, there may be a few oak in the actual pinewoods (PL. IX.*a*), and some scattered pine in oakwood. Beyond the most northerly pinewoods in Sutherlandshire, there were oakwoods in the past and today there are relict woodlands of birch with some scrubby oak and hazel. Along streams in practically every pinewood, there is a degenerate facies of alderwood.

THE NATIVE PINEWOOD COMMUNITIES

TREE SPECIES AND LARGER SHRUBS

The native pinewoods are relatively poor in species, but there is some variety, and those associated with pine may be found as single trees or in groups forming societies within the community. The frequencies of the species in the different groups of pinewoods are given in Table II.

The variation in the proportion of Scots pine and birches has been discussed in the previous section. The taxonomy of the birches in the Highlands is obscure and to some extent controversial. Tansley (1949) states that there are various forms hitherto attributed to *Betula pubescens*, but quotes Warburg's view that some of these should be put into a separate species. This has not been done, however, in the *Flora of the British Isles* (Clapham, 1952); two sub-species of *B. pubescens* are described, ssp. *pubescens* and ssp. *odorata*, and it is stated that the latter is perhaps the only sub-species in the Scottish Highlands. During the study of the pinewoods, typical *B. pubescens* and *B. verrucosa* have been found, both in eastern and western regions, but there are many individual trees that cannot be assigned with accuracy to them or to the named sub-species; we call these intermediates, because as yet there is no conclusive evidence that they are hybrids.

Oak is a rare species in the pinewoods but is commoner at the lower elevations in the west. Both the sessile oak (*Quercus petraea*) and the pedunculate (*Q. robur*) are to be found, and also many trees that are intermediate in their botanical characteristics. Ash (*Fraxinus excelsior*) is rarely found in pinewoods, although there may be an occasional tree amongst alder or oak along streams and roads, for example at Ardgour. Aspen (*Populus tremula*) is a minor species in most of the pinewoods, and it does not compete successfully with the pine, being often found beside streams and occasionally in clearings. In this respect, the Scottish native pinewoods differ from those in Scandinavia where there is often more aspen. The alder (*Alnus glutinosa*) often replaces the pine on the moister sites of river banks and wet alluvial pastures, and it sometimes grows in a mixed society with birches, rowan (*Sorbus aucuparia*), and *Salix* spp. which may include *S. atrocinerea*, *S. aurita*, *S. caprea*, *S. pentandra*. McVean (1953, 1955-6) has recently studied the ecology of alder. The rowan is a characteristic species of all the native pinewoods, as individual trees, in groups in clearings, or as an underwood. There is an occasional bird-cherry (*Prunus padus*) in a few of the pinewoods, for example at Rothiemurchus and at Barisdale.

The most important of the larger shrubs is the juniper (*Juniperus communis*); two sub-species have been described, ssp. *communis*, erect or spreading, and ssp. *nana*, procumbent. Three forms have been found in the pinewoods, procumbent, bushy, and columnar (PL. XI), the latter being similar to var. *suecica* (Dallimore, 1954). The columnar form attains the greatest height, but the bushy may reach 20 ft. (6 m.). The juniper is less common in the Deeside woodlands than in the Speyside, where all forms are to be found. In the Rannoch and Strath Glass Groups, juniper is common, but mainly of the bushy type. In the western districts, it is generally present, but usually as small bushes on the steep sides of gullies where it has escaped grazing. The holly (*Ilex aquifolium*) is less common than the juniper except in western woods, but is to be found in most, usually as a dwarf bush. Hazel (*Corylus avellana*) was only found in a few woods in the Rannoch, Great Glen and Southern Groups and only on the banks of streams.

TABLE II

FREQUENCE OF TREE SPECIES AND LARGER SHRUBS IN THE NATURAL PINEWOODS OF SCOTLAND

Group of native pinewoods	Pinus silvestris	Betula spp.	Quercus spp.	Populus tremula	Alnus glutinosa	Sorbus aucuparia	Juniperus communis	Ilex aquifolium
Deeside	D	O-LF	Absent	R-O	LF	O	LF	R
Speyside	D	O-LF	R	R	LF	O	F	R
Rannoch	CD	CD-LD	R	R	LF	O	LF	R
Great Glen	D-CD	CD-LD	O-LF	R-O	LF	O	O	O
Strath Glass	D-CD	CD-LD	R	R	LF	O	O	O
Wester Ross	D-CD	CD-LD	O	R-O	LF	O	R	O
Northern	CD	CD-LD	O	R	LF	O	R	O
Southern	D-CD	CD-LD	R	R-O	LF	O	R	O

D = dominant,   CD = co-dominant,   LD = locally dominant,   F = frequent, LF = locally frequent,   O = occasional, and R = rare.

THE FIELD LAYER COMMUNITIES

There are a number of these in every native pinewood of any extent. They vary according to, first the tree dominants and particularly the proportion of pine and birches, secondly the degree of stocking and thus the amount of shade cast, and thirdly the soil and particularly its water status. Nineteen field layer communities have been defined and the species and their frequency are listed in Appendix I.

I. COMMUNITIES WHERE SCOTS PINE IS DOMINANT AND THE BIRCHES ARE NOT MORE THAN LOCALLY FREQUENT

1. WELL STOCKED STANDS, 70 TO 90 PER CENT. CANOPY

Community No. 1. A dry moss community.

It is found in fully stocked stands on very dry soils. Typically there are only mosses such as *Rhytidiadelphus triquetrus* (*Hylocomium triquetrum*), *H. splendens*, *Hypnum cupressiforme*, and *Dicranum scoparium*, but half the surface of the soil may be covered by litter. This community is common but local in the eastern pinewoods.

Community No. 2. A moist moss community.

It is found under full canopy, but where the soil is moister. It is much richer in species, which include *Vaccinium vitis-idaea*, *V. myrtillus*, and *Deschampsia flexuosa*. The mosses often form a mat up to 6 in. (15·2 cm.) deep and there are not only species of *Hylocomium* and *Hypnum*, but the moisture-loving *Polytrichum commune* and *Sphagnum palustre* (*S. cymbifolium*) which may form cushions. This community is common in the west, particularly in the Wester Ross pinewoods.

Community No. 3. A *Vaccinium*/*Deschampsia*/*Hypnaceous* moss community.

This community is widespread in pinewoods in all parts of Scotland under close canopy and on the drier soils. *Vaccinium vitis-idaea* and *V. myrtillus* are the co-dominants; with *Calluna vulgaris*, *Deschampsia flexuosa* and *Luzula pilosa*. The moss layer consists of *Pleurozium* (*Hypnum*) *schreberi*, *Hypnum cupressiforme*, *Hylocomium splendens*, *Rhytidiadelphus triquetrus*, *R. loreus* (*Hylocomium loreum*), and *Dicranum* and *Dicranella* spp. *V. myrtillus* tends to be less luxuriant in the west. Where there is a little more light one finds typical pinewood species such as *Pyrola media*, *Ramischia secunda* and *Goodyera repens*.

Community No. 4. A *Deschampsia flexuosa*/*Hypnaceous* moss community.

Also on the drier soils, but under less complete canopy, this community may be found temporarily after thinning or felling, particularly in eastern and central Scotland. *D. flexuosa* is the dominant, but *Calluna* and *Vaccinium* tend to re-establish themselves. *Trientalis europaea* may be locally frequent. The principal mosses are the same as in No. 3.

Community No. 5. A dry *Calluna*/*Vaccinium*/*Deschampsia* moss community.

This community occurs frequently in eastern pinewoods on the drier soils under about 70 per cent. canopy. *Calluna*, *V. myrtillus* and *V. vitis-idaea* are locally domin-ant or co-dominant. In addition to *D. flexuosa*, there are a number of herbs such as *Luzula pilosa* and *Melampyrum sylvaticum*, while *Pyrola*, *Trientalis* and *Goodyera* may be present. The moss layer is not well developed, and the species are similar to No. 3.

Community No. 6. A moist *Calluna/Vaccinium/Deschampsia*/moss community.

On moister soils in many pinewoods, one gets a community dominated by rank growing *Calluna* with a much better developed moss layer richer in species compared with No. 5. There are also more moisture-loving species, such as *Erica tetralix* and *Sphagnum* spp., while *Carex* spp. and *Molinia* may be constituents.

2. OPEN STANDS, 10 TO 69 PER CENT. CANOPY

Community No. 7. A grass pinewood community.

This is not a typical pinewood community, but is sometimes found adjoining improved pastures grazed by sheep, and under about a 50 per cent. canopy. It is dominated by grasses such as *Agrostis, Anthoxanthum, Festuca* spp., and there are usually a considerable number of herbs. In addition to *Hypnum* and *Hylocomium* spp., there are *Pseudoscleropodium (Brachythecium) purum* and *Polytrichum commune*.

Community No. 8. A moist *Calluna/Vaccinium/Eriophorum/Sphagnum* community.

When drainage conditions deteriorate in No. 6, one gets this community by the invasion of *Eriophorum angustifolium, E. vaginatum, Trichophorum (Scirpus) caespitosum* and *Sphagnum* and there may be development of shallow peaty humus. It is common throughout the Scottish pinewoods, but in the west the next community is more widespread under similar conditions.

Community No. 9. A *Calluna/Molinia* community.

In this community, *Calluna* and *Molinia* are locally dominant and *Carex* and *Eriophorum* spp. and *Erica tetralix* are important constituents. The moss species are few in number and include *Sphagnum*. It is a very common community in the high rainfall districts in the west, but is only found in the east on very wet peaty soils.

3. UNDER SCATTERED PINE, LESS THAN 10 PER CENT CANOPY

Community No. 10. A *Callunetum*.

When Communities No. 5 and No. 6 are growing under scattered pine, *Calluna* tends to become luxuriant and to smother the other constituents, but *Erica cinerea, E. tetralix* and *Vaccinium vitis-idaea* tend to persist as subsidiary species. Moss species are few, but the lichen *Cladonia sylvatica* may be frequent. The community is common in the east, and there are all gradations from No. 5 and No. 6 to this community depending on canopy conditions.

Community No. 11. A *Calluna/Trichophorum* community.

This is a variant of No. 10 under wetter conditions. It is found throughout the Scottish pinewoods, but is commoner in the west, and is often found at the margins where the trees thin out. *Calluna* is generally co-dominant with *Trichophorum*; *Eriophorum, Erica* and *Vaccinium* spp. are usually present, while the principal lower plants are *Cladonia sylvatica, Rhacomitrium lanuginosum*, and *Sphagnum palustre*.

Community No. 12. A *Molinia/Trichophorum* community.

Under still wetter conditions in pinewood margins, this community develops, or No. 15. *Molinia* dominates along with *Trichophorum*, and the *Eriophorum* spp. are also important constituents. Both *Sphagnum* spp. are frequent to locally abundant. It is widespread in the west.

II. Communities under stands in which the Birches are abundant or co-dominant

Community No. 13. A *Calluna/*grass*/Vaccinium/*moss community.

In this community there is more pine than in the next and it is found under variable canopy closure. It is general throughout Scotland, but commoner in the west. It is dominated by *Calluna* along with *Vaccinium* spp., but the grasses, *Agrostis* and *Festuca* spp., *Deschampsia flexuosa*, and *Anthoxanthum odoratum* are important constituents. The moss species are numerous, but less well developed than in the next community.

Community No. 14. A grass/moss community.

This is found, particularly in the west, where there is more birch, and on moister and probably more fertile soils. While the usual shrubs are present, the grasses are richer in species, such as *Agrostis*, *Anthoxanthum odoratum*, *Deschampsia flexuosa*, and *Holcus*, and greater in amount. There are also more herb species than in any other community, for example, *Lysimachia nemorum*, *Ranunculus ficaria*, and *Viola riviniana*. The moss layer is well developed, and includes moisture-loving species.

III. Flush and bog communities of pinewood

In most of the pinewoods there has been little, if any, artificial drainage, and there are often flush and bog communities under conditions of topography that do not permit natural drainage. Some of the bog communities are also found at the margins of the woods, preventing their spread. In such communities, there are only scattered and usually stunted pine or none.

Community No. 15. An *Eriophorum/Trichophorum/Sphagnum* bog community.

This community is the most important of the bog communities, and may cover large areas, particularly in the west. The peat is 12 in. (30 cm.) or more in depth. In the wettest conditions *Eriophorum angustifolium* and *E. vaginatum* dominate the other species and there is much *Sphagnum* and *Narthecium ossifragum*. In somewhat drier conditions *Trichophorum caespitosum*, *Calluna* and *Erica tetralix* increase and are locally dominant.

Community No. 16. A *Molinia* flush community.

This is a common but local community, very rare within the eastern pinewoods, but often characteristic of the western, where it is spreading in the more open woods. The peat is usually 6 in. (15·2 cm.) or more in depth. It is dominated by *Molinia caerulea*, with either the tussock or diffuse habit, and it tends to smother the other constituents such as *Carex* and *Eriophorum* spp., *Trichophorum caespitosum*, and *Erica tetralix*. The moss layer consists of *Sphagnum* and *Polytrichum* spp.

Community No. 17. A *Juncus communis* agg. flush or bog community.

This community is common, but does not cover large areas. It is dominated by *Juncus effusus* and *J. conglomeratus*.

Community No. 18. *Juncus articulatus* flush or bog community.

It is never more than local, even in the west, and is only found under very wet conditions.

Community No. 19. A *Sphagnum* spp. bog community.

This community is found on completely water-logged peat. In addition to *Sphagnum* spp. there are *Carex* and *Eriophorum* spp., *Narthecium ossifragum* and occasionally *Drosera* species.

PLANTS OF PARTICULAR INTEREST IN THE NATIVE PINEWOODS

A number of species such as *Linnaea borealis*, *Goodyera repens*, *Trientalis europaea*, *Listera cordata*, *Moneses* (*Pyrola*) *uniflora*, *Pyrola media*, *P. minor*, and *Ramischia* (*Pyrola*) *secunda* are typical of the native pinewoods. Although so common in many Scandinavian natural woods, Linnaeus' favourite flower, *L. borealis*, is rare in the native pinewoods of Scotland, and was only found in Deeside, although it has been recorded from Speyside (Walton, 1949). The orchid, *Goodyera repens* (PL. XII.*a*), is widespread on the drier soils and under close canopy in the eastern pinewoods and as far north as Amat, but is less common west of the Great Glen. *Trientalis europaea* is commonest in the Deeside woods and locally at Glen Moriston. It is scattered thinly throughout the native pinewoods of Speyside, Strath Glass, and in the Northern Group, but is rarer in the Southern, Rannoch, and Wester Ross pinewoods. It is found growing not only on the litter of pine needles but in grassy birchwoods. *Listera cordata* is commonest in the inland pinewoods from Rannoch to Speyside, but was found as far north as Strath Vaich in Ross and Cromarty, and as far west as Loch Maree. It usually grows amongst hypnaceous mosses under tall heather under an irregular pine canopy, but it was found also amongst short grasses on river banks. The wintergreens are represented by four species of which *Pyrola media* is by far the commonest, and it is in all the pinewoods, although more frequent in the east than in the west. *P. minor* is more local in its distribution. *Ramischia* (*Pyrola*) *secunda* (PL. XII.*b*) and *Moneses* (*Pyrola*) *uniflora* are rarer, and unexpectedly no specimen of *P. rotundifolia* was found. *Vaccinium uliginosum* is rare in Scottish pinewoods although common in Scandinavian.

The next group consists of plants which are considered to be typical of a mountain and not a pinewood habitat, but they may be found in woodlands, particularly in the west where alpine species come down to lower altitudes under the influence of the extreme oceanic climate, and at the upper limit in eastern pinewoods. For example, *Salix herbacea* was found on wet scree at about 500 ft. (150 m.) in the Loch Maree pinewoods. *Empetrum hermaphroditum* grows near the pine limit in the eastern woods, but not usually under pine. The black bearberry (*Arctous alpina*), a rare species, is growing near the upper limit of the pine on a boulder at Achnashellach, on a rocky knoll in Glen Cannich and on a cliff at Loch Maree. The cloudberry (*Rubus chamaemorus*), whose yellow fruit is so prized in Scandinavian countries where it is found in boggy patches in the natural forest and at quite low elevations, is found in Deeside and Speyside pinewoods at 1700 to 1900 ft. (510 to 570 m.), and in one of the pinewoods at Loch Maree as low as 700 to 800 ft. (210 to 240 m.). The alpine lady's mantle (*Alchemilla alpina*) may be seen, not only at the upper limit of the pinewoods, but also on river shingle within them, for example at Rannoch. *Polygonum viviparum* is occasionally found in grassy communities at the higher altitudes in the pinewoods. The Scottish asphodel (*Tofieldia pusilla*) is not uncommon on moist peaty gravels under scattered pine. Three saxifrages, *S. aizoides*, *S. stellaris*, and *S. oppositifolia*, which are usually found in the eastern mountains well above the limit of the pine, grow in woodlands in the west. *S. aizoides* (PL. XII.*c*) is not uncommon on wet rocks and river shingle, *stellaris* is growing at Loch Maree among *Sphagnum* in springs and wet rocky crevices, while *oppositifolia* is thinly scattered along the upper margins of some of the larger pinewoods in the Strath Glass, Deeside, and Wester Ross, and occasionally in the Northern groups. The *Lycopodiaceae* are well represented in the native pinewoods. *Lycopodium selago* is common in all of them on peaty open places, while *L. clavatum* grows usually on drier sites and is less common in the west. *L. alpinum* is to be found in all the pinewoods extending beyond 1500 ft. (450 m.) in the east and above about 1000 ft. (300 m.) in the west. *L. annotinum* (PL. XII.*d*) is rarer, but was found in the Deeside, Speyside, and Strath Glass woodlands, while *L. inundatum* has been recorded at Glenmore in Speyside (Walton, 1949).

The next group of plants to be discussed is also unexpected in the native pinewoods. The wood sage (*Teucrium scorodonia*), a common plant in many Highland oakwoods, is found also at the lower fringe of native pinewoods and sometimes under pine canopy, particularly in some woodlands in the Great Glen, Strath Glass, and the Northern woods groups. In Glen Moriston, a number of plants of *Melica nutans* and *Sanicula europaea* were seen on a pocket of base rich soil. *Gentian-*

ella amarella, often found also on calcareous sites, may grow on acid soils on the margins of pinewoods along with *Calluna* and *Deschampsia flexuosa*. A number of orchids, other than *Goodyera repens* and *Listera cordata*, are found in the pinewoods, although not typical of them. The variable *Orchis maculata* is quite common in all the larger native woodlands, particularly on *Molinia* flushes in clearings in the forest. *Gymnadenia conopsea* may accompany it on such sites, but is more often found in short open *Calluna* on dry humus. *Platanthera bifolia*, a plant of grassy pastures, sometimes strays into such sites in the open parts of the pinewoods, for example at Glen Moriston and Glengarry. Coming to the lovers of wet places, *Parnassia palustris*, although rare, is to be found occasionally on bogs and beside streams in the more western pinewoods. The sundews, *Drosera rotundifolia* and *D. intermedia*, as well as *Pinguicula vulgaris*, are also found on open, wet, boggy places.

AGE, GROWTH AND STOCKING

The native pinewoods are uneven-aged, but old trees predominate, and there is not a complete gradation of age classes. As a rule, there are areas of trees of about the same age, but in them there may be scattered older trees and groups of younger in open places. The age structure, therefore, is semi-irregular. This is typical also of natural pine forests in other countries. The maximum age found from ring counts and borings is about 300 years; trees of this age, however, are often healthy and growing steadily if very slowly, hence this is not the maximum physical age of Scots pine in its Scottish habitat. This is confirmed by the discovery of a stump at Arkaig which gave a ring count of 395. Most of the pine, however, are under these ages, and while trees of 200 years old are common, 140 to 190 years is the principal older age class. There is often a good representation of trees of ages between 100 and 140 years, for example about 120 years, but trees under 100 years are local in their distribution. Age and size are not always closely correlated, and small trees at the upper fringes of woods may be over 200 years old. The other tree species in the pinewoods are shorter lived, and are rarely more than 100 years old, except for an occasional oak.

The pine is usually the dominant in the pinewood community, and the associated trees do not attain the same height. The average height of the pine in most of the pinewoods is between 45 and 55 ft. (13·5 and 16·5 m.). On well drained and sheltered sites trees up to 70 ft. (21 m.) are not uncommon, and very occasionally there are groups of trees up to about 90 ft. (27 m.) in height. While the height growth of the pine is, therefore, not spectacular, it must be remembered that many of the trees on the more favourable sites, which are usually also the more accessible, have been felled in the past. The average girth at breast height

(4 ft. 3 in., 1·28 m.) usually lies between five and six feet (1·5 and 1·8 m.). Trees with girths up to about 9 ft. (2·7 m.) are not infrequent, and at Glen Orchy, Arkaig and Guisachan records of 15 ft. (4·5 m.), 12 ft. 6 in. (3·75 m.) and 11 ft. (3·3 m.) respectively were obtained. In the oldest trees, the current rate of diameter growth is low, and there may be 50 rings to the inch (20 rings per cm.). Historical records indicate that the maximum heights and girths have not changed appreciably during the past two centuries. Jones (1945) in a paper entitled "The structure and reproduction of the virgin forest of the north temperate zone", gives data which show that the native pinewoods of Scotland have certain similarities in structure, age, and growth to virgin forests in temperate climates.

The stocking in the native pinewoods is on the whole both low and irregular (PL. I, III, and V.*a*). There are areas, sometimes extending to several acres, in some of the woods which are well stocked, particularly in the 100 to 150 age class, and this class is more numerous in the woods in Deeside (PL. VI.*a*), Speyside, and Glen Moriston (PL. VII.*a*). As a rule, however, the stocking is open, under 70 per cent. canopy, and the pine are often short boled with deep crowns. In places there are only scattered trees. There are no doubt different reasons for the low and irregular stocking. In all the woods, felling has taken place from time to time and every year a few old trees die. On the other hand initial natural regeneration may have been sparse or many of the seedlings may have been destroyed by grazing animals. There is some historical evidence for all these causes of poor stocking in individual woods.

PATHOGENIC FUNGI IN THE NATIVE PINEWOODS

In spite of the age of so many of the trees, the native pinewoods are remarkably free from rots and other diseases caused by pathogenic fungi. Trees even of about 300 years old when felled are often quite sound.

A certain amount of stem rot caused by *Trametes pini* is to be found, and the characteristic bracket fructifications are to be seen occasionally in most of the pinewoods, and somewhat more frequently in Ballochbuie. The fructifications are usually on trees more than 140 years old, but one or two were observed on trees about 110 to 120 years old. This fungus is very rarely seen in plantations in Scotland, no doubt because there are few over 100 years old. It can cause serious and extensive rot in the stem, but, as only an occasional tree has been attacked, the amount of damage is relatively small.

Fomes annosus, which is the principal cause of heart rot in plantations of Scots pine and other conifers in Scotland, is not an important disease in the native pinewoods. It can attack and kill young trees, but no mortality in young regeneration due to this cause was seen in the native pinewoods. There is a certain amount of heart rot in most of them, and, while the fructifications of this fungus were not always found, it was probably the cause in many instances. *Polyporus schweinitzii* was found in one or two of the native pinewoods, but it is not common, and heart rot due to it is not important. Occasional fructifications of *Armillaria mellea* were seen at the base of pines.

The rust, *Peridermium pini*, was identified in the Deeside woods and the Black Wood of Rannoch, and it is probably present in the others. It is not causing much damage. At Rothiemurchus and Rannoch a few pine, about 120 years old, were dying back from the top and their stems bore long, black, resinous scars. The cause has not yet been determined; it may have been lightning.

The needle cast fungus (*Lophodermium pinastri*) is to be found in all the native pinewoods, but it is not a serious disease. There is evidence that certain strains of pine, including the Scottish, are more resistant than others (Ruzicka, 1929; Wiedemann, 1930).

Polyporus betulinus is common and widespread on dying birch, and *Fomes fomentarius* may be found on stumps and dead logs of the same species.

The Fauna of the Native Pinewoods

Most of the larger native pinewoods support an animal and bird population that is characteristic and includes a number of uncommon species. There is often a large number of predators and carnivores, the remote and inaccessible parts of the forests serving as a refuge out of reach of gamekeepers and others whose duty it is to protect grouse and sheep, and they live their natural, comparatively undisturbed, lives. The fauna of these woods has, of course, been modified by man in the past, but, at least in recent times, it has been altered to a less extent than the fauna of woodlands nearer to human habitation.

The prehistoric fauna of Scotland was principally a forest fauna, comparable in some ways to that of the woodlands of Northern Europe and Northern America today. There were the red deer, roe deer, elk, caribou, brown bear, lynx, wild cat, wolf, fox, pine marten, polecat, stoat, weasel, and badger, and birds such as the crossbill, grouse, capercailzie, woodpecker, jay, and magpie. Many of these species such as the elk, caribou, brown bear, lynx and wolf have for long been extinct in Scotland, but several characteristic species still remain (Ritchie, 1920).

THE MAMMALS

Red deer (*Cervus elaphus*) are plentiful in all the unfenced parts of the larger native pinewoods. They are excluded from some, such as parts of Glenmore,

Rannoch, Glentanar, and Achnashellach, but in these areas they are common around the margins and sometimes stray into the woodlands when the fences are covered with snow in the winter or collapse under the weight of accumulated ice. Most of the native pinewoods have been at one time or another part of a sporting estate in which the deer were encouraged and protected for shooting, and this has often given rise to abnormally high populations within the woodlands. Large herds of fifty or more roam in the majority of the natural pinewoods until biting insects drive them to the higher ground in the summer. They use the woodlands as winter shelter and grazing, and they may do much damage to young pine seedlings. Deer do not only eat Scots pine as a last resort; they were seen browsing on young pine in Strathfarrar with ample grass pasture within twenty yards.

The roe deer (*Capreolus capreolus*) is a shy animal and is not so often seen, but nevertheless each woodland has a number, and they contribute their quota of damage to the pine regeneration. They are found principally in small herds of three to six animals.

The Japanese Sika deer (*Sika nippon*) was introduced into Scotland by Sir Arthur Bignold at Loch Rosque in Ross-shire in 1887 (Ritchie, 1920), and has since extended its range and invaded some of the natural pinewoods of the Northern Group.

Sheep are to be found in most of the unfenced native pinewoods, and sometimes find access into fenced woodlands. They may be seen grazing side by side with red deer and may also damage young pine seedlings. It is known that in the past, when cattle were more numerous in the Highlands, they did some damage to natural regeneration of pine. The grazing is poor, however, and today cattle are only found in a few woodlands.

Goats (*Capra hircus*) live independent of man in or near the old pinewoods in the glens east of Loch Shiel in Ardgour, and on the largest of the pine-clad islands on Loch Maree. They are large and quite untamed, but in the opinion of most they are feral (Darling, 1947; Matthews, 1952; Watt, 1937).

The rabbit (*Oryctolagus cuniculus*) and the blue or alpine hare (*Lepus timidus*) are to be found in most pinewoods. The former, however, is not common within the actual woodlands, and has seldom caused much damage. The alpine hare, which usually keeps to high ground, frequently visits pinewoods extending above 1000 ft. (300 m.), and there are a great many in Speyside and Deeside, particularly at Mar. They feed on the bark of young trees at the forest margins, but are seldom sufficiently numerous to be a serious pest.

The red squirrel (*Sciurus vulgaris*) is a forest-dwelling species in the native pinewoods. They are relatively numerous in Deeside, Speyside, and Rannoch, but are rarely seen elsewhere. At the present time they are not a serious pest, but in the past they have caused considerable damage to the pine, for example in the woodland known as "the Bush" in Glentanar. No damage to pine regeneration by mice or voles was seen, and the populations appear to be low, due no doubt to the large number of predators.

The other species of mammals in the pinewoods are the small carnivores, the pine marten (*Martes martes*), the wild cat (*Felis silvestris*), the fox (*Vulpes vulpes*), the otter (*Lutra lutra*), the stoat (*Mustela erminea*), the weasel (*Mustela nivalis*), and also the badger (*Meles meles*) which is more catholic in its choice of food. The pine marten is a comparatively rare species in Scotland, but it is quite common in the old pinewoods of Wester Ross, and is present in others. From the evidence of live specimens or recent skins, the wild cat is to be found in all the groups of pinewoods. Feral cats are quite common in the pinewoods near to human habitation. At the present time the polecat (*Mustela putorius*) is very scarce and probably extinct in Scotland. Specimens were taken in Sutherland for scientific purposes in 1905-7, but there are very few, if any, definite records of it since that time. Foxes are numerous in all the pinewoods (Darling, 1947; Tetley, 1939). The badger is comparatively rare in the stands of pine in the native forests, but is occasionally found in the birchwoods within their boundaries.

Apart from the deer, none of the wild mammals is harmful to the forest, although farmers deplore the numbers of foxes which take refuge in these old woodlands. It is to be hoped that the comparatively rare species such as the pine marten and wild cat will remain part of their fauna.

THE BIRDS

The native pinewoods contain a varied bird population, including game birds, ducks, waders, and divers, as well as carnivorous and insectivorous species.

The principal game birds are red grouse, black grouse or black game, capercailzie or capercaillie, woodcock, wood-pigeon, and ptarmigan. The red grouse (*Lagopus scoticus*) and ptarmigan (*L. mutus*) are essentially marginal species inhabiting open ground, but the former frequently enter the forest in severe weather and the latter do so occasionally. A more regular visitor to the woods is the black grouse (*Lyrurus tetrix*), and it is numerous in Speyside and Deeside, while there are a few in Rannoch and the Great Glen. Where they are common, they do a considerable amount of damage to the buds of Scots pine. The capercailzie (*Tetrao urogallus*), originally an indigenous species, became extinct in Scotland about 1770; after abortive attempts by the Earl of Fife to introduce Swedish birds at Mar Lodge in Deeside in 1827 and 1829, it was successfully re-established at

PLATE V

a

b

NATURAL REGENERATION IN NATIVE PINEWOODS

a) Black Wood of Rannoch, pine and birch regeneration in dry and moist
*Calluna/Vaccinium/Deschampsia/*moss Nos. 5 and 6 on podsolised, sandy soil.

b) Rothiemurchus, young pine regeneration in *Callunetum* No. 10, previously
burned, on dry podsolised sand and gravel, with older regeneration in the
background.

Taymouth in 1837 and 1838. Twenty-five years later it was estimated that there were between 1000 and 2000 birds in the area. Capercailzie from Taymouth, and fresh importations from Sweden in 1846, were transported to various parts of Scotland (Ritchie, 1920); and it is now found in most of the native pinewoods except in the extreme west and south (Baxter, 1953; Ritchie, 1920). Where it is numerous, for example in the Black Wood of Rannoch, it is responsible for appreciable damage to the pine shoots, including the leaders of young trees. The woodcock (*Scolopax rusticola*) and wood-pigeon (*Columba palumbus*) are found in most native pinewoods, although the latter is rare in those of the extreme north. Most specimens of both were seen in Speyside and Deeside.

The native forests provide a refuge for a number of predators such as the buzzard (*Buteo buteo*), the kestrel (*Falco tinnunculus*), the long-eared owl (*Asio otus*), and the sparrow-hawk (*Accipiter nisus*), both within and along the margins of nearly all the woodlands, the kestrel being the most common. Buzzards were seen more often in western forests, particularly in Strath Glass. The peregrine falcon (*Falco peregrinus*) occasionally visits the woodlands, and at one time frequented the cliffs near Rhidorroch Forest. It has, however, suffered considerable persecution, and is now comparatively rare in or near the pine areas. The hooded crow (*Corvus cornix*) is in all the pinewoods, and a few ravens (*C. corax*) and carrion crows (*C. corone*) frequent some of the woodlands, while jays (*Garrulus glandarius*) were seen at Rannoch. The golden eagle (*Aquila chrysaëtos*) nests in the vicinity of all the larger pinewoods and frequently flies over them. In one native pine-wood, in an eastern district, a golden eagle has nested in a Scots pine tree for two or three successive seasons. Such a nesting place has also been recorded elsewhere (Baxter, 1953).

The watercourses in the pinewoods support an avifauna of their own, the heron (*Ardea cinerea*), the oyster-catcher (*Haematopus ostralegus*), the dipper (*Cinclus cinclus*), the sandpiper (*Tringa hypoleucos*), the black-headed gull (*Larus ridibundus*), and the mallard (*Anas platyrhynchos*). Cormorants (*Phalacrocorax carbo*) and even an occasional shag (*P. aristotelis*) may be seen feeding in the lochs by the pinewoods, particularly west of the Great Glen. The goosander (*Mergus merganser*) and red-breasted merganser (*M. serrator*) occasionally visit pinewoods, especially in the west, and the latter species breeds in the vicinity of Coulin and Loch Maree.

A great many small insectivorous and seed-eating birds inhabit the pinewoods, and the former are no doubt partly responsible for the relative freedom from serious insect attacks. The most common are the chaffinch (*Fringilla coelebs*), the coal titmouse (*Parus ater*), and the long-tailed titmouse (*Aegithalos caudatus*). The most unusual, however, is the crested titmouse (*Parus cristatus*), a species that is

G

uncommon in this country; it was seen in Abernethy, Rothiemurchus, Glen Feshie and the Dulnan Valley, and once in Glen Affric. Small colonies have recently been recorded in Mar Forest (Macgregor, 1955), Glengarry, and elsewhere (Baxter, 1953). The crossbill (*Loxia curvirostra*) is locally frequent in the pinewoods of Speyside and Deeside, occasional in the Great Glen, Strath Glass, and Wester Ross, and rare in other groups. Considerable flocks of these birds were seen in Abernethy and Rothiemurchus Forests, but they are not so common as to constitute a serious pest in spite of their habit of feeding on Scots pine seeds. The siskin (*Carduelis spinus*) was seen in all geographical groups except the Northern. There are a great many in Speyside, the Great Glen, and Strath Glass. The tree-creeper (*Certhia familiaris*) is an inhabitant of the pinewoods of Speyside and Deeside, and the robin (*Erithacus rubecula*), and the wren (*Troglodytes troglodytes*) are common in all of them. The great spotted woodpecker (*Dendrocopos major*) is an inhabitant of the natural pinewoods in Deeside, Speyside, the Great Glen, and Strath Glass. The evidence of landowners, gamekeepers and others suggests that it occurs in all the other groups, but this requires confirmation. Baxter and Rintoul (1953) have recently discussed the distribution of this species.

The old pinewoods contain a limited number of reptilia. Two lizards occur in all pine areas, the viviparous lizard (*Lacerta vivipara*), and the slow worm (*Anguis fragilis*). The former is common. The adder (*Vipera berus*), the only native species of snake in Scotland, is distributed throughout all the geographical groups, and is common in the Deeside pinewoods of Glentanar and Mar. The toad (*Bufo bufo*), the frog (*Rana temporia*), and the palmate newt (*Triturus helveticus*) were seen in all the pine areas.

INSECT PESTS

The native pinewoods are remarkably free from serious damage by insects. There are a number of potential pests, but the populations are not usually high. The most common is the larger pine shoot beetle (*Myelophilus piniperda*) which is found in all the pinewoods; it causes appreciable damage to the crowns of younger trees in a number of them. The smaller species (*Myelophilus minor*) is also present in the native pinewoods, but is more local; adult beetles or recently made galleries were found in Glentanar, Ballochbuie, Rothiemurchus, Glen Loy, Glen Mallie, Loch Arkaig, and Glen Moriston, but it was not found in the extreme north or west. Beetles of the genus *Pityogenes* are very common in most areas, particularly parts of Speyside, but they cause no damage. *Pissodes pini* is present, but in small numbers. The birch bark beetle (*Scolytus ratzeburgi*) was found in all the groups of native pinewoods except the Northern and Southern (Carlisle, 1951).

Longhorn beetles of the family *Cerambycidae* breed in pine logs and stumps, *Rhagium mordax* and *R. bifasciatum* being found in most of the woodlands, and *Acanthocinus aedilis* was recorded in two locations in Deeside but not in the other geographical groups.

The pine weevil (*Hylobius abietis*), a normal inhabitant of all the pinewoods, is responsible for a certain amount of damage to young pine regeneration. Its numbers vary considerably from year to year, but there is no record of it being a serious pest in any of the natural pinewoods.

The most common of the lepidopterous potential pests are the pine shoot moth (*Evetria turionana*), the pine resin gall moth (*E. resinella*), and the pine looper (*Bupalus piniarius*). Pine looper caterpillars were seen in Deeside, Speyside, and Rannoch from 1953 to 1955, but comparatively few were seen in the other geographical groups. The populations of these species are too low to cause serious damage.

The only common Hymenopterous pests are the pine saw-flies (*Neodiprion sertifer* and *Diprion pini*). They are not abundant in these woods, but are widely distributed. A less common species is the yellow and black wood wasp (*Urocerus (Sirex) gigas*).

The pine *Adelges* (*Anisophleba pini*) is to be found on young pine shoots in most pinewoods, but is unimportant.

In many of the native pinewoods, there is a large number of anthills up to 2 ft. 6 in. (·75 m.) in height, and these mounds of litter are made by the wood ant (*Formica rufa*). In summer, thousands of these ants can be seen travelling up and down the pine stems carrying pine litter, resin, and insects, and they probably help to reduce the populations of potential insect pests (Thalenhorst, 1956). The anthills are most common in Deeside and Speyside, and are comparatively rare in the north and west. A list of other species of ants characteristic of eastern native pinewoods is quoted by Fraser Darling (1947).

NATURAL REGENERATION

We have seen already that there has been relatively little natural regeneration during the past century, most of the pine being over 100 years old. During this period the woodlands, with a few exceptions, have been open to intensive grazing by red deer and sheep. While this is the principal reason why seedlings have not grown into trees, it does not entirely explain the comparative lack of young seedlings. If the native pinewoods are to be perpetuated by natural means, the first step is to try and find out the causes.

General silvicultural knowledge about Scots pine throws a little light on this problem. This and most other species of pine are intolerant of shade, and seed-lings coming up under close canopy do not survive for long. Moreover for this reason, and because this species does not usually grow fast initially when regener-ated naturally, it does not compete successfully, either with most other tree species or with luxuriant field layer communities. While Scots pine, when established, will grow well on fertile soils, it is often found in nature on poor soils and under the more unfavourable climatic conditions, because there is then less competition from other trees and plants. For the same reasons, it often regenerates freely on disturbed soils or when the field layer communities are destroyed by fire, pro-vided, of course, that there is a sufficient seed source within reach. While its winged seed is disseminated over long distances, it is rare that enough to secure well stocked regeneration falls beyond a distance equal to about twice the height of the seed trees. Scots pine tends to regenerate freely, therefore, first where there is a large seed supply, secondly in the open or under a very light tree canopy, thirdly when the field layer communities are open and not luxuriant or when they have been destroyed, and lastly when the mineral soil is exposed or there is not a continuous layer of raw humus. Thus, like some other species in this genus, Scots pine may regenerate freely after catastrophic happenings provided a suffi-cient seed source remains. It can also be regenerated naturally under controlled silviculture by appropriate methods, and these will be discussed later.

Some further light is shed by the past history of the pinewoods. Most of the surviving native pine are between about 140 and 190 years old, and, making due allowance for the reduction in their number in the intervening period by felling and natural causes, the pinewoods must have contained much more regeneration in the eighteenth century and the beginning of the last than today. While most of the woodlands have been subject to some felling and grazing by domestic as well as wild animals for over two millennia, the historical evidence suggests that they were well stocked at the beginning of the seventeenth century or later, when the first large scale exploitation began for other than local needs. This is certainly true for some of the most important forests, for example Abernethy, Rothie-murchus, and Glenmore. Contemporary evidence indicates that there was pro-lific natural regeneration of pine in parts of these forests at the beginning of the last century, following the extensive felling towards the end of the previous century. It came up in the open, on dry heath communities, and sometimes was so dense as to form a carpet of seedlings (Grant, 1898; Grigor, 1834; Lauder, 1834). The Scots pine's characteristic of coming up in the open is also illustrated by a remark made at the end of the eighteenth century during a legal dispute relating to Ballochbuie Forest: "These highland fir woods shift their stances" (Michie,

1901). There was also good regeneration after a fire in 1746 at Abernethy, and other examples could be quoted. In some forests, however, where there had been heavy and indiscriminate felling which reduced the available seed supply, and in the more westerly forests with more luxuriant field layer communities, such as Rannoch and Arkaig, the amount of regeneration was already giving cause for anxiety in the middle of the eighteenth century, and direct sowing and planting were being done to augment it (anon., 1745-81; anon., 1745-85). The grazing problem in the native pinewoods is not a new one. There have been red and roe deer in them during most of post-glacial time, and the woodlands were part of the hunting forests of the king, or their noble owners. Until the middle of the eighteenth century the deer had a natural predator – other than man – in the wolf, but it is not known whether a natural increase in the population of deer followed the extermination of the wolf. In the middle of the last century, however, many of the regions in which the native pinewoods are located were turned into deer forests, and, as the rents obtained were high, the head of deer was increased, sometimes by winter feeding. This is undoubtedly one reason for the decline in the successful establishment of any regeneration that came up during the past century. There have also been domestic grazing animals in at least some of the woodlands since late prehistoric times. Until the second half of the eighteenth century the flocks were mixed, and consisted of the small black Highland cattle, the small native sheep, goats, and a few horses. Such records as are available indicate that the numbers were not large, and it was sometimes the practice to house the sheep indoors during the winter (Darling, 1955; Robertson, 1794; Robertson, 1808; Walker, 1808). Even so, the regeneration was being severely damaged in some instances, particularly by goats, and about the middle of the eighteenth century enclosures by ditch and dyke were made, for example at Rannoch, Arkaig, and Barisdale when the estates were in the hands of the Commissioners for the Forfeited Estates (anon., 1745-81; anon, 1745-85). After that time, sheep runs were formed in the Highlands with increasing flocks of sheep of the blackfaced and Cheviot breeds from the south of Scotland, and the numbers of both cattle and goats declined (Robertson, 1794); this trend has continued until the present day, although recently there has been an increase in the number of cattle, for example at Glentanar and at Conaglen in Ardgour. Not only were some of the native woodlands destroyed by fire to improve the sheep pastures (Stuart, 1848), but there is evidence of increasing damage to regeneration by sheep in many of the woodlands.

The current problems of natural regeneration can now be considered. In many of the native pinewoods grazing, particularly by deer and sheep, continues.

It is of interest, however, to consider what is happening in these woodlands where grazing animals are fenced out. Red deer have been largely excluded from Glentanar since 1936, and, while some cattle graze in the woods, there is a definite increase in the amount of established regeneration (PL. VI.*a*). All grazing animals are excluded from the whole or part of native pinewoods belonging to the Forestry Commission at Glenmore, Rannoch, Glen Moriston, Glen Loy, Guisachan, and Achnashellach. Some increase in growing regeneration has resulted at Rannoch (PL. V.*a*), but very little elsewhere so far.

The next problem to be considered is whether the quantity and quality of the seed produced by the old trees is sufficient to secure regeneration. There are no long term data for the periodicity of heavy cone crops in the native pinewoods, but such evidence as is available indicates that the cycle is between three and six years, the same as for the species generally in Scotland. Heavy cone production is not to be expected from old trees, but the open structure of the woodlands and the resulting well developed crowns should increase it. On balance, production is lower than in younger planted woodlands. The size of the seed is less than the average for the species, and the seedlings are thus smaller for the first few years, even when raised in fertile forest nurseries. Consequently, they are less well equipped to survive under competition. Tests made of samples of seed collected in a wide range of the pinewoods showed that the quality of the seed is good. Thus, while there may not be sufficient seed in all the woods, there is enough in a heavy seed year for an appreciable amount of natural regeneration.

Apart from grazing and the quantity of seed, the principal limiting factors to successful regeneration are the condition of the soil, and the competition from field layer communities, under conditions where there is sufficient light for the development of pine seedlings. In many of the pinewoods there are occasional seedlings coming up in open places and on disturbed soil, such as eroded river banks, along paths, and on river shingle (PL. VI.*a*), but rarely in any number. Although in the woodlands as a whole the stocking is often open, and there is sufficient light, the present conditions of the soil and the vegetation do not appear to permit much, if any, regeneration.

Observations show that the relationship between field layer communities and natural regeneration of pine is complex and the evidence sometimes conflicting. On the whole there is most regeneration in communities dominated by *Calluna*, particularly *Callunetum* No. 10, and there are examples of this at Glentanar, the north part of Abernethy (PL. VI.*b*), Rothiemurchus (PL. V.*b*), and Rannoch. On the other hand, there is scarcely a seedling to be found in *Callunetum* with seed-bearing trees nearby at Ballochbuie, Glen Affric, and Glen Strathfarrar. There is also some regeneration in *Calluna/Molinia* community No. 9 at Loch Maree and to a lesser extent at Glen Affric, but at the best the trees are growing slowly, probably because the community is growing on peat up to 18 in. (46 cm.) deep. The influence of the field layer communities depends not only on their floristic composition, but also on their luxuriance and the stage of the development of their dominants. For example in *Callunetum* and other heather-rich communities, the evidence indicates that pine regeneration is more successful when the *Calluna* is short, under 12 in. (30 cm.) in height, but not when it exhibits dense crop structure. On the other hand, when the heather is tall but open and straggling, pine may come in, provided there is no deep layer of living and dead mosses. The presence of some plants of *Vaccinium* spp. is not adverse to regeneration (PL. v.*a*), but competition from dense and vigorous *V. myrtillus* substantially reduces it. When there is an abundance of grasses in the field layer communities, for example in *Deschampsia flexuosa/Hypnaceous* moss No. 4, grass pinewood No. 7, *Calluna/grass/Vaccinium/*moss No. 16, grass/moss No. 14, and *Molinia* flush No. 16, there is rarely any established regeneration. While competition by the grasses is no doubt a factor, it is partly because the grass attracts grazing animals and any seedlings are browsed after germination. The litter and humus horizons of the soils have an influence. Where there is a felt-like layer of raw humus, there is usually little regeneration, but when it is both shallow and loose there may be some. The effect of the depth of litter and raw humus is sometimes not clear; deep layers are usually adverse, but there are sometimes seedlings under such conditions, and their survival probably depends on whether or no they die from lack of water in the first summer before the roots penetrate to mineral horizons. Many seedlings are killed by frost-lift during the first winter and spring after germination, particularly on mineral soils. Seedlings are often to be found on the principal bog community, *Eriophorum/Trichophorum/Sphagnum* No. 15. The layer of *Sphagnum*, moist and in summer warm, provides ideal conditions for germination, and the roots of the seedlings ramify and develop mycorrhiza. Their survival appears to depend on whether the roots are able to penetrate to and survive in the underlying peat. Examples of prolonged survival were seen at Ballochbuie (PL. IX.*b*), Abernethy, Loch Maree, Amat, and elsewhere, but at Affric the roots grow near the surface of the *Sphagnum* and the seedlings die in a few years. Such regeneration rarely, if ever, results in vigorous trees, but it emphasises the importance of suitable conditions for the germination of the seed.

The importance of grazing has been discussed already. In addition to damage by deer and sheep, capercailzie often deform seedlings by eating buds and shoots.

Other biotic causes are not important in reducing regeneration. There is a little destruction of cones by squirrels and crossbills, and in some forests the pine weevil may kill seedlings.

At various times, experiments have been carried out to stimulate natural regeneration, principally by endeavouring to create more favourable conditions for the germination of the seed and the growth of the seedlings, but sometimes adding to the natural source of seed by sowings. In 1883, an experiment was carried out at Ballochbuie after damage by wind. About 20 trees per acre (50 per ha.) were left, and the ground cleared of *Calluna* and *Vaccinium* which was heaped and burned. Cone production was poor in the two subsequent years, and in 1886 single spadefuls of soil were turned over and seed sown in each patch; this was supplemented by a good seed-fall in the same year, and a promising crop of seedlings followed (anon., 1887). Their later development, however, is not known, but some trees that probably resulted from this experiment are still growing in the forest. At various times since 1930, the Forestry Commission has carried out experiments on this subject at Glenmore, Glengarry, Guisachan, Glen Loy, and Rannoch. The treatments tried included pulling up the vegetation, killing it with sodium chlorate, burning, soil cultivation of different kinds, and sowings both of Scots pine and other conifers. J. A. B. Macdonald (1952), discussing the results, concluded: "The results have been distinctly disappointing. At best, unaided natural regeneration is erratic, undependable and a long-drawn-out process. Heather killing alone is insufficient to give much advantage, and although costly soil working is an improvement, the growth which follows has even there been extremely slow compared with plantation standards. Apart from this, the risk of insufficient seed falling at the right time is a very grave one." An experiment carried out by Mr Duncan Ross, head forester at Glentanar, is also of interest. In an area where there was a strong growth of *Calluna* up to 3 ft. (0·9 m.) in height, and in the open but adjoining a pine stand, the heather and other vegetation was removed by screefing patches about three feet square (0·9 m.²), and the soil loosened with a mattock. A fair crop of pine seedlings resulted, but grasses and heather seedlings also came in, and these appeared to attract grazing animals, and most of the seedlings were destroyed by browsing.

It is relevant to consider the methods which are normally used to regenerate Scots pine stands naturally in this and other countries. One such method is called the Uniform or Shelterwood Compartment System (Troup, 1952). It was tried in part of Dalliefour Wood in the Forestry Commission's Alltcailleach Forest, Ballater, Aberdeenshire, about mid-way between Glentanar and Ballochbuie native pinewoods. This trial was begun in 1939 in a plantation of Scots pine and a few European larch, 20 acres (8 ha.) in extent, the trees being then about 90 years old and of native Scottish origin. The site is an old river terrace and the parent material of the soil is sand and gravel. The soil is podsolised with an inch or two of raw humus. The wood was not fully stocked, and there were established field layer communities which, however, were not growing strongly. The communities varied with the microtopography, the principal ones being *Vaccinium/Deschampsia/Hypnaceous* moss No. 3 and *Calluna/Vaccinium/Deschampsia*/moss No. 5. No burning or soil cultivation was done. The Uniform System technique for natural regeneration was applied, and a seeding felling to provide the required light conditions for young seedlings and to reduce root competition for water and nutrients was made in 1939-40, the number of trees being reduced to 34 per acre (85 per ha.); a wind blow in 1942 reduced the number by a further 7. There were heavy seed years in 1941 and 1947, and from both a good crop of pine seedlings sprang up. The seed trees were not removed about 1950, as they should have been, because of policy reasons, but 15 years after the seeding felling there were over 5,000 pine seedlings per acre (12,000 per ha.), ranging in height up to 10 ft. (3 m.). While the distribution was uneven, such a result in the native pinewoods would remove all doubts about their perpetuation. On the Seafield Property in Speyside, there are a number of examples of naturally regenerated pinewoods up to 70 years old, such as Curr Wood and Balnagown Wood, which originated from plantations, but it is believed that the latter were raised from seed collected in Abernethy Forest; hence they are of native strains. The evidence of what took place is that in most instances the mature planted crop was removed by successive cuts over a relatively short period, probably about 10 years, thus in a way similar to the Uniform System technique. The soils are dry fluvio-glacial or morainic sands and gravels, and it is probable that the ground vegetation was sparse at the time when the regeneration took place, hence it is not surprising that dense regeneration resulted, even when there was some grazing by sheep.

In the natural forests of Norway, Sweden, and Finland the Uniform System technique is also applied to pine. In these countries pure pine is usually found on drier soils, and often with field layer communities similar to the better stocked parts of the native pinewoods in Scotland. Areas of about 10 acres (4 ha.) or more are dealt with at one place. The crop may be opened up by one seeding felling, but sometimes, for example in Finland, it is done in two fellings separated by a few years. The number of the trees left per acre varies but is often about 20 (50 per ha.). When the area is stocked with regeneration a final felling is carried out. Except in the far north, the seed supply is generally adequate, and good regeneration is often got in five to ten years. Sometimes, however, a smaller number of trees is left and seed is also sown in prepared patches; this increases the chance of a good crop of seedlings in a shorter time.

It is important that the principal native pinewoods in Scotland be perpetuated for a number of reasons. They are one of the most interesting survivals of our native vegetation, and they are the home of a distinctive flora and fauna. The trees remain healthy to an advanced age and are resistant to insect pests and fungal diseases. As will be shown in succeeding chapters, the pine exhibit a wide range of morphological variations, some of which at least are genetically controlled, and future progeny trials may demonstrate similar physiological variations. Some of these strains are already known to have good silvicultural qualities. They can be perpetuated elsewhere, but future generations of foresters may find that other variations may be useful for practical purposes; hence it is desirable that the whole range should be perpetuated in at least some of the native woods.

The natural regeneration of the native pinewoods is clearly full of difficulties, and further research is necessary. On the evidence presented, however, it would appear best to start from such fully stocked stands as there are, particularly on the drier sites with, for example, communities Nos. 1 to 6. If the trees have good crowns, the site is sheltered, and the risk of wind blow not serious, one could start to open them up at once. If not, then careful thinning will be necessary to build up the crowns and adapt the trees to increased wind pressure. In the light of the available evidence reviewed above, the most promising technique to secure natural regeneration is that of the Uniform System, but with an important modification. Normally in marking a seeding felling one leaves the best phenotypes as seedbearers. In a few selected native woods, however, it would be desirable to leave a range of the different types, so that all could be perpetuated to meet the possibility that future generations of foresters may prize some types now thought to be undesirable. It is clearly of the greatest importance that, whatever technique is used, the opening up of the crop should coincide with a heavy seed year; this can be predicted one year ahead, because the cone takes two years to mature. If a good crop of seedlings can be got at once, the increased luxuriance of the field layer communities following the increase in light and decreased root competition is not likely to be serious. If, however, the field layer is well established before the felling takes place, or the raw humus layer is continuous and felty, some soil cultivation or controlled burning may be necessary; but there is then the risk of thereby increasing the amount of grasses, for example *Deschampsia flexuosa* which usually decreases the chance of seedling survival. The better stocked areas are not extensive in any of the native pinewoods, and such measures, even if successful, will only begin to solve the problem of their perpetuation. The new regeneration, however, would in due course increase the amount of seed available, and it is to be expected that the area regenerated could be extended gradually. It might be necessary to supplement the natural regeneration by planting or sowing, and the former is more likely to be successful in the light of past experience. It is important however, that the seed of Scots pine should be collected in the wood where it is to be used; other origins should not be introduced.

The bog communities in the pinewoods can only be stocked with trees, whether Scots pine or other species, after adequate drainage. In many instances, it will be uneconomic to do so, and they should then be left to nature.

Finally there is the grazing question. If good crops of regeneration can be got, it will be less critical, but unless sheep are excluded and the deer population is kept at a low level, the task will be much more difficult, perhaps impossible.

CHAPTER 4

THE DEESIDE GROUP OF NATIVE PINEWOODS

THREE NATIVE pinewoods have survived in Deeside: Glentanar, Balloch-buie and Mar (see Fig. 2). In addition to these woodlands, there are others that contain Scots pine which were almost certainly regenerated naturally from native pine, but they are amongst planted pine, although the latter may have been raised from seed collected in native pinewoods. Examples of these are Garmaddie Wood on the Balmoral Estate and some woodlands on the Invercauld Estate and elsewhere. A former owner of the Invercauld Estate, Mr James Farquharson (1775), said in a letter dated 1775 that he planted Scots pine in such a way that they appeared natural. Such woodlands are best considered semi-natural, because while they almost certainly occupy sites that were previously native pinewoods and genetically the trees are of native origin, most of the trees in them have been planted. In addition, on Deeside there are Scots pine wood-lands which have been planted on sites which may or may not have carried native pinewoods in the past, but from the evidence of the trees themselves are likely to have been raised from seed collected in local native pinewoods. Good examples of these are the plantation at the Tower of Ess on the Glentanar Estate (PL. XVIII), and Dalliefour on the Forestry Commission's Alltcailleach Forest. Particularly westwards from Aboyne, Scots pine regenerates naturally in the absence of grazing in open places in and adjoining planted pine woodlands, for example at Headinsch near Pannanich and on Craigendinnie at Aboyne, and is obviously very much at home.

The pinewoods in Deeside were already well known in early times because in 1621, King James VI and I (1621) asked the Earl of Mar to send him seed for use in England. It was about this time also that some of these woodlands began to be exploited for use beyond their immediate neighbourhood, for example Glentanar. Up to that time they were much more extensive than they are today. The scattered remnants in Mar Forest were probably one large native pinewood. Ballochbuie extended along the north-facing slopes eastwards as far as Abergeldie; there is a seventeenth-century record of "firs of immense size" covering the slopes to the summit of Creag Ghiubhais (1593 ft., 478 m.) and incidentally the name means the hill of the firs (Macfarlane, 1908). There were pinewoods on the north side of the river on Invercauld Estate between Braemar and Ballater, but their extent and location is not known. Eastwards from Ballater, there appears to have been pinewood on the slopes of Pannanich which may have connected with the Glentanar woodlands, which in turn may have continued into part of the Forest of Birse. Nevertheless, Upper Deeside was never one large pine forest. There are eighteenth-century records of extensive birchwoods with little or no pine, for example the woodlands of Coripherige and Tornraw at Castleton of Braemar (Michie, 1901), while in the valley between Braemar and Ballater there were extensive birchwoods in the middle of the last century (Crombie, 1861). There are still relict communities of birch with alder, aspen and hazel along the river. Eastwards from Ballater, oak was almost certainly a constituent of the valley woods on the more fertile soils and on south-facing slopes; there are still surviving semi-natural oakwoods, for example on Craigendarroch at Ballater (Dickie, 1843; Tansley, 1949), and at Dinnet Bridge.

While felling for other than local needs had begun in some parts of Deeside during the seventeenth century, it was only during the next century that this trade reached considerable proportions. The River Dee and its tributaries were used to float logs from as far up the river as the Linn of Dee, west of Braemar, to Aberdeen (Cordiner, 1780; Sinclair, 1791-9). There were difficulties, however, and floating was only successful when the river was in flood; when bridges came to be built over the river, they suffered. The bridge at Potarch was destroyed by logs between 1810 and 1812, and the second bridge at Ballater in the "muckle spate" of 1829. As early as 1797, there was a proposal to build a canal from Aboyne to Hazelhead, near Aberdeen, to float timber from Glentanar, but the scheme did not come to fruition (Fraser, 1921). The building of the railway to Ballater in 1854 helped to solve the transport problem. There was a plan to construct a tramway for twelve miles beyond the railhead at that village to enable Ballochbuie Forest to be exploited, but Queen Victoria intervened, took a lease of the forest, and subsequently acquired it in 1878 (Fraser, 1921). There has been relatively little felling in the native pinewoods since that time; the emergency demands for timber in the two world wars during this century led to some felling, but only to a limited extent. There has been some destruction also by fire and exceptional gales such as that on 31 January 1953, but not on a catastrophic scale except for the fire at Glentanar in 1920. There is evidence, however, of a slow shrinking of the woodlands through the death of old trees on the margins as well as within the woodlands themselves; but during the last ten years, some interest has arisen in their perpetuation by natural regeneration and other means.

GLENTANAR

Owner: The Lord Glentanar.

Location: The parish of Aboyne and Glentanar, Aberdeenshire. Latitude, 57° 1′ N.; Longitude, 2° 53′ W. National Grid Reference 37 (NO)/470920. Ordnance Survey Maps: 1 in. to 1 mile, 44 (Scotland), 1946 edition; 6 in. to 1 mile, Aberdeenshire 92 N.E., S.E. and S.W., 93 N.W. and S.W., 101 N.E., 1902–03 edition.

The forest lies two to six miles (3·2 to 9·6 km.) south-west and south of Aboyne (see Fig. 13). There is a mixed birch and pinewood in the loop of the River Dee at Cambus o' May, locally called Torphantrick, which may be a small relict native pinewood, but there is doubt as to its origin and it is excluded from this study.

FIG. 13. Glentanar (see p. XVI for key to Figs. 13 to 37)

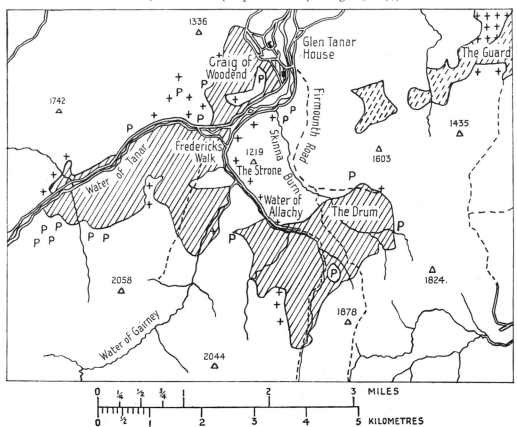

HISTORY

From the fifteenth until the end of the last century, Glentanar was more or less continuously in the possession of the Earls and Marquises of Huntly. From at least the beginning of the seventeenth century, there were feu charters to vassals who had rights of timber for their own use, but the superior otherwise retained the timber and had the right to erect sawmills driven by water and wind (Huntly, 1894). Travellers in the middle of the seventeenth century mentioned the immense forest of tall firs at Glentanar (Macfarlane, 1908), and Blaeu's *Atlas*, 1654, shows trees in this region. Writers such as Allan Ramsay (1721) and Lightfoot (1777) made allusion to the "wild pine" in this forest in the eighteenth century, and there is the following brief description of it in 1725: "The country is mountainous, not very fertile, the people living more by trafficking in timber than husbandry, this wood they have from the Wood of Glentanar, which lies on the south side of the said parish, and is the only ornament of the place. It is very large in extent, 10 to 12 miles (16 to 19·2 km.) in circumference, tho' not full in all places. The timber in this wood, which is all fir, grows to a great height and bigness, the whole country round being served in fir-timber out of it, to the considerable advantage of the Earl of Aboyne who is Heretour of it as he is all that parish" (Robertson, 1725). At the end of that century, the annual revenue from the forest was from £400 to £500 and the price of the timber was rising. Selected trees were removed, squared by the axe, and sold at threepence to sixpence per cubic foot; according to the first *Statistical Account* there was at that time no local sawmill, but the saw-pits found in Allachy Wood during this study may have been used at that time. There were two fires in the forest in the second half of the eighteenth century; according to the first *Statistical Account* young growth was destroyed, but the old trees were only singed. When the price of timber fell after the Napoleonic Wars the timber trade declined, and it is recorded in 1841 that the cost of carting the timber to Aberdeen was almost as great as the price obtained for it, most trees being too heavy for floating except when the river was in flood (Smith, 1874). During the second half of the nineteenth century, large areas of moor on the south side of the River Dee were enclosed and planted with Scots pine, European larch and broadleaved species, but, as far as is known, there was no planting in the native pinewoods, then estimated to extend to 6000 acres (2400 ha.), except perhaps on Craigendinnie (Smith, 1874). There is a record, but without details, of two fires during the nineteenth century (anon., 1903), and there was a catastrophic fire which began during very dry conditions on 14 June 1920, and was not finally extinguished until 1 July; it destroyed 1362 acres (545 ha.) of old pine, and no natural regeneration followed. Since that time there have been only minor fires in the native pinewoods. The gale of 31 January 1953 caused considerable damage, particularly in Frederick's Walk, Craig of Woodend and the woodlands adjoining the Water of Gairney.

There are a few abandoned crofts within the forest, and there has no doubt been some grazing by domestic animals for a long period. Prior to the middle of the last century, goats were pastured in the forest; these were then replaced by sheep, and at one time it is estimated that there were 7000 head in the forest (anon., 1956b; Glentanar, 1948). At the end of the century, the importance of sporting interests led to the preservation of deer, and in the early decades of this century the population reached a high level. For a number of reasons, the proprietor decided in 1936 to exclude red deer by means of a ring fence, and, while this is not entirely effective, it has greatly reduced the incidence of browsing by deer, but some hill cattle and ponies graze in the forest. While extensive fellings took place in plantations on the Glentanar Estate during the 1939-45 War, there was little felling in the native pinewoods.

THE HABITAT

Climate. For this and all other forests, the rainfall data are taken from the map of the average annual rainfall 1881-1915 (anon., 1949). The temperature data are from the *Climatological Atlas of the British Isles* (anon., 1952b). The isotherms in that publication, however, have been corrected to sea-level using 1° F. per 300 ft. (0·56° C. per 91 m.), and the values have been recalculated for the average altitude of each pinewood.

Mean annual rainfall		35 in.	889 mm.
Temperatures:	Mean annual	44° F.	6·7° C.
	January mean	36° F.	2·2° C.
	July mean	54° F.	12·2° C.

Climatic sub-province (Anderson, 1955) A1b.

Topography. The forest is growing in valleys drained by four streams that flow northwards into the River Dee. These are the Tanar, which is fed by the Skinna and the Allachy, the latter joined by the Gairney. The woodlands clothe the slopes of the valleys, the range in altitude being about 600 (180 m.) to 1400 ft. (420 m.), but there are scattered trees up to about 1500 ft. (450 m.). The forest is sheltered from the south and south-west by a number of hills ranging from 1824 ft. (547 m.) to 3077 ft. (923 m.), the highest being Mount Keen. An ancient highway, the Firmounth road, runs southward through the forest up the Skinna burn.

PLATE VI

NATURAL REGENERATION IN NATIVE PINEWOODS

a) Glentanar, on river shingle, with well grown, natural pine about 120 years old in the background.

b) Abernethy, pine regeneration in *Callunetum* No. 10 on sand and gravel under an open shelterwood.

Geology and Soils. The underlying rock in most of the forest is granite, with two small areas of quartz porphyry along the River Tanar and some impure limestone at its northern end. The solid rock is mantled by glacial drift of varying depths up to at least 20 ft. (6 m.), principally moraines and fluvio-glacial deposits containing much granitic material. Its texture is light and usually sandy and gravelly. Along the river courses there are banks of stony alluvium (anon., 1948 *a* and *b*; anon., 1897). The natural drainage is good, and there are few peat bogs within the boundaries of the woodlands, but beyond their upper limits there are peat bogs in places.

There is usually a layer, up to 3 in. (7·6 cm.) deep, of raw humus composed of the remains of pine needles and ground vegetation plants. The gritty, light textured soils show podsolisation with a distinct but not deep A horizon.

THE FOREST

Tree species and larger shrubs. The native pinewoods consist almost entirely of Scots pine. There are a few scattered birches – verrucose, pubescent, and intermediates – within the pine stands, and there is a detached birchwood at the Shiel of Glentanar, four miles (6·4 km.) south-west of the nearest pine. There are also some aspen, principally in open places such as along roadsides, while rowan is scattered thinly throughout the forest, and alder is found along the banks of streams. Juniper grows throughout the forest, but is more abundant in open places in the Allachy valley and the Drum woods, and is usually of the bushy and procumbent types.

Field layer. The communities within the native pinewoods have been classified and listed in Chapter 3 and Appendix I.

In well stocked stands, the principal community is *Vaccinium/Deschampsia/ Hypnaceous* moss No. 3, with No. 1, a dry moss community, very local. In the open stands, dry and moist *Calluna/Vaccinium/Deschampsia/*moss communities Nos. 5 and 6 predominate, with small areas of the grass pinewood community No. 7 around ruined crofts and adjacent to cultivated ground. Bracken (*Pteridium aquilinum*) is spreading to an unusual extent for an eastern native pinewood in communities Nos. 3, 5 and 6, and is beginning to form almost pure societies. As one approaches the upper margins of the woods and the pines become scattered, the characteristic communities are *Callunetum* No. 10, and *Calluna/Trichophorum* No. 11, in which *Erica tetralix* may become co-dominant after burning. The principal bog community within the woodlands is usually *Juncus communis* agg. No. 17, but with *Calluna* more abundant and luxuriant than typical, and within it there may be small pockets of *Sphagnum* bog No. 19, and a few patches of

H

Calluna/Molinia community No. 9. Beyond the margins of the pinewoods there are tracts of the bog community *Eriophorum/Trichophorum/Sphagnum* No. 15, particularly at the head waters of the Gairney, and it may spread under scattered pine.

A plant list, based on all the native pinewoods, is given in Appendix II. Of the less common plants, *Goodyera repens* (PL. XII.*a*) and *Trientalis europaea* are unusually widespread. *Pyrola media* and *P. minor* are to be found here and there throughout the forest, but *Listera cordata* is rare. The rock rose (*Helianthemum chamaecistus*) was found not far from the limestone area referred to above, while another unexpected species in a pinewood is *Achillea ptarmica* which grows in the Allachy valley. *Juncus alpinus* is to be found here and there along the upper margins of the woodlands.

Age structure. Most of the forest consists of trees about 130 to 190 years old, but there is a representation of most age classes in groups of varying size. Recently felled stumps have shown up to 240 annual rings, and there may be older trees in the forest. In Frederick's Walk and in the Drum, there are considerable areas of well stocked pinewoods from 120 to 140 years old, with scattered older trees which were probably the parent trees. Age classes below 100 years are poorly represented, but there are patches of regeneration under 20 years old which have come up following the restriction of grazing by red deer.

Growth and stocking. The maximum height attained by the pines is 75 ft. (22·5 m.), but this is exceptional, and even on the lower and sheltered slopes the usual height is 50 ft. (15·0 m.). The largest tree measured was 10 ft. 6 in. (3·15 m.) in girth at breast height, and there are a number between seven and eight feet in girth (2·1 to 2·4 m.), but the average of the older trees is between four and five feet (1·2 and 1·5 m.) so that they have 15 to 20 rings per in. (6 to 8 per cm.) on the average, although the oldest trees may show 40 to 60 rings per in. (16 to 24 per cm.) towards the perimeter of the stem.

The stocking is very variable, ranging from scattered trees at the upper fringes to almost fully stocked stands sometimes extending over several acres. The better but typical irregularly stocked stands carry between 500 and 1000 hoppus ft. per acre (45 to 90 m.³ per ha.).

Fauna. There are few red deer in the woodlands since the forest was enclosed by a deer fence in 1936, and the population of roe deer is not high. Even before the rabbits were decimated by myxomatosis in 1955, their numbers were small. Mountain hares come into the woodlands in the winter, and do some damage to young pines, but this is not serious. Red squirrels have peeled the stems of the pines in the past, but are not now numerous, while their predators, the pine martens, were exterminated between 1870 and 1880 (Macgregor, 1955). Both the golden eagle and the kestrel frequent the forest. Of the birds that do damage to the pine, capercailzie are numerous, but black grouse are few. There is an occasional greater spotted woodpecker, while crossbills appear to be increasing in number. The smaller birds include the chaffinch, coal tit, pied wagtail, robin, tree-creeper, and, on the lower ground, the wren. There are large numbers of adders and some slow worms and common lizards.

Natural regeneration. Most of the older pine in the forest originated during the hundred years from about the middle of the eighteenth century. During this period the forest was being exploited, and there would be open areas permitting the development of any natural regeneration. As already mentioned, there was grazing by goats at this time, but they could not have been sufficiently numerous to destroy completely the young trees. The almost complete cessation of established regeneration after the middle of the last century was probably due first, to the heavy sheep stock in the forest, and, from the end of the last century, to the rise in the population of red deer. The numbers of the latter began to decline after the 1914-18 War, and since the forest was enclosed in 1936 regeneration has begun to appear. It is usually found in open places, particularly along tracks, on shingle beside streams (PL. VI.*a*), and around isolated old pines, and in field layer communities dominated by *Calluna vulgaris*, such as *Callunetum* No. 10, and dry to moist *Calluna/Vaccinium/Deschampsia/*moss Nos. 5 and 6. There is little regeneration where there is a dense growth of *Vaccinium* spp. On the edges of woodlands there may be some regeneration on the *Calluna/Trichophorum* community No. 11, and seedlings do appear on bog community No. 15 but do not persist. Few seedlings are to be found within the better stocked stands, and this is probably due partly to the amount of shade and root competition and partly to the typical layer of raw humus, which reduces the chance of successful root penetration before the organic layer dries out in the summer.

BALLOCHBUIE

Owner: Her Majesty the Queen.

Location: The parish of Braemar and Crathie, Aberdeenshire. Latitude, 56° 59′ N.; Longitude, 3° 19′ W. National Grid Reference 37 (NO)/200895. Ordnance Survey Maps: 1 in. to 1 mile, 44 and 50 (Scotland) 1946 edition; 6 in. to 1 mile, Aberdeenshire Nos. 98 and 99, 1902-03 edition.

The forest stretches southward from the River Dee, 3 miles (4·8 km.) east of Braemar (see Fig. 14). In earlier times the area of the natural forest was more extensive. The strip between the river and Danzig Shiel has been modified by planting, including the use of non-indigenous species, and has been excluded from the present study. The forest appeared to have stretched to Creag Choinnich on the west, but this is now planted woodland. The woods of Garmaddie on the east were also part of the forest. These were felled at the end of the eighteenth and the beginning of the nineteenth century (anon., 1887), and, while Garmaddie may contain naturally regenerated trees, it is probably mainly planted, and is best considered to be a semi-natural woodland.

HISTORY

This region was part of the ancient Earldom of Mar. Previous to the seventeenth century, the Earls of Mar had granted small properties to their vassals, first on verbal missives, and from at least 1632 on written charters (Michie, 1901). In

FIG. 14. Ballochbuie

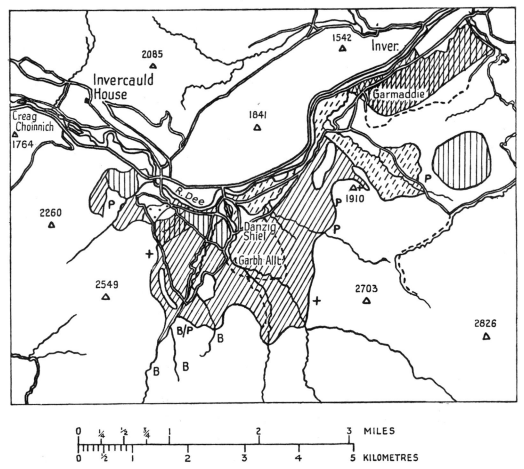

these the Earl reserved the whole of the natural pinewoods whether on his personal property or that of his vassals. These woods included part of Ballochbuie east of the Garbh Allt, at that time called the Garwalt burn or Garrawalt. The part between that burn and Creag Choinnich, termed Craigkynoch at that time, was already the personal property of the Farquharsons of Invercauld. The Earls of Mar, while reserving the natural pinewoods, had granted servitudes to their vassals and the latter's tenants for timber for building and for working of the land. The Mar estate was forfeited after the rising in 1715, when John Erskine, eleventh Earl of Mar raised the standard of King James on the Braes of Mar, and was purchased from the Crown in 1724 by James Erskine and sold to Lord Braco, later Earl of Fife, in 1735. In earlier times the Earls of Mar had been mainly interested in the woods from the point of view of hunting, but by the eighteenth century and the opening up of the country following the 1715 rising, the timber was of more value, and the new owner became concerned about the effect of the servitudes on the forest. This led to lengthy legal battles. In 1782 the dispute between the Earls of Fife and Farquharson of Invercauld acting both for himself and other holders of servitudes was settled by arbitration, Farquharson obtaining the eastern half of Ballochbuie in return for giving up the servitudes in other pinewoods, such as at Mar Forest. From that date until 1878, the whole of Ballochbuie Forest belonged to Invercauld.

From the Invercauld Records (Michie, 1901), and such visitors to Invercauld as Thomas Pennant (1771), one can form some picture of the forest in the eighteenth century and earlier. In 1769, Pennant describes it as follows: "A magnificent forest of pines of many miles extent. Some of the trees are of vast size; I measured several that were ten, eleven and even twelve feet [3, 3·3 and 3·6 m.] in circumference, and near sixty feet [18 m.] high, forming a most beautiful column, with a fine verdant capital. These trees are of great age, having, as is supposed, seen two centuries. The value of these trees is considerable; Mr Farquharson informed me that, by sawing them and retailing them, he has got for eight hundred trees five-and-twenty shillings each; they are sawed in an adjacent sawmill into planks ten feet long, eleven inches broad, and three thick (3·0 m. × 28 cm. × 7·6 cm.], and sold for two shillings a piece." In the middle of the last century Macgillivray (1855) gave 12 ft. (3·6 m.) as the maximum girth at 4 ft. (1·2 m.) in Mar Forest, while in Ballochbuie in 1887 (anon., 1887), the largest girths at 5 ft. (1·5 m.) from the ground ranged up to 14 ft. (4·2 m.) with volumes of from 100 to 250 cu. ft. (3·6 to 9·0 m.³) per tree. The upper girth limit, therefore, appears to have remained relatively constant at least during the past two centuries.

In previous centuries, the amount of timber removed under the rights of servitude was probably not large in spite of the complaints of the Superior. Here, as elsewhere, there was also some damage by the cutting out of the resinous hearts of the trees for "candle-fir." There is still evidence of such damage in existing trees.

For many centuries the forest had been grazed by cattle, and there were also red and roe deer. Even the Earl of Fife, however, was prepared to accept some damage to natural regeneration by cattle grazing. In the eighteenth century natural regeneration appears to have been relatively prolific in the open spacings. The tendency of Scots pine to regenerate only in the open is illustrated by the remark already mentioned: "these Highland fir woods gradually shift their stances" (Michie, 1901). In one dispute, the Earl of Fife objected to the cultivation of land adjoining the forest because this prevented its spread, and twelve thousand young trees up to 9 ft. (2·7 m.) high had been destroyed on three acres (1·2 ha.).

Queen Victoria and the Prince Consort visited Ballochbuie in 1848 (Queen Victoria, 1868), and this led later to its preservation. Ballochbuie had escaped the extensive felling which had taken place during the first half of the last century in Mar Forest. About 1870, however, several thousand trees were sold to a firm of timber merchants in Aberdeen. Queen Victoria intervened and purchased the trees from the merchant, and in 1878 acquired also the land on which they were growing (anon., 1887; Fraser, 1921); thus ownership passed from Invercauld to the Queen. The storm of 28 December 1879, that destroyed the Tay Bridge, caused extensive windfall in Ballochbuie, and there was further damage on 6 March 1883 (anon., 1887). This led to some interesting attempts being made by Mr John Michie, then forester at Balmoral, to restock the parts of the forest opened up by the gales. A portion of the forest between the low and middle drives was fenced against deer. Some planting was done with three year seedlings of Scots pine, and one such plantation exists today. On Garrawalt hillock, west of the falls of Garbh Allt, an area was prepared for natural regeneration. The ground was cleared of *Calluna* and *Vaccinium* and the material heaped and burned. There were about twenty seed trees left per acre (50 per ha.) on the ground, but cone production was poor in 1884 and 1885, and in 1886 single spadefuls of soil were turned over in spots about six feet (1·8 m.) apart, and a few seeds sown in each. In the same year there was an abundant crop of cones, and it is recorded that there was a good crop of seedlings in the following year (anon., 1887). As it is known that pine seedlings were being raised at the forest nursery at Balmoral at that time from seed collected in Ballochbuie Forest, it is a reasonable assumption that the seed used was collected in Ballochbuie. There are still patches of pine on Garrawalt hillock which probably date from these experiments.

Since the forest was owned by the reigning sovereign there has been little felling except of dead and dying trees. The gale of 31 January 1953 did some further damage to the forest, and unfortunately some of the oldest and tallest trees were blown down.

THE HABITAT

Climate. Mean annual rainfall   35 in.   889 mm.
Temperatures: Mean annual   43° F.   6·1° C.
                        January mean   35° F.   1·7° C.
                        July mean   54° F.   12·2° C.
Climatic sub-province (Anderson, 1955) A1b and A2b.

Topography. The forest lies in an amphitheatre, open to the River Dee in the north, and surrounded by hills in the other directions. Most of the forest is at elevations of from 1000 (300 m.) to 1700 ft. (510 m.) above sea-level, but there are scattered pines up to about 1900 ft. (570 m.). The surrounding hills range from 2500 (750 m.) to 2900 ft. (870 m.). The general aspect is northerly, but there are both easterly and western aspects on the slopes. The basin is drained by the Garbh Allt and lesser tributary streams of the River Dee.

Geology and soils. Most of the forest is underlaid by granite of the Lochnagar mass, but there are Dalradian quartzite and graphite schists near the western boundary. The soils are derived from glacial deposits laid down in the closing phases of the Ice Age. The drifts consist principally of morainic sands and gravels, but there is some boulder clay, and fluvio-glacial deposits. Most of the rock material in the drifts is granite, but there is also some diorite, schists and limestone from surrounding formations. There are narrow strips of alluvium along the water courses (anon., 1911; anon., 1948).

Most of the soils are gritty and gravelly and show some podsolisation. There is usually a deep raw humus layer of the remains of ground vegetation plants, pine needles and bark, and this may exceed a foot (0·3 m.).

Most of the forest is on well drained slopes, but there are peat bogs up to several feet in depth in hollows. The pine has invaded these bogs, but it is generally of small size (PL. IX.*b*).

THE FOREST

Tree species and larger shrubs. The forest is predominantly Scots pine, birch being uncommon and principally on margins, but there is a small birchwood at the north-west of the forest. Both *Betula pubescens* and *B. verrucosa*, as well as intermediates, are present. There are a few aspen and alder, principally along streams, while rowan is scattered thinly throughout the forest. There is an occasional larch and Norway spruce here and there, either naturally regenerated from seed carried either by wind or birds from planted woods in the vicinity or planted. Juniper is of the bushy type (PL. XI.*b*), and is rare in the western half but locally frequent in the east and south-east of the forest. There are a few holly bushes, but they never attain more than six feet (1·8 m.) in height.

The field layer. Under close canopy the principal community is the *Vaccinium/Deschampsia/Hypnaceous* moss community No. 3; in more open pinewood the communities are, with increasing moisture, the dry *Calluna/Vaccinium/Deschampsia* moss No. 5, the moist *Calluna/Vaccinium/Deschampsia/*moss No. 6, and the moist *Calluna/Vaccinium/Eriophorum/Sphagnum* No. 8 community. Locally in open places there is the *Callunetum* community No. 10. The principal bog type is the *Eriophorum/Trichophorum/Sphagnum* No. 15, while there are very local patches of *Juncus communis* No. 17 and *Sphagnum* spp. bog No. 19.

Among the rarer plants found was one plant each of *Linnaea borealis* and *Moneses uniflora; Ramischia (Pyrola) secunda* on two locations (PL. XII.*b*), and *Listera cordata* on a number; *Empetrum hermaphroditum* is present at the upper fringe of the forest amongst rocks.

Age structure. The forest is uneven-aged, but the oldest age classes predominate. There are only occasional trees or small groups under 100 years, but there are a number of stands between 100 and 150 years. The trees in the greater part of the forest are in the 150 to 200 age class (PL. VII.*b*), and the maximum age attained is about 300 years.

Growth and stocking. The maximum height of the pine is 90 ft. (27 m.), but this is exceptional, and the mean height, even on the lower and well drained slopes, is about 50 to 55 ft. (15 to 16·5 m.). The maximum girth at breast height is about 9 ft. (2·7 m.), and the mean for the older age classes on the lower slopes is between 6 and 7 ft. (1·8 and 2·1 m.). The rate of growth is, therefore, slow and in the oldest trees there may be over 50 rings to the inch (20 per cm.) in the outer parts of the stem.

The stocking is very variable, ranging from very open forest to fully stocked groups, which on the lower and well drained slopes may be quite extensive. The forest as a whole, however, is understocked.

Fauna. Red deer are numerous in the forest during the winter, and there are also roe deer. Neither rabbits nor mountain hares, which come into the forest in the upper margins, are sufficiently numerous to do any damage to the trees. There are red squirrels but the population is low. The Scottish wild cat is said to be an inhabitant of the forest, but the polecat is extinct, although it was common at the end of the eighteenth century in this district (Millar, 1909), and one was killed in 1890 (Macgregor, 1955). Of the birds that might do damage to trees, there are capercailzie, black grouse, and crossbills, but they are not sufficiently numerous to be important from that point of view.

While a few sheep stray into the margins of the forest, there is now no appreciable grazing by domestic animals.

The forest is remarkably free from insects potentially injurious to the trees, but both *Myelophilus piniperda* and *M. minor* are to be found.

Natural regeneration. The evidence of the age structure of the forest, together with the historical records, show that the pine regenerated relatively freely in the eighteenth century. Damage to young trees by the grazing of cattle was referred to at that time, and no doubt red and roe deer did some browsing, but there was sufficient natural regeneration to ensure the perpetuation of the forest, although stocking in the resulting age classes today is often open. The experiments carried out in the 1880's with natural regeneration, direct sowing, and planting have been discussed already. Since that time, there has been very little natural regeneration, and in most parts of the forest one has to search in order to find even one seedling. In spite of the age of the trees, there is good cone production periodically, and the germination of the seed is normal. Where the plants in the field layer form a deep mat of vegetation, and there is a thick layer of raw humus underneath, one is not surprised that few seedlings can germinate and survive; but where the vegetation is rich in *Calluna* up to about a foot (0·3 m.) high, the raw humus is thin, and sand and gravel are exposed in places, one would expect a good crop of seedlings after a heavy seed year: nevertheless there are only a few on such sites. When seedlings grow above the vegetation, they tend to be grazed by deer, but the primary cause of the lack of natural regeneration is the failure of the seed to germinate and the seedlings to survive, and this requires further study.

MAR

Owner: The trustees of the late Duke of Fife.

Location: The parish of Braemar and Crathie. Latitude, 57° to 57° 3′ N.; Longitude, 3° 30′ to 3° 36′ W. National Grid Reference 37 (NO)/035932 to 37 (NO)/085955. Ordinance Survey Maps: 1 in. to 1 mile, 43 (Scotland), 1947 edition; 6 in. to 1 mile, Aberdeenshire 88 and 97, 1902–03 edition.

The native pinewoods are located on the south-east face of the Cairngorm Mountains, in glens three to six miles (5 to 10 km.) west and north-west of Braemar (see Fig. 15). The woods lie in three valleys, the Quoich, the Derry, and

Luibeg whose waters drain into the River Dee, and give their names to the surviving remnants of what was a much larger pinewood in earlier times. There are native pine at Lui amongst birch, but as many of the trees in this woodland have been planted, it is not included in the present study.

HISTORY

As already mentioned, the lands in Upper Deeside previously belonged to the Earldom of Mar, the history of which has been described by Simpson (1949). The earls used their estate mainly for hunting deer and other game. Land was let to their vassals, but, as already mentioned, the earls generally retained the rights to the fir woodlands of natural growth, subject to servitudes of timber for the

Fig. 15. Mar

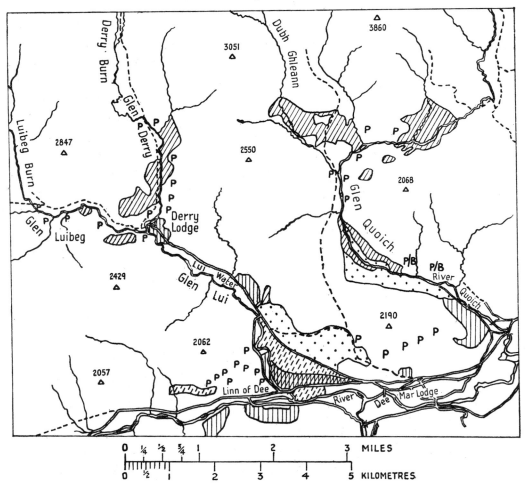

vassals' own use, which as we have seen led later to legal disputes. There does not appear to have been much exploitation of the pinewoods, except for local use before the beginning of the eighteenth century. A sawmill was built in 1695 at the mouth of Glen Quoich, and there were annual fellings of pine in the more accessible places in that glen (Cordiner, 1780). Following the rising in 1715, the estate was forfeited and ultimately came into the possession of Lord Braco, later the Earl of Fife, in 1735. It is clear that he realised the commercial value of the timber, hence his desire to limit the depredations of his tenants. Charles Cordiner (1780) gives a glimpse of conditions in Mar Forest in 1776. Prior to his visit, a large part of the woodlands in Luibeg and Glen Derry had been felled and the logs floated down the Lui Water to a sawmill below the Linn of Dee, which also received logs from woodlands further up the Dee. The forest contained many dead, dying, and rotten trees, and there must have been many old trees in it at that time; a tree 70 ft. (21 m.) long and 13 ft. (3·96 m.) in girth is mentioned. There was also young regeneration coming up in Glen Quoich. At that time some of the crofts in Luibeg had been abandoned. It is known that during the period from 1811 to 1855, many of the best remaining pine in the neighbourhood of Braemar were felled (Macgillivray, 1855), and there is reference at that time to the floating of timber from Mar down the River Dee (Loudon, 1838). Extensive fellings were carried out on the Mar Estate during the two wars of this century, but principally in planted woodlands. In recent years there have been small fires in Glen Quoich and Glen Derry which have killed scattered pine over several acres. There has been a large number of red and roe deer in Mar Forest since at least the end of the eighteenth century (Cordiner, 1780; Sinclair, 1791-9) and the population is still large.

THE HABITAT

Climate.   Mean annual rainfall   40 in.   1016 mm.
              Temperatures: Mean annual   42° F.   5·6° C.
                             January mean   34° F.   1·1° C.
                             July mean   53° F.   11·7° C.
Climatic sub-provinces (Anderson, 1955) A2b and B3c.

Topography. In Glen Quoich, the pinewood is near the junction of the Quoich Water and Dubh Ghleann, and on slopes between 1300 ft. (390 m.) and 1850 ft. (555 m.), but with scattered trees up to 2050 ft. (615 m.). The slopes are steep on the west side of the valley and moderate on the east; the aspects are variable but mainly southerly. The pinewood in Glen Derry is on a flat alluvial plain and adjacent slopes between 1360 ft. (408 m.) and 1750 ft. (525 m.), with scattered trees up to 2000 ft. (600 m.) above sea-level. In Luibeg, the pine is principally on undulating hillsides from 1360 ft. (408 m.) to 1700 ft. (510 m.), and with a general northerly aspect. Far up the valley a single stunted bushy pine referred to in Chapter 1 was found at 2800 ft. (840 m.) on a slope with a south-easterly aspect.

Geology and soils. The main mass of the Cairngorms is granite, but at their south-east limit the underlying strata are gneisses and other rocks of the Central Highland Granulites or Moine series, and there are also narrow belts of Dalradian quartzite. Moine gneiss underlies most of Glen Quoich with granite under the higher parts of the main pinewoods at the extreme north. Almost the whole area is mantled with glacial drift, while there is alluvium along the sides of streams. In Glen Derry, there is granite on the west side of the river which continues as a narrow band on the east for about a mile north of Derry Lodge, but most of the east side is on Moine rocks, principally gneisses with small zones of calcareous material and a little hornfels. Along the river there are alluvial deposits and local bogs, while the slopes are covered with glacial drift and there is boulder clay at the upper margin of the pinewoods and beyond. Luibeg is on granite overlaid by drift including boulder clay, with alluvial terraces along the river (anon., 1911; anon., 1913*a*; anon., 1948*b*).

The parent material of the soils over most of the area is glacial drift of varying texture, but all containing a high proportion of quartzose material. The better stocked parts of the pinewoods are growing on freely drained, coarse textured soils with a thin mat of raw humus and signs of podsolisation. In valley bottoms and also on slopes the drainage may be impeded, and the stocking is then generally more open with field layer communities characteristic of such stocking, while particularly in Glen Derry there are some peat bogs.

THE FOREST

Tree species and larger shrubs. In the native pinewoods, the pine predominates and the birches are subsidiary species, but in Glen Lui and other adjoining woods where there has been planting, there is more natural birch. Rowan is to be found as an occasional tree throughout the woodlands, and alder along streams, but aspen is absent although it is growing in the neighbouring woods to the south where there is also holly and dog rose. There are a few bushes of the procumbent type of juniper.

Field layer. In the well stocked parts of all three remnants in this forest, the same field layer communities are to be found. Under the closest canopy, the *Vaccinium/Deschampsia/Hypnaceous* moss No. 3 community, and, where a little more light reaches the forest floor, dry *Calluna/Vaccinium/Deschampsia/*moss No. 5

and locally the moist variant, No. 6, are characteristic. In open stands, there are patches of the *Deschampsia flexuosa/Hypnaceous* moss community No. 4 and the grass pinewood community No. 7. In open places at the upper margins of the woods, there is *Callunetum* No. 10 on dry sites and the *Calluna/Trichophorum* No. 11 and *Calluna/Vaccinium/Eriophorum/Sphagnum* No. 8 communities on moister soils. Particularly at Glen Derry under open and scattered pines at the margins of the woods where the natural drainage is poor, *Molinia caerulea* and *Trichophorum caespitosum* are invading communities Nos. 5 and 6, and there are patches of *Calluna/Molinia* No. 9, *Molinia* flush No. 16 and *Molinia/Trichophorum* No. 12 communities. The *Molinia*, however, is never so abundant and luxuriant as it is in the pinewoods of the western Highlands. In all the pinewoods, there are small areas of bog communities, principally *Eriophorum/Trichophorum/Sphagnum* No. 15 and the *Sphagnum* spp. No. 19.

Of the less common plants characteristic of pinewoods, there are *Pyrola media*, *Ramischia secunda* (PL. XII.*b*), *Trientalis europaea* and *Listera cordata*. On grassy patches *Gentianella amarella* and *Polygonum viviparum* are to be found. Above the upper limit of the pinewoods, there is the distinctive mountain flora of the Cairngorms, but a few species such as *Saxifraga aizoides* (PL. XX.*c*), *S. stellaris*, *Rubus chamaemorus*, *Alchemilla alpina*, *Lycopodium alpinum* and *L. annotinum* (PL. XII.*d*) descend to the margins of the woods at about 2000 ft. (600 m.).

Age structure. In the three pinewoods at Mar, there is less diversity in age than in the two other forests in Deeside. Most of the trees are between about 140 and 200 years old, even in Luibeg where the height is only 30 ft. (9·0 m.); the oldest, determined by borings, was 250 years old. Outwith that range, there are several trees about 100 years old, and a few seedlings at the edges of the woods under five years of age.

Growth and stocking. The tallest trees at Mar are beside the river in Glen Derry, where they reach 80 ft. (24 m.) and many are over 70 ft. (21 m.) in height, although the altitude is over 1350 ft. (405 m.). Elsewhere the average height is about 50 ft. (15 m.), except in Luibeg where they are smaller, while at the upper limit of the woodlands, about 1800 ft. (540 m.) above sea-level, the trees are stunted. On the more sheltered sites with good natural drainage, the girths at breast height are between four and six feet (1·2 to 1·8 m.). As in the other forests, the current rate of radial growth on old trees is very slow.

At Mar the stands are mostly open, but there are small areas which are well stocked; as in other forests there are only scattered trees at the margins.

Fauna. The red deer which shelter in or near the woodlands in winter and spring are numerous, and herds of up to 100 animals may be seen grazing at the edges of the woodlands. There are also a few roe deer, and mountain hares come into the woodlands in the winter, but their numbers are stated to be declining (Macgregor, 1955). The last pine marten in the district was killed in 1883, and the wild cat came to the verge of extinction about the same time, but after the 1914-18 War its numbers increased, and there are probably still some in the forest although there are no recent reliable records (Macgregor, 1955). There are a few red squirrels in the woodlands. Capercailzie are now numerous, with a few black grouse and an occasional crossbill. Members of the Cairngorm mountain fauna, such as the golden eagle, the ptarmigan, the snow bunting, the buzzard, and the raven sometimes come down to the tree limit. Macgregor (1955) has stated that there is now a colony of crested tits in Mar Forest.

Natural regeneration. As already mentioned, there are a few naturally regenerated pine seedlings on the edges of the woodlands, principally on the following field layer communities: *Callunetum* No. 10; *Calluna/Trichophorum* No. 11; and the dry and moist *Calluna/Vaccinium/Deschampsia*/moss Nos. 5 and 6. The age structure of the forest already described shows that there has been little successful regeneration for over 150 years, and the heavy incidence of grazing by deer during that period is almost certainly the principal reason. The present pine in Glen Derry probably grew up after the felling which was done before Cordiner's visit in 1776 (Cordiner, 1780), while the trees in Glen Quoich may be those that he saw as young seedlings at that time.

CHAPTER 5

THE SPEYSIDE GROUP OF NATIVE PINEWOODS

THE NATIVE pinewoods that have survived in the upper reaches of the River Spey and in the valleys of its tributaries are more extensive than most of the others elsewhere in Scotland. There are still large tracts in the forests of Abernethy, Rothiemurchus and Glenmore, and small remnants in the upper Dulnan Valley, Glen Feshie, and Glen Avon (see Fig. 2). There has been a good deal of planting in these native woodlands, particularly at Abernethy and Glenmore. There are also many Scots pine woodlands in this region which have been planted or regenerated naturally from planted pine, but by record or tradition, and the evidence of the trees themselves, they are of native origin. Some of these existing woodlands may occupy sites of earlier native pinewoods and in most instances their field layer communities are characteristic of the native woods. The most interesting of the plantations is that in the policies of Castle Grant near Grantown-on-Spey, which was planted at the beginning of the eighteenth century with plants raised from seed collected in Abernethy Forest. Before this wood was damaged in the gale of 31 January 1953 the better stocked parts had about 120 trees per acre (300 per ha.), and the average height was about 75 ft. (22·5 m.), but one of us measured a felled tree in 1919 which was 106 ft. (31·8 m.) to the tip of the tree. Another interesting stand is Curr Wood, near Broomhill, which originated about 1880 from dense natural regeneration, when the previous plantation, probably also raised from Abernethy seed, was removed by successive heavy thinnings. It contains Forestry Commission permanent sample plots which have been thinned periodically at different intensities since 1925. Balnagown Wood at Nethybridge has a similar history. It was regenerated naturally at the beginning of this century from a plantation which was almost certainly grown from Abernethy seed. There are still a few of the old parent trees scattered through this woodland. All such woodlands are best considered as semi-natural and are not described further.

Before the exploitation of the pinewoods began in the seventeenth century, the scanty historical evidence suggests that they were much more extensive than they are today. On the south side of the Spey, Abernethy Forest probably extended further down the river towards Grantown-on-Spey, and in the other direction joined on to Rothiemurchus and Glenmore Forests. Continuing westwards, the pine probably clothed the slopes of Glen Feshie and continued up the River Spey to beyond Kingussie; the original form of this name probably meant the head of the fir-wood. On the north side of the Spey, the more fertile land along the river appears to have been covered with woods of alder and birch with some aspen, and there are still some surviving relict communities of these species. There are records of natural pinewoods in the Dulnan Valley towards its head waters beyond Carrbridge which were not cut until the middle of the last century, and there are still scattered remnants of them (Loudon, 1838; Macfarlane, 1908). There are a few oaks in Strathspey, for example at Loch Pityoulish, at Inchriach and near Kingussie. They are probably all planted, because there are no early references to this species in Upper Speyside.

The first efforts to extract the timber from the Strathspey pinewoods appear to have been made in the early decades of the seventeenth century, both from Abernethy and the Upper Dulnan Valley. In the latter instance the timber went to Inverness (Macfarlane, 1908). While there were thus some efforts to exploit the pinewoods at that time, and there is occasional reference to the use of the rivers for floating timber, it was not until the next century that this work really got under way. That the value of timber was realised is seen by the measures taken to prevent theft and damage to the trees in the forests. This is shown by some of the penalties enforced locally by the Baron Baillies in the Regality Courts. In 1693, burning heather too close to the pinewoods rendered the culprit liable to be nailed to the gallows with a ten-penny nail through the ear, and in 1722 the penalty for stealing timber was a fine of £10 Scots for a first offence, rising to £40 Scots for the third, and any subsequent offence rendered the offender liable to hanging (Forsyth, 1900; Johnson, 1956). The developments in the early decades of the eighteenth century appear to have been due to the activities and imagination of a picturesque gentleman, Aaron Hill, who amongst his many exploits in different parts of the world had been manager of the Drury Lane Theatre, and was also a poet. After a visit to the Spey valley in 1726, he persuaded the York Building Company of the practicability of exploiting Abernethy Forest, and it purchased 60,000 of the best pine from Sir James Grant for £7,000 sterling. The Company began operations in 1728 with great vigour, bringing 120 horses, waggons and other equipment to the forest; sawmills were erected, and in 1730 an iron foundry was built near Nethybridge, charcoal for smelting being made from the smaller trees, and the iron ore brought by ponies from the Lecht which

Glen Moriston, a densely stocked natural pine stand, about 110 years old, and 50 ft. (15 m.) high, near Torgyle Bridge.

PLATE VII

THE PINEWOOD COMMUNITIES

b) Ballochbuie, a well stocked pine stand, ranging in age from 140 to 220 years, and 50 ft. (15 m.) high.

is to the east of the forest. Extravagance rather than efficiency appears to have characterised these operations, and the venture came to an end in 1737; but for the first time the floating of timber on the River Spey became efficient, and the problem of the economic extraction of the timber on a relatively large scale to centres of consumption was solved. Prior to that time, the rafts of deals were small, and a man preceded them in a so-called coracle, a small boat with a wicker-work frame covered with hide, and which was attached to the raft by ropes (Hornell, 1946). If the raft stuck on a rock, the man went behind the raft and loosened it. This was found to be slow and awkward, and in due course, Aaron Hill built large rafts of 60 to 80 trees bound together, deals being used to form a platform. Two men, fore and aft, each with a guiding oar, navigated this large raft down to the sea. Sunken rocks in the Spey caused obstructions, and these were re-moved when the river was low by building fires on the rocks, and throwing water on them while they were still hot so that they cracked (Chambers, 1861; Forsyth, 1897; Forsyth, 1900; Murray, 1883; Sinclair, 1791-9). After the York Building Company gave up operations, the work continued, and the exploitation of Rothiemurchus and Glenmore forests began. The activities at Rothiemurchus at the beginning of the nineteenth century and before have been graphically and entertainingly described in the *Memoirs of a Highland Lady* (1898) by Elizabeth Grant, the daughter of the proprietor. In 1813, the sawmilling in Rothiemurchus had been centralised near the Spey at Inverdruie, and the logs were floated down the tributary streams. Lochs such as Einich and Morlich were dammed and pro-vided with sluices so that the water was available when needed. On the banks of the Spey, the logs to form the base of the raft were fitted with iron plugs, while other logs went to the sawmill for conversion to deals, being kept in water until required, as is the practice today in the Scandinavian countries and North America. The deals then formed the platform of the raft as already described. The floating down the Spey was done by men whose trade it was. They lived at Ballindalloch further down the Spey and came up annually to float the timber when the river was in spate. After earlier unsuccessful attempts had been made to work the timber in Glenmore, the Duke of Gordon sold the trees in 1783 for £10,000 to Osborne and Dodsworth of Kingston-upon-Hull to be felled in the space of 26 years, but they completed the work in 1805. According to contemporary accounts (Donald-son, 1794, Sinclair, 1791-9), the trees were assembled in Loch Morlich in the heart of the forest and floated down the Rivers Luineag and Druie to the Spey after the Luineag had been deepened and straightened, and even the tall trees to be used for masts were brought down successfully. The timber was then floated down the Spey on what were termed "loose floats" to Garmouth at the mouth

I

of the river. Osborne had two sawmills there, one powered by a windmill operating 36 to 40 saws, and one by water driving 30 to 36 saws. The manufactured timber was distributed by sea along the coasts from Skye to Aberdeen, and some of it went to Hull and the King's yards at Deptford and Woolwich. These timber operations were favoured by the shortage of timber during the Napoleonic Wars and prices were high; for example at Garmouth deals 2 to 3 in. (5·1 to 7·6 cm.) thick, 10 in. (25 cm.) broad, and 10 to 12 ft. (3·0 to 3·6 m.) in length fetched over 1s. per cubic foot, more than a day's wage of a man. The pine timber was also used for the building of ships at Garmouth (Sinclair, 1791-9), and it was considered that they were equal to those constructed of oak. During the period of Osborne's operations 47 sail of ships of a total of upwards of 19,000 tons (19,300 tonnes) burden were built, the largest being 1050 tons (1056 tonnes). This is recorded on a brass plaque on a board cut from the largest Scots pine tree at Glenmore and presented to the Duke of Gordon by William Osborne; it is now in the Forestry Department of the University of Aberdeen. After the Napoleonic Wars, exploitation of the pinewoods still continued, and in 1839 about 90 men were employed in Abernethy Forest, earning about £7 each per annum. In the second half of the last century the timber trade declined, although the railway had been opened in 1863. The sporting value of the forests rose, and they were turned into deer forests, in some instances the crofters being resettled in other parts of the estate. The next major fellings in the native pinewoods were during the 1914-18 War, when the Canadian Forestry Corps operated both at Glenmore and Abernethy, and there was felling also in Rothiemurchus. On this occasion some of the logs from Glenmore were conveyed along a tramway alongside the stream in the Sluggan Pass. At Abernethy, about 10 to 15 seed trees per acre (25 to 38 trees per ha.) were left in the hope of natural seeding, but unfortunately most of the seed trees were destroyed by fire during brush-burning operations. After that war there was extensive planting both in Abernethy and Glenmore which will be referred to later. During and immediately after the 1939-45 War, there was considerable felling at Rothiemurchus and Glenmore.

ABERNETHY

Owner: The Countess of Seafield.

Location: The Parish of Abernethy and Kincardine, Inverness-shire. Latitude, 57° 14′ N.; Longitude, 3° 39′ W. National Grid Reference 28 (NH)/990180 and 38 (NJ)/030140. Ordnance Survey Maps: 1 in. to 1 mile, 43 (Scotland) 1947 edition; 6 in. to 1 mile, Inverness-shire 46A, 46, 59, 60 and 75, 1902-03 edition.

The forest is on the east bank of the River Spey between Boat of Garten and Nethybridge, stretching south-eastwards towards the Cairngorm Mountains, and adjoining Glenmore Forest (see Fig. 16). Abernethy Forest is in two blocks, the northern around Loch Garten and the southern lying south of Forest Lodge.

HISTORY

By tradition, the barony of Abernethy belonged at one time to the Comyns, Lords of Badenoch, but these lands have been in the hands of the Grants since the time of Robert the Bruce in the fourteenth century (Fraser, 1883). At the beginning of the seventeenth century, there is a record of a "firr forest, twenty-four miles [38 km.] in compass" in the parish of Abernethy. This native pinewood

Fig. 16. Abernethy

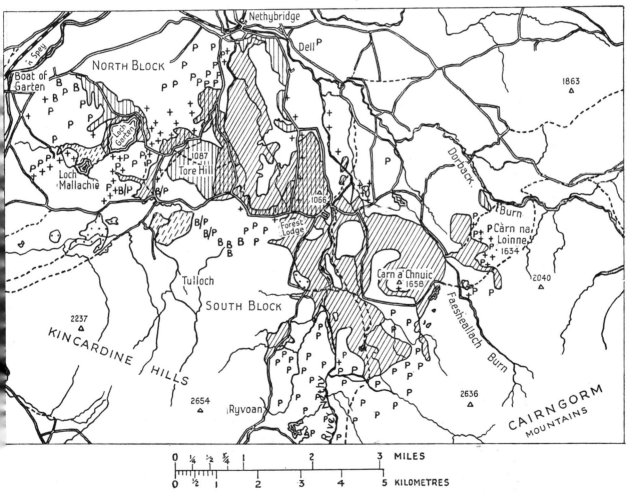

had only to meet local needs for timber at this time but there were already two sawmills in it (Macfarlane, 1908). Natural regeneration was probably not seriously damaged by the grazing of the crofters' animals. In 1631, part of the forest was leased for forty years to Captain John Mason, who reported to the Commissioners of the Navy that the timber was suitable for naval purposes, but it is not known if any was extracted at that time (Forsyth, 1897; Fraser, 1949; Johnson, 1956). Efforts to market pine for ship's masts were again made at the beginning of the eighteenth century by the owner of the estate, but without success owing to extraction difficulties (Sinclair, 1791-9). The operations of the York Building Company in this forest have already been described, and this appears to have been the first large scale exploitation of Abernethy Forest. The felling continued after the Company ceased work, and at the end of the eighteenth century there were four sawmills in the forest, and timber was still being rafted down the Spey (Sinclair, 1791-9). James Robertson (1771) while on one of his journeys to the Highlands to survey the flora for the Commissioners of the Forfeited Estates, reported that there was a boring mill at Abernethy, and also at Rothiemurchus, at which wooden pipes were prepared for supplying London with water. This work was no doubt started by the York Building Company. He also mentioned that none of the trees were large; only one measured 13 ft. in circumference and 50 ft. in height. John Grigor (1834, 1868, 1881), the well known nurseryman of Forres, visited Abernethy Forest about 1830. He mentions that there had been a serious fire in the forest in 1746, and that a new crop of trees had grown up after it. There is a record from another source of a fire in 1770 (Fraser, 1883). At the time of Grigor's visit, most of the trees in the woods were 45 (13·5 m.) to 65 ft. (19·5 m.) in height, and the largest he saw was 12 ft. (3·6 m.) in girth at 8 ft. (2·4 m.) from the ground. Felling was still being carried out and the ring counts gave ages up to 242 years. He also observed that the rate of growth was good up to 70 years, but thereafter decreased. Some of the old pine had been thrown down during the great flood of 1829, and he noted that the roots did not penetrate below a foot in depth where there was a compacted gravel layer in the soil. At that time the working of the forest was centred on the River Nethy which was used to float the timber to the Spey. In the middle of the last century, a forest nursery, still in use, was made near Nethybridge, and the natural regeneration of pine was completed by planting in the northern part of the forest, particularly round Loch Garten, and along the Nethybridge-Boat of Garten road; while there are no definite records, it is believed that the pine plants were raised from seed collected from native trees in the forest. In the middle of the last century, efforts were made to improve the forest, about 3800 acres (1520 ha.), including 113 acres

(45·2 ha.) of plantation, being enclosed by dykes to protect the trees from grazing and thinnings were made in the woods (Johnson, 1956). In 1869, the higher land at the southern end of the forest was turned into an enclosed deer forest, and the crofters moved to other parts of the estate (Johnson, 1956). In 1896, the well-known German forester, Adam Schwappach, visited Speyside and was impressed by the natural regeneration of Scots pine, but criticised the failure to complete gaps by moving seedlings from the denser patches (Schwappach, 1897). Elwes and Henry (1908) give some information about the forest at the beginning of this century, when trees up to 60 ft. (18 m.) high and 14 ft. (4·2 m.) in girth were seen. In the 1914-18 War, 400 acres (160 ha.) were felled in the north block, and 120 acres (48 ha.) in the south. As already mentioned, seed trees were left in the former but most were destroyed by fire (Johnson, 1956). Nevertheless there was some natural regeneration in patches, and these areas were subsequently filled up by planting, the pine plants being raised from Abernethy seed. In the northern block, therefore, part is almost entirely planted, part is a mixture of planted and naturally regenerated trees, and part is entirely natural; the southern block is natural. In the south block, there has been practically no felling since that time, but in the 1939-45 War about 1235 acres (494 ha.) were felled in the north block, of which 154 acres (62 ha.) were natural pine and the remainder mainly planted.

THE HABITAT

Climate.	Mean annual rainfall	30–35 in.	762–889 mm.
	Temperatures: Mean annual	43° F.	6·1° C.
	January mean	35° F.	1·7° C.
	July mean	54° F.	12·2° C.

Climatic sub-province (Anderson, 1955) B2c.

Topography. The forest lies on undulating ground moulded by the retreating ice and water action during the last stages of the Ice Age. This type of topography is seen most clearly in the southern block. There are no steep slopes except in the vicinity of the River Nethy which in places has cut deeply into the morainic and other glacial deposits. The range in altitude is from 700 (210 m.) to 1500 ft. (450 m.) above sea-level, and there are three rounded hills in the forest, Tore Hill (1087 ft., 326 m.), Càrn a'Chnuic (1653 ft., 496 m.) and Càrn na Loinne (1634 ft., 490 m.), with open scrubby pine to near the summits of the two higher hills. The general aspect is north to north-west, and the forest is sheltered to the south and south-west by the Cairngorm Mountains and the ridge formed by the Kincardine Hills.

Geology and Soils. The underlying rocks belong to the Central Highland

Granulites or Moine series of gneisses and schists, often rich in quartz and sometimes micaceous, and with a small area of granite in the neighbourhood of Loch Garten and Tore Hill. The whole region is mantled with morainic, fluvio-glacial and lacustrine deposits – as the ice retreated a number of lakes were formed (anon., 1895; anon., 1914; Charlesworth, 1956; Read, 1948). The parent material of the soils is largely sand and gravel derived not only from the Moine rocks, but also from granite, and in places is very deep. There are extensive peat bogs in the hollows, particularly in the neighbourhood of Loch Garten, Faesheallach burn, and at the southern margin of the forest (anon., 1895; anon., 1914).

The soils are generally podsolised with a raw humus covering, and in places there is a compacted gravel horizon which impedes the downward penetration of the pine roots. The best growth is on freely drained soils; on the peat bogs the trees are stunted.

THE FOREST

Tree species and larger shrubs. In the parts of the forest where there has been no planting, Scots pine is almost the only species, with only a few scattered birches, both verrucose and pubescent. As in other native pinewoods, there are rowan scattered throughout the forest, and alder is to be found along the rivers. Juniper is abundant in the northern block, and less common in the southern; all three types, procumbent, bushy, and columnar are found, and the latter may reach 20 ft. (6·0 m.) in height. North of Tulloch there are birchwoods in the neighbourhood of the crofts. In the northern block where there has been planting, there is in addition to pine, Norway and Sitka spruces, larch and other non-indigenous species.

Field layer. Where the stands are well stocked, the principal community is *Vaccinium/Deschampsia/Hypnaceous* moss No. 3, with small areas of the dry moss community No. 1. In the former, *Vaccinium vitis-idaea* frequently dominates *V. myrtillus.* Under the open stands, the dry and moist *Calluna/Vaccinium/Deschampsia/*moss communities Nos. 5 and 6 predominate, but sometimes there is more *Empetrum nigrum* than is typical for these communities, and there may be a little bracken. In such stands as well as under scattered pine, the field layer is often *Callunetum* No. 10, and in the latter instance there may be a vigorous growth of *Arctostaphylos uva-ursi.* There are also patches of grassy pastures that resemble community No. 7, probably due to cultivation in the past. Where the drainage is slightly impeded, there may be community No. 11, *Calluna/Trichophorum,* and occasionally, No. 9, *Calluna/Molinia.* The bog communities are principally *Eriophorum/Trichophorum/Sphagnum* No. 15, with local patches of *Sphagnum* bog No. 19, and less commonly *Juncus communis* agg. flush No. 17.

The typical pinewood species, *Pyrola media, Goodyera repens* (PL. XII.*a*), and *Listera cordata* are found in the forest, and above 1300 ft. (390 m.) on the south-east margin there are *Rubus chamaemorus* and *Lycopodium alpinum*.

Age structure. Abernethy Forest is one of the few native pinewoods in Scotland where a range of age classes is to be found. The oldest trees are more than 200 years old, and, while trees over 150 years are common throughout the woods, they seldom form even-aged groups. Particularly in the southern block, almost all the closed stands of some extent are between 50 and 120 years, with a few under 50. Scattered through these are the original mother trees, generally over 140 years old. There is an abundance of natural regeneration under 30 years of age, particularly in the northern block. It has come up in open places along roads, and on felled areas where an occasional seed tree has been left. Owing to the completion of the natural regeneration by planting in this block, it is, however, not always easy to assess how much is natural. There is a poorer representation of the youngest age classes in the southern block. There are many scattered stunted trees of undetermined age on the many peat bogs in the forest.

Growth and stocking. The tallest tree measured in this forest was 65 ft. (19·5 m.) high. In the northern block, the average height is between 40 (12 m.) and 50 ft. (15 m.), and in the southern, where the altitude is higher, 35 (10·5 m.) to 45 ft. (13·5 m.). It must be kept in mind that most of the largest trees have been felled in the past. The maximum girth measured at breast height was 9 ft. 4 in. (2·8 m.) and the trees over about 130 years of age averaged about 5 ft. (1·5 m.). The Woodlands Department of the Strathspey estates estimate that, in the southern block and over large areas, the average volume of the 50 to 100 year old pine is about 1000 cu. ft. hoppus per acre (90 m.³ per ha.). Height growth up to about 50 years is moderately rapid for the site conditions and averages almost one foot (0·3 m.) per annum. The current rate of diameter growth is similar to that noted by Grigor (1834) over a century ago, that is normal growth up to about 70 to 80 years, falling off thereafter, and there may be up to 60 rings in the last inch (24 rings per cm.).

The stocking is variable. In the northern block, the older trees often stand singly or in small groups over young natural regeneration or planted trees. In the heart of the southern block, there are large areas where the stocking is good, but at the southern and eastern margins there are only scattered trees.

Fauna. As already mentioned, the southern block is a deer forest, and there are many red and a few roe deer. There are also sheep and a few cattle, while mountain hares come into the southern, upland margins. In the northern block, there are only a few red deer, and the population of roe is not large. Red squirrels have done much damage in the past to the younger Scots pine, but the numbers are not now large. The wild cat is said to inhabit the forest, and there are certainly feral cats, and also a few badgers. Crossbills are numerous and can be seen opening the green cones in the summer, and capercailzie and black grouse do some damage to the trees. There are many small insectivorous birds of which the chaffinch, the coal tit, and the siskin are the commonest, and there are also many crested tits.

The only important insect pest in the forest is *Myelophilus piniperda* which has caused severe damage to groups of pine at the south-east margin of the forest.

Natural regeneration. The age structure of the forest shows that good regeneration must have followed the exploitation of the forest in the eighteenth century and later, because many of the older trees in the forest, as well as those felled this century, date from that time. There is also Grigor's observation that good regeneration followed in parts of the forest destroyed by the fire of 1746. The distinctive thing about Abernethy Forest is the relative abundance of natural regeneration which has come up during this century, and there would have been much more if most of the seed trees left during the felling in the 1914-18 War had not been destroyed by fire; any that escaped are now surrounded by natural regeneration. As already mentioned, regeneration is still continuing in open places. It is most prolific on freely drained sands and gravels with only a thin covering of raw humus, and in communities dominated by *Calluna*, such as *Callunetum* No. 10 (PL. VI.*b*), *Calluna/Vaccinium/Deschampsia/*moss No. 5, and *Calluna/Trichophorum* No. 11, most being in Nos. 10 and 5. There is also regeneration on the bogs, such as *Eriophorum/Trichophorum/Sphagnum* community No. 5, but the trees do not reach any size. The causes of the good regeneration in this forest appear to be the relatively thin and loose layer of raw humus, which permits the seed or seedling roots to reach the mineral soil, and the freely drained coarse-textured and relatively unfertile soils which favour the young pine in competition with the field layer communities. The influence of the grazing factor is demonstrated by the different results in the northern and southern blocks. As already noted, there is grazing by red deer and sheep in the latter, and natural regeneration is much less common and is often damaged by grazing.

ROTHIEMURCHUS

Owners: Col. J. P. Grant. Small areas at the south-west of the native pinewood to be described belong to Major J. H. Drake of Inshriach and the Forestry Commission.

Location: The parish of Duthil and Rothiemurchus, Inverness-shire. Latitude, 57° 9′ N.; Longitude, 3° 47′ W. National Grid Reference 28 (NH)/920080. Ordnance Survey Maps: 1 in. to 1 mile, 43 (Scotland), 1947 edition; 6 in. to 1 mile, Inverness-shire 73, 74, 88 and 89, 1902–03 edition.

The forest stretches eastwards from the River Spey near Aviemore for a distance of about four miles (6·4 km.) (see Fig. 17, PL. I).

HISTORY

These lands have been in the possession of the Grants since the sixteenth century. No historical references to the condition of woods are known before the next century, but the small farms scattered throughout the forest probably date from early times, and there must have been some grazing by cattle and other animals for a long period. At the beginning of the seventeenth century, travellers recorded great fir woods at Rothiemurchus (Macfarlane, 1908) and one meaning that has been given to the name is the "plain of the firs." Later in that century, their extent was stated to be two miles (3·2 km.) long and very broad, and there was already a sawmill in these woods (Macfarlane, 1908). The large-scale exploitation of the forest at Rothiemurchus began later than in Abernethy, but before the end of the eighteenth century timber from Rothiemurchus was being floated down the Spey to Garmouth (Sinclair, 1791-9). The timber was sawn in small sawmills scattered throughout the forest, and located beside streams which supplied the power; the deals were then carted to the Spey. Under the stimulus of the high prices for timber during the Napoleonic Wars, the exploitation was greatly expanded about the beginning of the last century, and reference has already been made to Elizabeth Grant's vivid description of work in the woods at that time, when the sawing had been centralised near the River Spey. When the felling at Rothiemurchus was at its peak, the annual revenue was between £10,000 and £20,000 (anon., 1845; Lauder, 1834). About 1820, an attempt was made to systematise the felling and protect the regeneration. The forest was divided into sections, and the fellings concentrated in one at a time, which was then protected by a stout fence. When this was done, it is stated that immediately there was a carpet of inch-high (2·5 cm.) plants struggling in the heather, and in a few years time a thicket of trees. This attempt came too late, however, to save the whole forest. Sir Thomas Dick Lauder (1834) and John Grigor (1834) both visited Rothiemurchus about 1830. The former appears to have known the forest before the heavy fellings had taken place, and was struck by the scene of devastation. Both, however, refer to the extent and abundance of the natural regeneration. Lauder said that the seedlings were coming up as thick as they do in a nurseryman's seed bed. At the time of Grigor's visit, some of the regeneration was about 30 years old, thus dating from the beginning of the heavy fellings, and was already almost 30 ft. (9 m.) high. Thus in this forest also, prolific natural regeneration followed the heavy exploitation of the timber. There appears to have been little felling in Rothiemurchus for a considerable time thereafter, but there was an extensive fire in 1899 at the south-east of Loch an Eilein and the killed trees were later felled. The last occasion when floating was used was in 1903, when trees were brought down the River Luineag using the sluice at Loch Morlich (Cash, 1905b). There was again felling during the 1914-18 War and some regeneration followed. In the 1939-45 War the fellings were heavy in the scattered woodlands that remained.

THE HABITAT

Climate.	Mean annual rainfall	45 in.	1143 mm.
	Temperatures: Mean annual	44° F.	6·7° C.
	January mean	36° F.	2·2° C.
	July mean	55° F.	12·8° C.

Climatic sub-province (Anderson, 1955) A2b, B2c and B3c.

Topography. The "plain of the firs" is an apt description of the topography of this forest. It is, however, an undulating plain studded with knolls of glacial material, and there are some deeply eroded river banks (see PL. 1). The general aspect is north-westerly and the forest stretches on to the steep hills to the south. The region is drained by the River Druie and its tributaries, the Luineag which flows out of Loch Morlich, and the Am Beanaidh out of Loch Einich. The well-known Loch an Eilein is at the south-west margin of the forest. The general elevation of the main plain rises from about 750 ft. (225 m.) near the Spey to about 1200 ft. (360 m.) as one proceeds southwards, and, on the hills to the south, the pine reaches one of the highest points in any native pinewood, namely 2050 ft. (615 m.) on Creag Fhiaclach.

Geology and soils. The underlying rocks over most of the forest are mica schists and siliceous granulites of the Central Highland Granulites or Moine series, but the higher ground to the south is on granite of the Cairngorm mass. North and north-west of Loch an Eilein, there are gneisses and schists with some crystalline white marble and calc-silicate rock, and here birch predominates. The soils, however, are derived mainly from glacial drifts, which over most of the forest are morainic in origin, but, particularly towards the River Spey, fluvio-glacial sands and gravels predominate. These glacial deposits consist mainly of rocks of the Moine series, and were laid down by the local Glenmore glacier, but they also contain granitic material (anon., 1914; Anderson, 1949).

The best groups and stands of pine are growing on freely drained sands and gravels, often on knolls and terraces. Such soils generally have a thin layer of raw humus and are weakly podsolised. As the drainage becomes poorer, the depth of the raw humus increases, and in hollows and on other low-lying ground there are peat bogs of varying depth.

THE FOREST

Tree species and larger shrubs. Over most of the forest, Scots pine is the only tree species, but here and there and particularly along the streams there is an occasional birch or rowan. North and north-west of Loch an Eilein where the soils are better, birches – verrucose, pubescent or intermediate – predominate, together with a few aspen, holly, and *Prunus padus*. There are a few alder in the lower reaches of the River Druie. Juniper is to be found throughout the forest in all three forms (PL. IX.*a*).

Field layer. In the few well stocked stands in this forest, the same communities are to be found as in Abernethy, namely Nos. 3, 5 and 6. In the open stands and under scattered pine, *Callunetum* No. 10 is the principal community on knolls and ridges; on their lower slopes *Trichophorum caespitosum* is invading this community, and on the less well drained sites it becomes *Calluna/Trichophorum* No. 11. As the peat becomes deeper and wetter, *Calluna/Molinia* No. 9 is local but common, and the still deeper bogs are covered with *Eriophorum/Trichophorum/Sphagnum* No. 15, with local peat hags of *Sphagnum* community No. 19, while there are scattered areas of *Juncus communis* agg. flushes No. 17.

At Rothiemurchus, there is a considerable number of the less common species found in pinewoods, such as *Listera cordata*, *Goodyera repens* (PL. XII.*a*), *Pyrola media*, *Ramischia secunda* (PL. XII.*b*). *Moneses uniflora*, *Trientalis europaea*, and *Linnaea borealis.* On wet peaty areas, *Tofieldia pusilla* and more rarely *Parnassia palustris* are to be found. At the upper fringe of the forest, between 1700 ft. (510 m.) and 2000 ft. (600 m.), there are a number of mountain species, such as *Empetrum hermaphroditum*, *Saxifraga oppositifolia*, *S. aizoides* (PL. XX.*c*), *Rubus chamaemorus*, *Juncus trifidus* and *Lycopodium alpinum*. *L. selago*, *L. clavatum* and the rarer *L. annotinum* (PL. XII.*d*) are to be found throughout the forest.

Age structure. This forest is also uneven-aged with a predominance of older trees. There are groups over 190 years old and ring counts gave a maximum age of 310 years. The commonest age class, however, is that between 180 and 120 years. There is a poorer representation of trees under the latter age, except that regeneration under 20 years old is abundant locally, particularly in the Luineag valley where regeneration has come up in patches, the nearby seed trees being of various ages up to 150 years, but principally between 40 and 80 years old. On the more poorly drained soils and at the higher altitudes, there are many small trees, no more than 30 ft. (9 m.) high, which may nevertheless be over 150 years old. On the other hand on freely drained sands and gravels, trees up to 9 ft. (2·7 m.) in girth were found to be about 130 years old.

Growth and stocking. The tallest tree measured was 70 ft. (21 m.) in height, but the average is between 45 (13·5 m.) and 50 ft. (15 m.). The maximum girth is 12 ft. (3·6 m.), but the average girth of trees about 150 years old is between 5 (1·5 m.) and 6 ft. (1·8 m.). There is the same fall off in diameter increment with age as already mentioned in other forests.

At the lower elevation the forest is now open, with large bare areas or with only scattered trees. There are, however, some well stocked stands in the more inaccessible places towards the southern boundary. The stocking in this forest today, therefore, is even more open than when it was described by Sir Thomas Dick Lauder over a century ago after the heavy fellings during the Napoleonic Wars (Lauder, 1834).

Fauna. There are records of red and roe deer in this forest as far back as the seventeenth century (Macfarlane, 1908), and the former are still numerous. A few sheep and cattle graze in the woodlands in the present as in the past. Rabbits were formerly numerous on the lower ground, and mountain hares invade the upper margins of the woodlands in winter, while there are a few red squirrels. The wild cat is believed to be in the woods and foxes are common. Of the birds that may injure the pine, there are large flocks of crossbills, and capercailzie and black grouse are numerous. The population of the smaller birds is unusually high for a native pinewood, chiefly the chaffinch and the tits, the crested tit being common. The predatory birds in or near the forest include the golden eagle, the buzzard, the kestrel, the sparrow-hawk, the peregrine falcon, and the raven, while the osprey has nested at various times on an island in Loch an Eilein (Cash, 1905a).

The harmful insect species are the same as in other forests, and *Myelophilus piniperda* and also *M. minor* are doing damage in places.

Natural regeneration. It has already been mentioned that prolific regeneration followed the heavy fellings made about 150 years ago (Grigor, 1834; Lauder, 1834), and most of the older trees that survived into this century date from that time. The evidence of the present age structure suggests that there was relatively little regeneration during the second half of the last century, but some followed the fellings in the 1914-18 War, particularly along the River Luineag. Just before the last War, there was some good regeneration of pine after burning near the Glenmore boundary. Since then young pine has come up in places, particularly along the road and river from Coylumbridge to Loch Morlich, probably also after burning (PL. v.*b*). Recent successful regeneration has almost always been on knolls and banks of freely drained sands and gravels, with a discontinuous layer of raw humus, and amongst field layer communities dominated by *Calluna*, such as No. 10, and also in Nos. 5 and 6 when they are to be found in the open. As in other forests, there are pine seedlings in the communities containing *Tricho-phorum caespitosum*, Nos. 11 and 15, but their rate of growth is poor.

Unlike Abernethy and Glenmore forests, there has been no planting in the native pinewoods at Rothiemurchus for a long period, and the older planted areas are shown on the map in Fig. 17.

GLENMORE

Owners: The Forestry Commission. A small part of this pinewood is on the Pityoulish estate, belonging to Sir Herbert Ogilvy.

Location: The parish of Kincardine, Inverness-shire. Latitude, 57° 10′ N.; Longitude, 3° 42′ W. National Grid Reference 28 (NH)/980090. Ordnance Survey Maps: 1 in. to 1 mile, 43 (Scotland) 1947 edition; 6 in. to 1 mile, Inverness-shire 74, 1902 edition.

This forest lies to the east of Rothiemurchus and in the valley between Cairngorm and the Kincardine Hills (see Fig. 17).

HISTORY

In ancient times Glenmore belonged to the Stewarts of Kincardine. In 1685 an Act of the Scottish Parliament (VOL. VIII, p. 499) ratified its ownership by the Duke of Gordon. In 1923, it was sold by the Duke of Richmond and Gordon to the Forestry Commission. In the middle of the seventeenth century, there is a reference to a great fir woodland at Glenmore and at that time there was also much birch in it. Timber was already being extracted and floated down the Luineag and Druie rivers to the Spey (Macfarlane, 1908). The first large-scale exploitation began in 1783 when, as already mentioned, the Duke of Gordon sold the larger trees in part of the forest to Osborne and Dodsworth of Kingston-upon-Hull for a sum of £10,000. At that time the forest was described as the oldest, the largest, and the best quality fir-wood in Scotland (Fraser, 1949; Sinclair, 1791-9). These operations were successful and were completed in 1805, four years before the end of the contract. Not only the face of the forest was changed, but also the way of life in the glen. In the words of a local bard "our ears are stunned by the crash of falling trees and the clamours of the Sassenachs" (Forsyth, 1900). The plank of Scots pine presented to the Duke of Gordon by William Osborne has been referred to already. It is of interest that the top of this tree, the Lady of the Glen, was still lying undecayed in the forest in 1914 (Leslie, 1916).

FIG. 17. Rothiemurchus and Glenmore

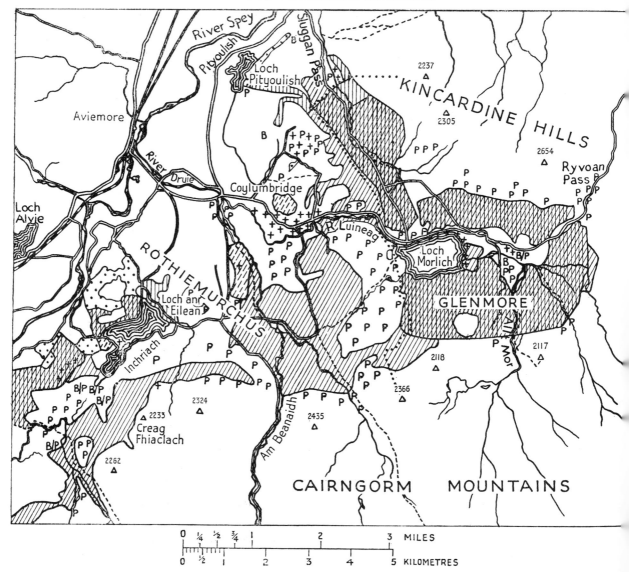

Lauder (1834), when he visited Glenmore about 1830, found that the forest was fast replenishing itself, and he was impressed by the gigantic skeleton trees, over 20 ft. (6 m.) in girth, that had been too decayed to justify felling. Before the middle of the last century, the forest was turned into a sheep-run. Later the sheep were removed and it became a deer forest (Forsyth, 1897; Fraser, 1949). The regeneration that came up earlier was no doubt safely established before this intensive grazing took place. There was no further heavy felling in the forest until the 1914-18 War, when the lumbering was done by the Canadian Forestry Corps. Glenmore was acquired by the Forestry Commission in 1923, the woodlands were fenced against red deer, and over 2500 acres (1000 ha.) have been planted, using not only Scots pine, but also Norway and Sitka spruces and other species. There was little felling during the 1939-45 War, but immediately after the war about 200 acres (80 ha.) of woodland were cut (Fraser, 1956). During recent years some of the old woodland on the south side of the loch has been destroyed by forest fires. Glenmore became a National Forest Park in 1948.

THE HABITAT

Climate. Mean annual rainfall 45 in. 1143 mm.
Temperature: Mean annual 43° F. 6·1° C.
January mean 35° F. 1·7° C.
July mean 54° F. 12·2° C.
Climatic sub-province (Anderson, 1955) B2c and B3c.

Topography. Loch Morlich is the central topographical feature of Glenmore, and it is believed that it was formed by the melting of a local glacier at the end of the Ice Age. On the south side, the pinewoods are growing on the lower slopes of Cairngorm, and on the north on those of the Kincardine Hills. At the east there is the narrow steep-sided gorge, the Ryvoan Pass, and at the north-west the Sluggan Pass which leads to the Spey. Except in places the slopes are only moderate. The general aspect of the woods south of the loch is north-westerly, and those on the north side south to south-westerly. The Allt Mor and its tributaries drain into the eastern end of Loch Morlich, forming an alluvial plain near it, and the overflow from the loch feeds Luineag, a tributary of the Druie. The altitude of Loch Morlich is 1046 ft. (314 m.), and the tree limit of the surrounding native pinewoods is at about 1600 ft. (480 m.), with scattered trees to about 1750 ft. (525 m.).

Geology and soils. The rocks underlying most of this forest are schists and siliceous granulites of the Central Highland Granulites of Moine age, with thin veins of pegmatite, and there are intrusions of felsite and porphyry at the tree limit on the Kincardine Hills. Near the upper limit of the pine south of Loch Morlich, granite is the solid rock. Except for alluvium along the streams, the whole area is mantled with glacial deposits, laid down as the Glenmore glacier shrank. These are principally morainic in origin, consisting mainly of metamorphic material but with some granite. These deposits are a mixture of sand, gravel and clay, tending to be more clayey on the slopes of the Kincardine Hills. Peat bogs are common in the hollows, particularly south of the loch (anon., 1914; Anderson, 1956).

The soils are similar to those already described for Rothiemurchus.

THE FOREST

Tree species and larger shrubs. As in the other pinewoods already described, Scots pine is the principal native and naturally regenerated species throughout the forest. There are a few copses and some scattered trees of birch and rowan, with some alder on alluvial terraces. There is less juniper than in Rothiemurchus and it is principally of the bushy type.

Reference has already been made to the extensive planting that has been carried out during the past thirty years, using not only Scots pine, which was sometimes not of native origin, but also a range of non-indigenous conifers.

Field layer. The communities within the native pinewoods are the same as those already described for Rothiemurchus. The less common species are also the same, but *Lycopodium inundatum* and *Chamaepericlymenum* (*Cornus*) *suecicum* have been recorded (Walton, 1956).

Age structure. The native pines are usually over 140 years old, the maximum age determined by borings being 240. There are a few trees here and there between 139 and 20 years. There are some groups of naturally regenerated seedlings up to 20 years old, particularly on river shingle, on sandy shores of the loch, and occasionally along paths.

Growth and stocking. The tallest trees surviving do not exceed 65 ft. (19·5 m.) in height and these are few, but before the extensive felling in the 1914-18 War, trees up to 70 ft. (21 m.) were not uncommon on both sides of the loch. Today the average height of the older trees is between 45 (13·5 m.) and 50 ft. (15·0 m.). Age/height analyses made in 1919 of well grown trees, then about 150 years old, showed that height growth was slow to begin with, and over 20 years elapsed before the trees reached 10 ft. (3·0 m.) in height. This has also been observed more recently. The average girth is about 5 ft. (1·5 m.) at breast height, but occasional trees may reach 10 ft. (3·0 m.).

PLATE VIII

THE PINEWOOD AND BIRCHWOOD COMMUNITIES

a) Glen Affric, pinewood on the north aspect and birchwood on the south.

b) Glen Strathfarrar, pinewoods fringed with birchwood.

As a result of the extensive fellings and damage by fire during the last 40 years, there are only scattered old pine standing amongst planted trees over most of the forest, except for a few well stocked groups south and south-west of Loch Morlich, particularly at the upper margin of the woodlands.

Fauna. The woodlands have been fenced against red deer since they were acquired by the Forestry Commission, while there is no grazing by domestic animals. The local fauna is described in the Glenmore National Forest Park Guide (Gordon, 1956).

Natural regeneration. As in the other Speyside forests already described, the existing old trees date from the fellings made over 150 years ago, and the prolific regeneration that followed has already been mentioned. The evidence of the existing age structure suggests that there was relatively little natural regeneration after the middle of the last century, due perhaps either to the grazing first by sheep and then by deer, or to the then well stocked condition of the forest. One would have expected that natural regeneration would have been more prolific during the past thirty years since grazing was substantially reduced. As mentioned in Chapter 3, this problem has been investigated by the Forestry Commission since 1930, principally by means of methods of soil cultivation and burning, particularly when there was a good cone crop. A measure of success was attained, but mortality was high due to frost lift, and damage by insects, black grouse and capercailzie, and the problem is still unsolved (Macdonald, 1952).

GLEN FESHIE

Owner: Sir George Macpherson-Grant, Bt.

Location: The parishes of Kingussie and Insh, and Alvie, Inverness-shire. Latitude, 57° 3′ N.; Longitude, 3° 54′ W. National Grid Reference 27 (NN)/845990. Ordnance Survey Maps: 1 in. to 1 mile, 43 and 49 (Scotland) 1947 edition; 6 in. to 1 mile, Inverness-shire 88, 102, 103 and 118, 1902-03 edition.

The woodlands described are in Glen Feshie and Glen Tromie, south and south-east of the River Spey between Kincraig and Kingussie. In Glen Feshie, the principal surviving native pinewoods encircle Creag Mhigeachaidh and Creag Ghiubhsachan, while Badan Dubh covers the north-western side of Craig Dhubh, and there are woods on both sides of the valley near Glenfeshie Lodge, extending to about 11 miles up the glen from Kincraig. The native pine in Glen Tromie are on the east side of the valley opposite Glentromie Lodge. There are scattered pine between these woodlands (see Fig. 18).

FIG. 18. Glen Feshie

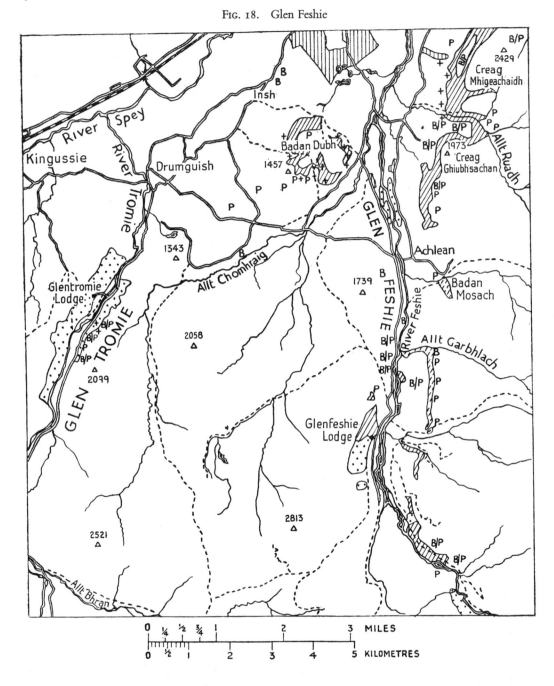

HISTORY

At one time the pinewoods were almost certainly part of a more or less continuous forest stretching up the valleys just mentioned. While place names are not conclusive evidence, there are many in this district containing modifications of the Gaelic word "giubhas," a pine. The earliest record of such woods which has been traced is the testimony of travellers at the beginning of the seventeenth century (Macfarlane, 1908). Towards the end of the next century, timber was being floated down the Spey from these as well as other Speyside pinewoods (Sinclair, 1791-9). During the great flood of 1829, there was much destruction of the trees growing along the River Feshie (Lauder, 1873). Queen Victoria visited Glen Feshie in 1860 and 1861 and remarked on the magnificent fir-trees as well as the birch and the juniper (Queen Victoria, 1868). It is believed that the pine on the lower slopes of Creag Mhigeachaidh were felled about 1870, after damage by snow, leaving the surviving upper fringe. During this century, there has been considerable felling in a number of these woods, particularly during the 1939-45 War when the Canadian Forestry Corps carried out the work. There have been red deer in these woods since at least the seventeenth century, and they are still numerous, while there is grazing by sheep.

THE HABITAT

Climate.	Mean annual rainfall		45-50 in.	1143-1270 mm.
	Temperature:	Mean annual	42° F.	5·6° C.
		January mean	34° F.	1·1° C.
		July mean	53° F.	11·7° C.
	Climatic sub-province (Anderson, 1955) A2b.			

Topography. These pinewoods are all growing on slopes, some of them gentle, but mostly steep and even precipitous near their upper limits. The aspect is generally westerly, and the altitudinal limits are 900 ft. (270 m.) and 1800 ft. (540 m.), with scattered trees up to about 2000 ft. (600 m.).

Geology and soils. The underlying rocks are schists of the Moine series which have not been differentiated by the Geological Survey, but the upper limit of the woodlands on the eastern side of Glen Feshie comes on to Cairngorm granite. The soil parent material in most of the woodlands is glacial drift, principally morainic, but there is boulder clay in places (anon., 1913). The glacial deposits consist of both schistose and granitic material, and, south of Glenfeshie Lodge, they contain a considerable amount of mica schist fragments. Along the River

Feshie there are extensive deposits of stony alluvium, often forming several terraces. The peat bogs are few.

In the pinewoods, there is a covering of raw humus usually not deep, the soils are stony, sandy loams, and there is some podsolisation which increases towards the higher altitudes. South of the Lodge where there is more mica schist in the deposits, the soils are moist brown loams with little or no leaching, becoming peaty in the wetter places. Here the pine tends to give way to birch and alder.

THE FOREST

Tree species and larger shrubs. Except on Badan Dubh, there is more birch in Glen Feshie woodlands than in the other native pinewoods in Speyside. Birch dominates the pine on the western side of the valley at Glenfeshie Lodge, at the southern limit in the glen, and in Glen Tromie. Alder is common along the streams and on wet ground, particularly near Glenfeshie Lodge and in Glen Tromie, and rowan is thinly scattered throughout the woods. Juniper in all three forms is to be found in all the woodlands, and is abundant in parts of Glen Tromie.

Field layer. Communities Nos. 3, 5 and 6 are characteristic of well stocked groups in this as in the other eastern native pinewoods, but in the densest parts of Badan Dubh the dry moss community No. 1 is to be found, while, where there was felling in this woodland during the last war, *Deschampsia flexuosa* has increased in Communities Nos. 3, 5 and 6 and they have become temporarily *Deschampsia flexuosa/Hypnaceous* moss community No. 4. On the more fertile soils at the south of the glen already mentioned, communities Nos. 5 and 6 are giving way, as the birch becomes dominant, to the *Calluna/grass/Vaccinium/*moss No. 13 and the grass/moss No. 14 communities. Scattered bracken is found in most of the woodlands. Under scattered pine, *Callunetum* No. 10, with an unusual amount of *Arctostaphylos uva-ursi*, is characteristic on the drier sites, and *Calluna/Trichophorum* No. 11 on the wetter, including the upper fringes of the woodlands where the latter community may grade into the bog communities *Eriophorum/Trichophorum/Sphagnum* No. 15, *Juncus communis* agg. No. 17, and *Sphagnum* No. 19.

The pinewoods have such typical species as *Pyrola media*, *Moneses uniflora*, *Goodyera repens* (PL. XII.*a*) and *Trientalis europaea*, the latter particularly where birch predominates. On moist screes at the south end of the forest and above 1700 ft. (510 m.), there are such mountain species as *Saxifraga aizoides* (PL. XII.*c*), *S. oppositifolia* and *Alchemilla alpina*.

Age structure. Most of the trees in the native pinewoods are over 130 years old, the oldest tree determined being 200 years, but there are records of up to

250 years at the time of felling during the last war (McIntosh, 1953). There are scattered groups and trees between 90 and 125 years, and in Badan Dubh several acres where the trees are 30 to 100 years old. There are only local groups under 30 years of age.

Growth and stocking. The tallest tree measured was 60 ft. (18 m.) high, but the average height of the older surviving trees is only about 40 ft. (12 m.). The average girth is between 4 and 5 ft. (1·2 and 1·5 m.), and the maximum 10 ft. (3 m.).

The stocking is variable, and over most of the area there are only scattered trees, but there are some well stocked stands and groups, particularly in Badan Dubh.

Fauna. It is similar to the adjoining pinewoods, but there is more grazing by deer and sheep.

Natural regeneration. During this century there has been little natural regeneration, except locally at Creag Mhigeachaidh and Badan Dubh. At the foot of the former and under scattered pine, there are groups of pine regeneration of various ages from a few years up to 45 years old. Growth is slow, for example less than three feet (0·9) m. may be attained in 15 years, but this is due partly to damage by fire, pine shoot beetle, grazing, black grouse and capercailzie, and, when the trees get beyond the risk of grazing, height growth is faster, and trees of 30 years old are about 15 ft. (4·5 m.) high. In Badan Dubh there are groups of healthy regeneration between 10 and 25 years old and 3 to 15 ft. (0·9 to 4·5 m.) high which came up adjoining isolated pine. It is of interest, however, that where *Deschampsia flexuosa* has increased in this woodland after felling, there is no regeneration. The regeneration is almost all in open places on freely drained stony soils with discontinuous raw humus, principally in the *Callunetum* No. 10 community, but occasionally in the dry and moist *Calluna/Vaccinium/Deschampsia/* moss communities Nos. 5 and 6.

DULNAN

Owner: The Countess of Seafield.

Location: The parish of Duthil and Rothiemurchus, Inverness-shire. Latitude, 57° 14′ N.; Longitude, 3° 56′ W. National Grid Reference 28 (NH)/ 830180. Ordnance Survey Maps: 1 in. to 1 mile, 38 and 43 (Scotland) 1947 edition; 6 in. to 1 mile, Inverness-shire 45, 57 and 58, 1902–03 edition.

The principal native pinewoods lie south-west of Carr Bridge on either side of the River Dulnan from Dalnahaitnach farm to the junction of the River Dulnan and Allt Ghiubhais. There are also scattered natural pine amongst planted trees near Carr Bridge, on Cam na Guaille and Beinn Ghuilbin.

GENERAL DESCRIPTION

There were previously extensive native pinewoods in the Dulnan Valley, and already in the seventeenth century timber was being transported to Inverness from these pinewoods (Macfarlane, 1908). In the early decades of last century, the River Dulnan was used to float the logs down to sawmills (Grigor, 1834, 1868, 1881). Most of the mature timber had been felled by the middle of the last century, and later there was extensive planting, particularly in the neighbourhood of Carr-bridge and at Kinveachy; most of these woodlands were felled during the last war, and after it there was a large fire in the Upper Dulnan valley adjoining the remnant to be described.

The surviving native pinewoods are growing on the moderately steep slopes of Garbh-mheall Mor on the south side of the River Dulnan, with a small stand on the north. The aspect is north-westerly, and the range of altitude is from 1020 ft. (306 m.) to 1500 ft. (450 m.). The underlying rock is granite. There are stony alluvial terraces along the river, and the remainder of the area is covered with glacial drift, both morainic and boulder clay. The stony, sandy loams are more strongly podsolised than usual, and there is iron pan on some of the alluvial flats.

The woodland to the south of the river is dominated by Scots pine, and the subsidiary tree species and field layer communities are those described for other Speyside forests. On the north side of the river, there is more birch and grasses, and the communities are Nos. 2, 4 and 12.

Most of the pine are between 60 and 100 years old, but the scattered old trees on the hillsides are older. The stocking is irregular, with densely stocked groups separated by more open woodland, and the height of the trees rarely exceeds 40 ft. (12 m.). On the south side of the river there is little recent regeneration, and only scattered trees under 30 years old. On the north side, however, there are many groups of recent natural regeneration coming up in the open in *Callunetum* No. 10 on an alluvial terrace. Growth is good when the trees get above grazing by red deer and sheep.

GLEN AVON

Owner: Col. O. Haigh.

Location: The parish of Kirkmichael, Banffshire. Latitude, 57° 9′ N.; Longitude, 3° 22′ W. National Grid Reference 38 (NJ)/177074. Ordnance Survey Maps: 1 in. to 1 mile, 44 (Scotland) 1947 edition; 6 in. to 1 mile, Banffshire 46, 1902 edition.

This remnant consists of about twelve pine trees near the Linn of Avon, about seven miles south of Tomintoul, and one tree about a mile farther up the valley.

GENERAL DESCRIPTION

At the end of the eighteenth century, the parish minister recorded in the first *Statistical Account* that there were scattered pine on the banks of the River Avon at the southern extremity of the parish; the present trees are no doubt their descendants. In the same account, it is mentioned that there were groves of alder, some of large dimensions, and it is of interest that there are still some large, old trees of that species between Delnabo and Torbain, south of Tomintoul.

The group of pine is growing on the steep, rocky banks of the river, the altitude being 1330 ft. (400 m.). The site is near the boundary between a mass of granite and quartzose mica-schists of the Dalradian series; there is limestone immediately to the east, on which birch is growing. The soil consists mainly of raw humus in the crevices of the schistose rocks.

Mixed with the pine are birch – mainly intermediate but some definitely verrucose and others pubescent, aspen, alder and a few small juniper. The field layer communities vary from *Callunetum* No. 10 to dry and moist *Calluna/Vaccinium/Deschampsia* Nos. 5 and 6. The only species of interest is *Alchemilla alpina* which is common in places.

The pine appear to be up to 140 years old. The maximum height is 35 ft. (10·5 m.), and the largest girth at breast height about 5 ft. (1·5 m.). There is a little natural regeneration, seedlings up to 6 ft. (1·8 m.) in height, but they have been heavily browsed by red deer.

CHAPTER 6

THE RANNOCH GROUP OF NATIVE PINEWOODS

IN THE heart of Perthshire there are two surviving native pinewoods, the Black Wood of Rannoch and the Old Wood of Meggernie in Glen Lyon. There are also groups or scattered old pine which may be the survivors of earlier native pinewoods, behind Ben Alder Lodge on Loch Ericht (National Grid Reference 27 (NN)/573787), and in the neighbourhood of Killin and in Glen Lochay (N.G.R. 27 (NN)/535350), at the western end of Loch Tay. No early historical references to native pinewoods in these latter districts have been found, however, and it is known that there was planting in Glen Lochay as early as the beginning of the seventeenth century (anon., 1855); hence their origin is uncertain, and, as they are no longer pinewoods in an ecological sense, they are not considered further.

It is probable that the existing native pinewoods were more extensive during historical times. The Black Wood of Rannoch may have spread up the valleys to the west and south-west, but two hundred years ago there was birchwood and not pine on these sites. The pine remains entombed in the peat on the Muir of Rannoch are, however, almost certainly principally of Sub-boreal age. At Meggernie, the pinewoods probably continued up the valleys of the Allt Conait and its tributaries, one of which is called Allt Ruighe Ghuibhas, suggesting that there was pine in this valley. Even as early as the beginning of the seventeenth century, and before extensive exploitation started, there are no historical references to other extensive pinewoods in this region.

Both at Rannoch and Meggernie, the birches are important constituents of the pinewoods, and at least in the former this has been so for two hundred years. There are now natural birchwoods containing a few oak on the north shore of Loch Rannoch on sites which in the eighteenth century were treeless, but at that time there were birches farther up the valleys of the Aulich and Killichonan Burns, and birch and oak at Dunalaster, to the east of the loch (anon., 1745-85). The Tummel valley is still clothed in birchwoods with a few oaks, and the latter increase as one proceeds down the valley. The pine stands in the Black Wood of

Rannoch are and have been surrounded by birchwoods for a long period, and there is evidence that each community has replaced the other in the course of the centuries (anon., 1745-85). In Glen Lyon, Roy's map of 1750 (Roy, 1750) shows a wood on the north side of the glen which today is a natural birchwood, and it is likely that in the past, as in the present, any natural woods further down the valley were birchwoods, oak coming in at the lower altitudes.

The available evidence suggests that these two pinewoods had only to meet the requirements of the small local population until the seventeenth century. The cattle, sheep, and goats from the crofts nearby grazed in the woodlands and no doubt did some damage to natural regeneration, but it could not have been catastrophic. From the second half of the seventeenth century there were successive heavy fellings, and the loch and the rivers were used to extract the timber. This will be described for each forest.

The Black Wood of Rannoch

Owners: The Forestry Commission and Major Allan Walmsley. The former owns the woods approximately east of Camghouran (see Fig. 19) and the latter the western section.

Location: The parish of Fortingall, Perthshire. Latitude, 56° 41′ N.; Longitude, 4° 19′ W. National Grid Reference 27 (NN)/580560. Ordnance Survey Maps: 1 in. to 1 mile, 55 (Scotland) 1947 edition; 6 in. to 1 mile, Perthshire 35 N.E. and S.E., 36 N.W., S.W., N.E., S.E. and 37 N.W., 1900 edition.

This forest lies on the south side of Loch Rannoch, the principal pinewoods being between the Dall Burn and Allt Camghouran (PL. II), but there are groups and scattered pine both east and west of these limits (see Fig. 19). The Muir of Rannoch is to the west.

HISTORY

These lands belonged to the Robertsons for many centuries, the first chief being a follower of King Robert the Bruce; and a new grant of the whole estate was given to Robert Robertson in 1439 for his part in apprehending the murderers of James I (Sinclair, 1905). In the past, the Black Wood of Rannoch has also been known as the Wood of Strowan and the Fir Wood of Carie. A large wood on the south side of Loch Rannoch and the River Tummel was referred to by travellers as early as about 1600 (Macfarlane, 1908), and there are records of heavy exploitation during the seventeenth century. The pine was converted into deals at sawmills, and in 1683 it was stated that 176,000 deals had been produced in the preceding years. When timber was floated on Loch Rannoch, it was sometimes scattered by storms and some went down the Rivers Tummel and Tay, being stolen on the way. Alexander Robertson, the twelfth Chief, was given powers by the Privy Council of Scotland in 1675 and 1683 to impose fines for such theft, an early example of a special law to protect timber during floating (Brown, 1915). The next chief came out in the Jacobite cause in 1689 and fought at the Battle of Killiecrankie. He was subsequently pardoned by Queen Anne and returned to his estate, but he came out again both in 1715 and 1745 (Sinclair, 1905). During this unsettled period, there was indiscriminate felling in the Black Wood of Rannoch. From 1749 the estate was administered by the Commissioners of the Forfeited Estates and their records throw light on the condition of the woodlands during the second half of the eighteenth century. Their local officers found that the woodlands were in a bad condition. The best and most accessible timber had been felled, the brush left on the ground was impeding drainage, and birch and alder had grown up after the felling of the pine; but there was some pine regeneration in the pole stage. When the Commissioners took over, there were two sawmills operating at Dall and Carie, but they were obsolete, described as "perhaps the most Gothick thing of their kind in the World," the saws being $\frac{1}{4}$ in.

FIG. 19.   The Black Wood of Rannoch

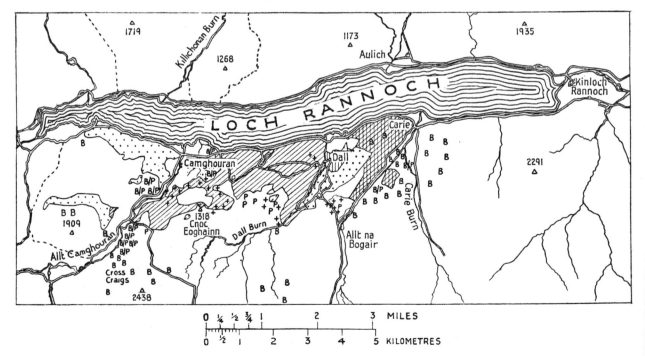

thick. Determined efforts were made to improve the condition of the woodlands both by reducing the number of trees felled in spite of the loss of revenue, and by taking steps to regenerate the crop. The annual felling was progressively reduced from 2000 trees in 1749 to 860 in 1753, and consisted of only 100 trees in 1776; but there was some windblow both in 1771 and 1779. The trees were marked and valued before felling, and saws were used for the first time for cross cutting into logs. In order to reduce damage to young regeneration by the grazing of cattle, sheep, horses, and goats, areas were enclosed in 1781 by ditch and dyke. Two years later a plan was made for the restocking of bare areas and this was approved by the Commissioners. It was proposed that swine be put into the woods for a year to break up the ground, and then cones dropped at distances of five or six feet (1·5 to 1·8 m.), the seed being released when the cones opened; or notches one to two inches (2·5 to 5·1 cm.) deep were to be made with a spade and a few seeds dropped in each notch; or where the heather and "fog" were very deep it was to be pulled up by the roots and cones dropped on the bare earth. There were also plans for planting 100,000 to 200,000 pine trees on short heather land previously grazed. It was recommended that the plants be taken from dense natural regeneration and cones collected from the best trees. It is not known how far this work was carried out, but it appears likely that something was done to repair earlier devastation, and it is known that birch and alder competing with the pine were cut out about this time. In 1758, a new sawmill was built, a water wheel supplying the power, and there was a log pond (PL. IV). There is a record of the material used and the sawing was to be done by frame saws, the total cost of the mill being £195. 14. 10 sterling. At that time the standing trees were valued at between 4s. and 5s. each; they were cut into two to three logs, and each log produced five deals which were sold at 9d. each, while the four backs fetched 2½d. apiece (anon., 1745-85). Timber from the Black Wood was used during the construction of General Wade's bridge over the River Tay at Aberfeldy, and later was used for the roof of the present church at Amulree. Timber from Rannoch was also used in house construction during the second half of the eighteenth century in Perth and Crieff (Whayman, 1953). The use of the resinous pine at Rannoch for the production of "stocks" or flambeaux for domestic illumination appears to have been on a larger scale than elsewhere. In 1751, it was reported that one in three of the larger trees in the Black Wood was chipped and hollowed out by makers of "candle-firr" (anon., 1745-85), and it has been stated that many thousands of tons were sent regularly to county fairs (Hunter, 1883). The estate was returned to the Robertsons about 1784. The next heavy exploitation of the forest was during the Napoleonic Wars, and a public company felled a great part of the Black Wood at the beginning of the last century. The enterprise ultimately failed because of transport difficulties, but ingenious attempts were made to solve them. Canals were dug in the Black Wood with locks and basins in which the timber was floated and collected, and the larger trees were slid down a mile-long sluice to the loch, where they were bound into rafts and taken down the Rivers Tummel and Tay; whether the river floating was on rafts or loose is not certain. It is recorded that some of the timber was carried out to the North Sea and was stranded on the shores of Holland (Hunter, 1883; Whayman, 1953). There is evidence that the number of sheep belonging to the tenants increased during the last decades of the eighteenth century. The estate was purchased by the Wentworth family in 1857, and the Black Wood became an enclosed deer forest in 1895. A new system of roads was constructed, often following the line of the earlier canals, and there was some planting of felled areas using Scots pine, probably of native origin. When the West Highland Railway was being constructed, over 1000 trees were felled for conversion into railway sleepers. Although the Black Wood was scheduled for felling in 1918, the end of the war saved it; but in the inter-war period there were regular annual fellings of about 350 trees for estate purposes. During the 1939-45 War, 8000 trees totalling about 235,000 hoppus feet (8,460 m.^{3}) were felled, the work being done by the Canadian Forestry Corps, but a small area in the vicinity of the Dall was left untouched (Whayman, 1953). The eastern portion of the Black Wood was acquired by the Forestry Commission in 1947, and deer and other grazing animals excluded.

THE HABITAT

Climate:	Mean annual rainfall		50 in.	1270 mm.
	Temperature:	Mean annual	44° F.	6·7° C.
		January mean	37° F.	2·8° C.
		July mean	55° F.	12·8° C.

Climatic sub-province (Anderson, 1955) B2e.

Topography. The forest is on undulating land drained by three streams, the Allt Camghouran, the Dall Burn, and the Allt na Bogair. As in many other native pinewoods, the aspect is northerly, but the slopes are not steep, except on Cross Craigs in the south-west where there are only scattered pine. The range in altitude of the woods is from 675 ft. (203 m.) to 1200 ft. (360 m.), with a few scattered trees up to 1400 ft. (420 m.). The birch goes to still higher altitudes. The woodlands are sheltered by higher ground, particularly to the south and east, the highest nearby hill being Schiehallion, 3547 ft. (1064 m.).

Geology and soils. The underlying rocks are principally siliceous schists and gneisses of the Central Highland Granulites of the Moine series. Towards the western end of the loch, there is a little quartz-porphyry and felsite, and at the eastern end of the forest narrow bands of porphyrite. In the neighbourhood of the Camghouran Burn, there are bands of bluish-white marble and calc-silicate rock; this impure limestone was worked in the eighteenth century and probably later (anon., 1745-85; anon., 1923). The region was heavily glaciated, and in the closing phases of the Ice Age much morainic and other material was deposited by the retreating local glaciers (Charlesworth, 1956). The drifts contain mainly schistose and gneissose material with numerous fragments of granite. There are alluvial flats at the mouth of the streams.

The soils in the drier parts of the Black Wood are podsolic. The raw humus layer is generally not deep compared with some other pinewoods. The A horizon, while variable, is generally less than 5 in. (12·7 cm.) in depth. As the drainage deteriorates the soils become peaty, and in the hollows there are numerous small peat bogs.

THE FOREST

Tree species and larger shrubs. Unlike the native pinewoods in Deeside and Speyside, the Black Wood of Rannoch contains much birch, with all gradations from pure pine to pure birch. The birches consist of the verrucose and pubescent species and also intermediates. There are both pedunculate and sessile oak nearby, though not in the pinewoods, for example near Carie and on the north side of the loch, but these trees may have been planted. Aspen is relatively rare and is found only in the birchwoods, but rowan is common throughout the forest. There is alder along the streams and in the wetter parts of the woods, and a little hazel and dog rose in the birchwoods, while low bushes of *Salix aurita* and *S. atrocinerea* are common in the wetter places. Juniper, generally of the bushy type, is comparatively common, particularly near Dall.

Field layer. The communities associated with the pine are as already described for other pinewoods. Under well stocked pine groups on freely drained knolls, there is the *Vaccinium/Deschampsia/Hypnaceous* moss community No. 3, and, under the more open pine where drainage is good, the dry and moist *Calluna/Vaccinium/Deschampsia/*moss communities Nos. 5 and 6, the heather being luxurious, and the *Deschampsia* and moss components well developed. These communities may be invaded by grasses and bracken, becoming the grass pinewood community No. 7, dominated locally by bracken. As the drainage deteriorates, and the soils become peaty, *Calluna/Molinia* community No. 9 is found. Under scattered pine,

Callunetum No. 10 occurs on drier ground both within the woodlands and at their south-east margin, while in wetter places *Molinia* flush No. 16 is common, sometimes invading open stands of pine and birch, and often containing such grasses as *Deschampsia caespitosa* and *Agrostis* spp. which are not typical of this community. *Calluna/Trichophorum* No. 11 is found at the upper margins of the woodlands, while the principal bog communities are *Eriophorum/Trichophorum/ Sphagnum* No. 15, *Juncus communis* agg. No. 17, *Juncus articulatus* No. 18, and *Sphagnum* spp. No. 19. In the birchwoods, the communities are *Calluna/grass/ Vaccinium/*moss No. 13, and the grass/moss community No. 14, but in some which probably contained pine in the past there are communities Nos. 5 and 6.

The Black Wood contains many typical pinewood species such as *Pyrola media, Listera cordata* and *Trientalis europaea.* In woodlands of both pine and birch there are *Gentianella amarella, Achillea ptarmica, Geum rivale, Anemone nemorosa, Geranium sylvaticum, Lysimachia nemorum, Lonicera periclymenum, Mercurialis perennis, Teucrium scorodonia,* and *Brachypodium sylvaticum.* At the upper margin of the woodlands, there are the orchids *Coeloglossum viride* and *Gymnadenia conopsea* as well as the usual mountain species.

Age structure. As in the other native pinewoods the age structure is irregular, the different ages being represented either by single trees or groups, but there is a better representation of the different age classes than in most other pinewoods. There are only scattered trees over 200 years of age, the oldest being about 250 years. Particularly at Dall, there are open stands between about 130 and 200 years old. The age class between 100 and 130 years is only represented by scattered trees throughout the woodlands, but there are groups between 30 and 100 years old. There are relatively few trees under 30 years old, except at Dall and at the southeast margin of the woodland.

Growth and stocking. The tallest pine measured was 65 ft. (19·5 m.) high, but while trees of 60 ft. (18 m.) are common, the average of the older pine does not exceed 50 ft. (15 m.). One tree measured was 14 ft. (4·2 m.) in girth at breast height, but although trees of 7 to 10 ft. (2·1 to 3·0 m.) are scattered throughout the pinewood, the average is between 6 and 7 ft. (1·8 to 2·1 m.). Diameter growth for the first ten years is slow, increasing up to about 90 years, after which it declines, becoming very slow after about 140 years.

The pattern of the mixture of pine and birch has already been mentioned. The stocking of the pine is generally open, but there are groups of trees, 20 to 40 ft. high (6 to 12 m.) which are fully and even over stocked. There are also well stocked groups about 60 to 70 years old at the upper margins of the woodlands which probably originated from planting, as there are remains of fences round them. Pine are scattered through the birchwoods at the west end and near the upper altitudinal limits of the woodlands.

Fauna. The part of the Black Wood owned by the Forestry Commission is fenced against deer, and thus there is no grazing by wild or domestic animals except by a few roe deer. The western section, however, is grazed by deer, numerous sheep, and a few cattle, although the sheep prefer the better grazing in the birchwoods. Until 1955, there were rabbits in the woodlands, and the red squirrel, while common, has done little damage. Black grouse and capercailzie are sufficiently numerous to do considerable damage to pine of all ages, and there are also crossbills. Of the predators, the rough-legged buzzard has recently been reported near the Wood, and the jay, uncommon in native pinewoods, was seen at Dall and Camghouran.

Among insects, *Myelophilus piniperda* is doing appreciable damage, and *Hylobius abietis* is attacking young regeneration. The Black Wood is the southermost station of *Thamnonoma brunneata*, the rare looper, the larvae feeding on *Vaccinium myrtillus* (Darling, 1947).

Natural regeneration. In this as in the other native pinewoods already described, some natural regeneration followed heavy exploitation, if there were scattered trees or adjoining stands to provide a source of seed. The oldest trees now in the wood date from the period of indiscriminate fellings in the first half of the eighteenth century, and regeneration was mentioned in reports made later to the Commissioners for the Forfeited Estates (anon., 1745-85). The trees now over 150 years old are no doubt in part the result of the improvement measures taken by the Commissioners, including the enclosures against grazing in 1781. There are also a considerable number of trees which originated during and immediately after the fellings at the beginning of the last century, and regeneration must have continued sporadically thereafter, in spite of the effect of increasing grazing by sheep and red deer. Regeneration under 30 years old is scarce, except near Dall where there are groups between older trees (see PL. V.*a*). Elsewhere, it is only found as single trees or small groups in open places in the Wood and on its edges, or along paths and streams. Where protected against grazing animals, it is healthy and growing well except for some damage by capercailzie, but outside the deer fence the young pine is badly browsed. The rate of growth is slow in the early years; measurements made near Dall showed that at 10 to 15 years a height of only 5 ft. (1·5 m.) might be attained, but the annual growth increases thereafter and in a few years it may exceed one foot (0·3 m.). The best of the recent regeneration within the forest is coming up on sites where the layer of raw humus is shallow, and principally amongst communities Nos. 5 and 6, the *Calluna* being tall and vigorous with a little *Molinia* and a well developed moss layer, but with no bracken. In the open and on knolls and other dry sites, the regeneration is usually in *Callunetum* No. 10, but occasionally in the *Calluna/Trichophorum* community No. 11. As elsewhere there are a few seedlings on bog communities Nos. 15 and 17, but they do not survive for long. In 1949, the Forestry Commission began experiments on methods to stimulate natural regeneration on *Calluna* and *Molinia*-covered sites, using hand cultivation, burning the vegetation, killing it with sodium chlorate, and pulling it up. The addition of phosphate and sowing pine seed was also tried. In the first two seasons some success was attained, but by the spring of 1951, after a bad winter and with continued attacks by *Hylobius abietis*, few pine seedlings remained on the *Calluna* site, while there was complete failure on *Molinia* due to frost and suppression by the vegetation. There was, however, a good crop of birch and rowan seedlings on the *Calluna* site (Macdonald, 1952). Since that date, bracken has become more luxuriant, and capercailzie have caused damage to these experiments.

THE OLD WOOD OF MEGGERNIE

Owner: Sir Ernest Wills, Bt.

Location: The parish of Fortingall, Perthshire. Latitude, 56° 35' N.; Longitude, 4° 22' W. National Grid Reference 27 (NN)/555455. Ordnance Survey Maps: 1 in. to 1 mile, 55 (Scotland) 1947 edition; 6 in. to 1 mile, Perthshire 57 N.W. and 56 N.E., 1900 edition.

The pinewoods in Glen Lyon lie 13 miles west of Fortingall. The principal woodland is on the south side of the glen across the river from Meggernie Castle. There is also a considerable area of scattered old pine to the west of the main wood and in the valley of Allt Conait (see Fig. 20).

HISTORY

The earlier owners of this part of Breadalbane were successively the McGregors, the Campbells, and the Menzies. There is an early seventeenth-century reference to the pinewoods in Glen Lyon: "A firr wood betwixt Dalmoir and Balemoulyn called Leakgour; it is 3 myl long and a myl broad; also Kreach na Keir, a wood of firr, 2 myl long and as much broad" (Macfarlane, 1908). The place names have not been found in early maps, but Balemoulyn is probably the Bail' a' Mhuilinn of modern maps, immediately east of the present native pinewood (see Fig. 20). About 1675 the owner, Robert Campbell, got into financial difficulties following alterations to Meggernie Castle and sold his pine forest in Glen Lyon to a company of merchants, headed by a certain Captain John Crawford. The timber was

PLATE IX

a) Conaglen, Ardgour. A pedunculate oak in the foreground to the right, with pine and birch in the background.

THE PINEWOOD COMMUNITIES

b) Ballochbuie, Stunted pine, 15-20 ft. (4·5-6·0 m.) high, and up to 90 years old on a deep peat bog.

converted at a sawmill erected nearby and the planks floated down the River
Lyon. The owner appears to have regretted the loss of his woodlands and the
damage to the fishings caused by the damming of the river and the floating of the
timber, and an action was brought against the purchaser. Before it was settled,
however, the local inhabitants took the law into their own hands, broke the dam
and burned the sawmill (Campbell, 1886). On the evidence of Roy's Map of
Scotland (Roy, 1750), the boundaries of the pinewoods in the middle of the
eighteenth century were similar to those of today. Felling must have continued,
because Sir Robert Menzies of Slismin said in 1763: "There was in Glen Lyon a
very great fir wood, which by extending the hagges [yearly cuttings] to a greater
extent than it could bear, is now quite exhausted" (Whayman, 1953). The
woodlands must have recovered, however, because in the great storm on 28
December 1879, which destroyed the Tay Bridge, there was great destruction to
the pinewoods in Glen Lyon, and some of the trees rooted in crevices of living

FIG. 20. The Old Wood of Meggernie

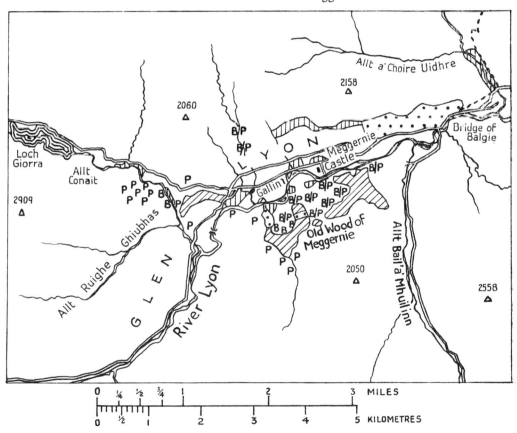

L

rock were broken to matchwood (Buchan, 1880). Many of the trees blown down at that time are still lying in the woods today, and a few bent over but still rooted are alive. About this time, the main pinewood was enclosed by a sheep fence, and since then there has been little felling.

THE HABITAT

Climate.	Mean annual rainfall	70 in.	1778 mm.
	Temperature: Mean annual	44° F.	6·7° C.
	January mean	37° F.	2·8° C.
	July mean	55° F.	12·8° C.

Climatic sub-province (Anderson, 1955) B2e.

Topography. The main wood is on moderately steep, undulating slopes with a north-westerly aspect. The range in altitude is from 750 ft. (225 m.) to 1300 ft. (390 m.), with scattered trees going a little higher. There are also old pine amongst planted trees in the steep-sided gorge of Allt Conait.

Geology and soils. The underlying rocks are Central Highland Granulites or Moine rocks, principally quartzose gneisses and schists rich in mica. They are covered with glacial deposits, deeper on the lower slopes and shallower on the upper, laid down by the retreating Lyon Glacier in the closing phases of the Ice Age. The boulders in the drifts are principally gneiss and schist. There is a narrow band of alluvium along the River Lyon, and there are numerous small bogs of no great depth, both within the wood and at its lower margin.

On freely drained sites, the soil is podsolised with a raw humus layer up to 3 in. (7·6 cm.) deep, and the texture is a stony, sandy loam, but on the lower slopes the soil is heavier. On the moister sites where there is soil compaction, the B horizon is gleyed with mottling.

THE FOREST

Tree species and larger shrubs. The woodland consists principally of Scots pine and birch, both as pure stands and in mixture. Some of the birch is definitely verrucose, some pubescent, but most intermediate. There is a considerable number of alder amongst the birch on the lower slopes, and rowan is growing vigorously in the birchwoods. No juniper was found in this wood.

Field layer. The communities are the same as already described for Rannoch, except that there is the dry moss Community No. 1 under dense pine, and, in communities Nos. 9, 11, 12 and 16, *Molinia* is less luxuriant, and there is more *Myrica gale*. The unusual species are also the same.

Age structure. This woodland also is uneven-aged with a predominance of the older age classes. The maximum age determined by borings was about 240 years, but most of the older trees are between 160 and 210. There are many trees about 100 years old surrounding older parents. The younger age classes are poorly represented; there are a few groups about 70 years old, and scattered trees under about 10.

Growth and stocking. The tallest tree measured was 55 ft. (16.5 m.) high, but the average of the older trees does not exceed 45 ft. (13·5 m.). The maximum girth is 10 ft. (3 m.), and the average between 7 and 8. The rate of diameter growth was found to be variable even on similar sites, some trees averaging about 8 rings to the inch (3·2 to the cm.) up to about 80 years old when there was a falling off, while others only averaged 30 rings to the inch from the beginning (11·8 to the cm.).

The stocking is very irregular and many of the trees are heavily branched. The central portion of the woodland consists of scattered trees, birch towards the west, and pine and birch towards the east. The stands of 100-year-old pine with older parent trees are usually well stocked and are principally at the east and south-west of the woodland. As already mentioned, there are scattered old trees along Allt Conait.

Fauna. Although the woodland is partially fenced, there is grazing by red deer, roe deer, sheep, and a few cattle; mountain hares are increasing. Both capercailzie and black grouse are common, but the crossbill has not been seen in recent years.

Of the insect pests of pine, *Meylophilus piniperda* is the most important, and the condition of the crowns of the hundred-year-old trees suggests that this pest caused serious damage in the past, for example after the storm of 1879.

Natural regeneration. Most of the old trees date from the period of exploitation about the middle of the eighteenth century. There are remains of a stone wall and ditch enclosure which may date from that period, when similar erections were being constructed at Rannoch, and which may have helped to protect any regeneration that came up. The trees now about a hundred years old may have developed following the enclosure during the second half of the last century. Since that time there has been little regeneration, and today there is only the occasional tree under ten years old, usually in *Callunetum* No. 10, *Calluna/Molinia* No. 9, and *Calluna/Trichophorum* No. 11. All the young regeneration is badly damaged by grazing.

CHAPTER 7

THE GREAT GLEN GROUP OF NATIVE PINEWOODS

THE Great Glen, a spectacular geological fault, runs from the Moray Firth to Loch Linnhe. In it are three lochs, Ness, Oich and Lochy, and these were joined before the middle of the last century to form the Caledonian Canal. The waters, particularly from the high rainfall areas to the west, come down the tributary valleys to the Great Glen. The surviving native pinewoods, described in this chapter, are in these valleys which from the north are Glen Moriston, Glen Loyne, Glengarry, Loch Arkaig, Glen Loy, Glen Nevis, and the glens in Ardgour, while Barisdale on the seaboard west of Glengarry is included in this group.

In addition to these woodlands, there are scattered old pine which may be the last survivors of earlier pinewoods, for example at the upper limit of Ruskich Wood on the western side of Loch Ness, Strath Errick on the eastern side, and in the valleys north and east of Kinlochleven. The scattered pine in Ruskich (N.G.R. 28 (NH)/470210) were described in the second *Statistical Account* in the middle of the last century as follows: "The top consists of native pine trees, with oaks, ashes and hoary hawthorns, stretching in detached stems and clumps along the precipitous rocks, and which, descending below, mingle themselves with dense woods of birch which cover all the lower declivities to the water's edge." Woodlands were shown in Blaeu's *Atlas* (1654) in what is now known as Strath Errick, but they had been largely exploited before the middle of the eighteenth century although there were still some pine as well as oak and other broadleaved species near Loch Ness (Macfarlane, 1908). There were woodlands on the lands of Callart (N.G.R. 27 (NN)/090605), now called Callert, north of Loch Leven, in the middle of the eighteenth century, and there are references to the cutting of pine as well as oak and ash while the estate was in the hands of the Commissioners of the Forfeited Estates, following the attainder of the then owner, Allan Cameron, after the rising in 1745 (anon., 1745-81). Later that century, however, Pennant (1771) referred to scattered pine trees only. A description, probably by Timothy Pont, of the country round Loch Eil about 1600, makes reference to "great fir-woods" as well as oakwoods to the north of Kinlocheil (Macfarlane, 1908). In previous centuries, therefore, there appear to have been extensive native pinewoods within the region covered by this Group that have now largely disappeared, and the descriptions of the surviving pinewoods that follow show that these also were more extensive in earlier times.

The pinewoods were only one of the natural woodland communities and there are many historical references to both oakwoods and birchwoods, and some persist to the present time. Many of the slopes along the Great Glen itself appeared to have been clothed with mixed woods of birch and oak, some of which survive, with perhaps scattered pine on rocky knolls, and in some instances pinewoods at their upper limit, for example in Ruskich Wood referred to above. There were similar woods in the lower reaches of the tributary valleys, such as Glen Moriston, Glen Garry, Glen Loy, and in Cona Glen in Ardgour, some of which survive. The surviving native pinewoods are almost always on the north facing or south sides of the valleys and lochs, and on the other side there are, or have been in the past, oakwoods and birchwoods. The most striking example is at Loch Arkaig, but in the past there were extensive oakwoods on the north side of Loch Eil, and the north side of Loch Garry.

The Great Glen has been a route from the west to the east since Neolithic times, and there must have been settlements along it for many centuries. There was shipbuilding from early historical times both at Inverness in the north and at the head of Loch Linnhe in the south, and at least some of the timber came from the forests in this region. The ship built in 1249 at Inverness by the Earl of St Pol and Blois to take himself and his followers to the Holy Land may have been built of Glen Urquhart oak and Glen Moriston pine (Mackay, 1914). In the sixteenth century, the pinewoods at Arkaig and elsewhere were being inspected by the King's surveyors for ships' masts (Speed, 1611), and a little later masts and other pine timber were being extracted from Glen Scaddle and Cona Glen in Ardgour and despatched by sea. About 1600 also, the oak in Loch Eil was being used for shipbuilding (Macfarlane, 1908). As already mentioned in chapter 2, a cargo of oak was brought by ship from Lochaber to Leith for use at Holyrood in 1535-36 (Paton, 1957). During all that time the timber from these forests was also being used locally for house building and other purposes, and the oak was being peeled to provide bark for tanning. As early as 1563 there was concern about the devastation of the woods, and Lord Lovat and the Laird of Grant obtained an order from the Earl of Moray as Sheriff of Inverness-shire prohibiting the cutting and peeling of trees in the neighbourhood of Loch Ness (Fraser, 1883). Particularly from the seventeenth century, there was felling, chiefly of birch but also of other species, for the production of charcoal for smelting iron ore, and later timber was exported to the Carron Iron Works for this purpose (Macadam, 1887; Mackay, 1914; Ritchie, 1920). During the troublous times of the eighteenth century, felling continued in the woodlands, but some efforts were made on forfeited estates to protect regeneration and limit fellings (anon., 1745-81). During the nineteenth century, there was an increase in the numbers first of sheep and later of red deer, and there were heavy fellings from time to time in the woods, culminating during the 1914-18 and 1939-45 Wars. During the last twenty-five years the Forestry Commission has acquired some of the native pinewoods, has endeavoured to get some natural regeneration of pine, and has carried out planting using a range of coniferous species.

GLEN MORISTON

Owner: The late Captain Grant of Invermoriston. Since the date of the survey, the principal areas of native pinewood have been acquired by the Forestry Commission.

Location: The parish of Urquhart and Glenmoriston, Inverness-shire. Latitude, 57° 10′ N.; Longitude, 4° 48′ W. National Grid Reference 28 (NH)/310120. Ordnance Survey Maps: 1 in. to 1 mile, 41 and 42 (Scotland), 1947 edition; 6 in. to 1 mile, Inverness-shire 53, 67 and 68, 1902-03 edition.

The pinewoods and scattered pine trees are in Glen Moriston, three to twelve miles west of Invermoriston on the west side of Loch Ness (see Fig. 21).

FIG. 21. Glen Moriston

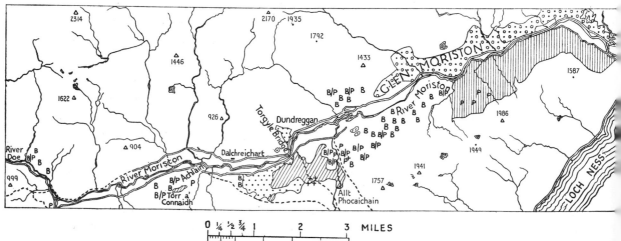

HISTORY

Mackay (1914) has described the past history of this region and the part played in Scottish history by its succession of noble owners. Glen Moriston came into the possession of the Grants towards the end of the fifteenth century, and from 1509 they were also foresters of Cluanie to the west, which had been a royal forest since the thirteenth century. Although remote, there was royal interest in the forest, and in 1573, during the reign of James VI, attempts were made to protect the trees and deer from graziers, cutters of timber, and peelers of trees. Early in the next century, there is a vivid picture of this glen: "Glenmoriestoune is a verie profitable and fertill little glen, or countrie both plenteous of corne and abundance of butter cheese and milk and great long woods of firr trees doth grow in that countrey. And the river doeth transport big Jests and Cutts of timber to the fresh water Loghnes . . . and there is ane little parish Church of timber in this countrey called Millergheard" (Macfarlane, 1908). In 1715, John Grant of Invermoriston joined the Stuart cause and the estate was forfeited. It was administered by the Commissioners of the Forfeited Estates for a period, but the local people proved unco-operative and the annual revenue was small. The estate was sold in 1730 to another branch of the Grant family and later came back into the possession of a descendant of the original owner. During the second half of the eighteenth century, there was a sale of timber, probably both pine and oak, for a sum of £2000 sterling (Mackay, 1914). The next heavy felling appears to have been at the beginning of the next century, when the pinewoods were leased for felling for a period of seven years bringing in an annual revenue of £800 (Robertson, 1808). At the prices of timber then current, this represented about 50,000 hoppus feet (1,800 m.³) per annum. About the same time the Carron Iron Works Co. of Falkirk bought a woodland eight miles up Glen Moriston for £900. The species is not recorded, but the timber appears to have been taken to Falkirk for smelting purposes (Ritchie, 1920). There were heavy fellings in the pinewoods in the 1914-18 War. After the war, the Forestry Commission acquired land in the glen for planting, and in 1953 it also purchased the pinewoods west of Torgyle Bridge. Since then the less vigorous old pine have been felled and the younger groups thinned. As we have seen already, there was a settled agricultural community in the glen as early as the beginning of the seventeenth century, and no doubt for many centuries before that time. There were twelve holdings in 1509, and the crofters kept cattle, sheep, and goats which must have grazed in the woodlands (Mackay, 1914). At the end of the eighteenth century and beginning of the next, the sheep population no doubt increased here as elsewhere, and later red deer were preserved. The regeneration in the woods, therefore, has had to contend with grazing animals during a long period.

THE HABITAT

Climate. Mean annual rainfall 60–70 in. 1524–1778 mm.
Temperature: Mean annual 45° F. 7·2° C.
January mean 37° F. 2·8° C.
July mean 55° F. 12·8° C.
Climatic sub-provinces (Anderson, 1955) B2b and B3a.

Topography. The principal native pinewoods, west of Allt Phocaichain, are on gently undulating slopes, and the scattered pine among birch and planted woodlands to the east are on moderate to locally steep slopes. The aspect is N.N.W., and the range of altitude is from 400 ft. (120 m.) to 1000 ft. (300 m.), with scattered trees up to about 1100 ft. (330 m.).

Geology and soils. The underlying rocks are schists and gneisses of the Moine series, with minor basic intrusions, for example along Allt Phocaichain. The slopes are covered with glacial deposits, principally moraines and terrace moraines, laid down by the Glen Moriston glacier as it retreated westwards at the end of the Ice Age (Charlesworth, 1956). There is alluvium along the water courses and peat bogs in the hollows.

The freely drained knolls of stony, sandy loams are podsolised, with a shallow layer of raw humus. At the base of the knolls and ridges, the drainage may be impeded, and there is then mottling in the B horizon. As the drainage deteriorates, the surface is covered with shallow peat up to 10 in. deep (25·4 cm.), and at the margins of the woods and in places within them the peat is up to 30 in. (0·76 m.) in depth.

THE FOREST

Tree species and larger shrubs. The native pinewoods in Glen Moriston are unusual, because there is some mingling of oak with pine as well as with birch. In earlier times, the north-facing, south side of the glen was covered with pine and birch – "the long firrwoods" of the early seventeenth century already referred to. At the beginning of the next century, there were pine and birch on the south side of the glen from near Dalnacaig in the east to the River Loyne in the west. At that time there was on the opposite side of the glen, young oak near Dalnacaig, and further up the glen birch and alder with some pine (Avery, 1725–30). Most of the present-day native pine are on the south side of the glen, east and west of Torgyle Bridge. There are pure groups of Scots pine, but many are in mixture with birches – verrucose, pubescent and intermediate, and there are also a few oak, mainly sessile. There is a small outlying stand of pine on Torr a' Chonnaidh, $2\frac{1}{2}$ miles west of Torgyle Bridge, and scattered trees still farther west as far as the River Doe. On the north side between Torgyle Bridge and Invermoriston, there are scattered pine amongst birch and oak. Rowan is common throughout the woods, with some aspen particularly in open places, and there are alder and willows along the streams. There are a few bushy juniper and hazel.

Field layer. The communities in this native pinewood are similar to those in other forests in this group in that *Molinia caerulea* is commoner than in the eastern pinewoods, although the natural drainage is better than at Arkaig and Glengarry. The flora, however, is richer, probably due to the presence of some basic rocks in the parent material of the soils. Under the densest groups of Scots pine on freely drained sites, there is either the dry moss community No. 1 or more rarely the moist moss No. 2, but the commonest in well stocked stands is the *Vaccinium/Deschampsia/Hypnaceous* moss No. 3, with *V. vitis-idaea* unusually prominent. In a few groups of dense pine regeneration up to 30 ft. high (9 m.) where there is good side lighting, there is almost pure, diffuse, short *Molinia* with a little *Calluna, Erica cinerea* and *E. tetralix* even on freely drained sites, an unusual community not included in the standard list. In the more open woodlands, there are the dry and moist *Calluna/Vaccinium/Deschampsia/*moss communities Nos. 5 and 6, with some scattered *Molinia* and bracken, the latter being locally vigorous and dense. Particularly where there is birch, there are patches of *Deschampsia flexuosa/Hypnaceous* moss No. 4 and the grass pinewood No. 7 communities. *Calluna/Molinia* No. 9 covers large areas of peaty ground under open woodland, particularly towards its upper limit, and it often contains *Myrica gale* and bracken. On similar sites, there are also tracts of *Molinia* flush community No. 16, with some bracken. On knolls there is *Callunetum* No. 10 grading into *Trichophorum/Sphagnum* No. 15, with local flushes of *Molinia* No. 16 and *Juncus communis* agg. No. 17, and the wettest are covered with *Sphagnum* community No. 19, sometimes with a little *Menyanthes trifoliata*.

The only unusual species typical of pinewoods which were found at Glen Moriston were *Pyrola media, P. minor* and *Trientalis europaea*. The latter is common in grassy places, and both white and pink colour variants are to be found. On the other hand, there are the limestone species *Sanicula europaea* and *Melica nutans*, which are very unusual in a native pinewood. A number of species more typical of oakwoods and birchwoods are to be found under pine, such as *Lysimachia nemorum, L. nummularia, Primula vulgaris* and *Viola* spp., while *Polygonum viviparum* is growing on grassy sites. The uncommon *Lycopodium annotinum* (PL. XII.*d*) occurs under mixed pine and birch, and *L. alpinum* grows at the upper limit of the woodlands.

Age structure. There are small stands, groups, and scattered pine between 130 and 200 years old. The most extensive stands, however, are between 90 and 120 years, for example near Torgyle Bridge (PL. VII.*a*). Some of the older trees are surrounded by younger age classes. There are relatively few trees under 50 years, some small groups between 20 and 49 years old, and hardly any under 20 years.

Growth and stocking. The tallest tree measured was 60 ft. (18·0 m.) high, and the average for trees over 100 years old is about 45 ft. (13·5 m.). The maximum girth was 9 ft. (2·7 m.), and the average for the older trees about 6 ft. (1·8 m.). Girth increment is slow to begin with, becomes good until about 70 to 80 years, and decreases again thereafter.

The stocking is irregular, with varying proportions of pine and birch, but there are areas of pure pine, between 90 and 120 years old, and up to two to three acres in extent, which are well stocked and at the time of the survey were even over stocked; they have since been thinned.

Fauna. The pinewood at Torr a' Chonnaidh in the west and the scattered pine in the Forestry Commission plantations to the east have been protected against grazing for a period of years, but the pinewoods in the vicinity of Torgyle Bridge were only enclosed in 1955-6. There are roe deer in the woods, rabbits were numerous until recent years, and there are a few red squirrels. Black grouse have been seen, but no capercailzie.

The only serious insect pest is *Myelophilus piniperda* which has pruned the crowns of trees in the pole stage.

Natural regeneration. As in other native pinewoods, the older age classes of pine are correlated with heavy fellings in the past. There are also many examples of dense naturally regenerated pine, 20 to 90 years old, surrounding old bushy crowned trees probably isolated during past exploitations. There is little regeneration under 20 years old, a few seedlings four to five years old in *Callunetum* and *Calluna/Molinia* on knolls at the south edge of the woodlands and along the banks of streams. There are also a few seedlings on the bog communities, but they are unlikely to survive.

GLEN LOYNE

Owner: The North of Scotland Hydro-Electric Board.

Location: Kilmonivaig parish, Inverness-shire. Latitude, 57° 5′ N.; Longitude, 5° 9′ W. National Grid Reference 28 (NH)/085050. Ordnance Survey Maps: 1 in. to 1 mile, 41 (Scotland) 1947 edition; 6 in. to 1 mile, Inverness-shire 80 and 81, 1875-80 edition.

The woodland, known locally as Etnach, lies on the south side of the River Loyne, three miles west of Loch Loyne. It is, therefore, between the Glengarry and Barisdale native pinewoods.

GENERAL DESCRIPTION

This wood is in the ancient Royal Forest of Cluanie, in which steps were taken to protect the trees as early as the sixteenth century as already mentioned in the account of Glen Moriston (Mackay, 1914). Avery, on his map of 1725-30, showed a wood of birch and pine at the eastern end of the south side of Loch Loyne, an area now treeless, but as his map ended at this point the present wood is not marked. Pennant in 1769 and the botanist Lightfoot in 1777 also mentioned natural pine in this district (Lightfoot, 1777; Pennant, 1771). The survivors in Glen Loyne are, therefore, the remnants of more extensive native pinewoods that must have been felled or otherwise destroyed after the closing decades of the eighteenth century, but no records of this have been found.

The rainfall is about 100 in. (2540 mm.) per annum. The wood is growing in an amphitheatre with a northerly aspect, and the altitudinal range is from 1000 ft. (300 m.) to 1300 ft. (390 m.). The underlying rocks are schists and gneisses of the Moine series, and they are mantled with deep morainic sands and gravels laid down by the retreating Loyne glacier in the closing phases of the Ice Age (Charlesworth, 1956). The soils are stony, sandy loams, with a raw humus covering 3 to 6 in. deep, and show slight leaching. The natural drainage is only moderate, and there are deep peat bogs to the north and east of the wood.

The surviving pine are scattered thinly among open birch which is mainly verrucose and of a small-leaved type. There are a few rowan and one or two small alder. Under the canopy of the pine, the field layer communities are Nos. 3, 5 and 6, as in other pinewoods, but *Molinia* is a constituent of these and other communities, and *Vaccinium vitis-idaea* is not common, except at the east end of the wood. Under both pine and birch, there are patches of communities Nos. 9, 13, 14 and 16.

The trees are between 130 and 200 years old, the tallest being about 45 ft. (13·5 m.), and the average girth about 6 ft. (1·8 m.). Both the pine and birch show signs of blasting by wind and many of the former are dying. There is no natural regeneration.

GLENGARRY

Owners: The woodlands on the south side of Loch Garry east of Greenfield are owned by the Forestry Commission and west of that place by Miss M. Ellice.

Location: The parish of Kilmonivaig, Inverness-shire. Latitude, 57° 4′ N.; Longitude, 4° 55′ W. National Grid Reference 28 (NH)/230010. Ordnance Survey Maps: 1 in. to 1 mile, 41 and 42 (Scotland), 1947 edition; 6 in. to 1 mile, Inverness-shire 96, 97, 81 and 82, 1904 edition.

The woodlands to be described are to the south and west of Loch Garry, 4 to 12 miles west of Invergarry on the road to Tomdoun (see Fig. 22).

HISTORY

Glengarry belonged to the Macdonnells from the sixteenth century. It was sold to the Marquis of Huntly about 1824, and belonged to Lord Ward, afterwards the Earl of Dudley, from 1840 to 1860, when it was purchased by Edward Ellice (anon., 1886). The Forestry Commission acquired part of the site carrying the native pinewoods in 1927, but most of the timber did not pass into the ownership of the Forestry Commission.

As in some of the pinewoods already described, the earliest reference which has been found is the information recorded by seventeenth century travellers which was later used in the preparation of Blaeu's *Atlas* (Blaeu, 1654; Macfarlane, 1908). During the first half of that century, there was a pinewood on the south-

FIG. 22.   Glengarry

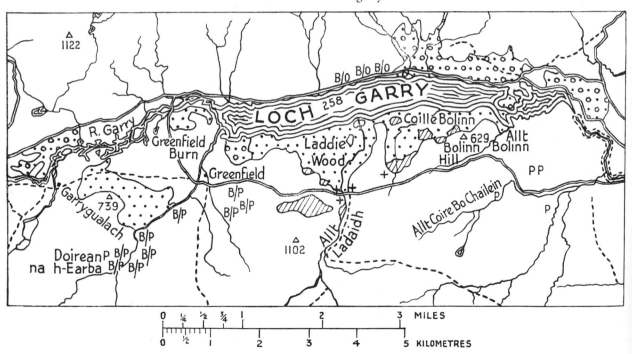

west side of Loch Garry, 10 to 12 miles long, and on the north side an oakwood (Macfarlane, 1908), remnants of which still remain. As at Loch Arkaig, therefore, the oakwoods had a southerly aspect and the pine a northerly. Avery's (1725-30) manuscript map showed oak, alder, and some pinewoods on the south side of the loch, and oak, birch and some pine on the north side. There was an iron mill in Invergarry about 1730 (Macadam, 1887), but it is unlikely that any timber from the pinewood was used for smelting. Pennant (1771) mentioned the pinewood in 1769, and a little later it was recorded that the neighbourhood of Loch Garry was closely wooded with pine on the southern side and birch and alder on the north (Robertson, 1808). At the beginning of this century, there were pine 70 to 80 ft. high (21 to 24 m.) and up to 16 ft. (4·8 m.) in girth at 5 ft. (1·5 m.) from the ground, and at that time there were four discernible age classes of trees: the very old; a class between 120 and 150 years which was not numerous; a class between 80 and 100 years which contained 15,000 to 20,000 trees; and the younger (Elwes, 1908). There was some felling in these woodlands during the 1914-18 War, and some of the logs were floated down the rock-strewn River Garry. A little later, trees felled west of Loch Garry were brought down the Greenfield Burn. In Greenfield at that time, there were well stocked groups of pine about 100 years old growing on sandy knolls, while on the surrounding peaty areas there were very old trees dying partly of age and partly of the effects of waterlogging. From 1930, there was extensive felling in the pinewoods, both of the trees reserved south of Loch Garry at the time of the Forestry Commission's purchase, and also in Greenfield to the west. In 1942, a fire swept up from Kilfinnan and killed many of the older trees and young regeneration then growing at the southern and western margins of the woods. The red deer population has been high since the middle of the last century, and there is also grazing by sheep, except within the Forestry Commission enclosure. As the result of all these causes, there are now few native pine surviving in this forest compared with even the recent past. At the eastern end, the Forestry Commission has replanted the area using different coniferous species. Since this area was studied, the level of Loch Garry has been raised by the North of Scotland Hydro-Electric Board.

THE HABITAT

Climate.   Mean annual rainfall   70 in.   1778 mm.
            Temperature: Mean annual   45° F.   6·1° C.
                         January mean   37° F.   2·8° C.
                         July mean   55° F.   12·8° C.
            Climatic sub-provinces (Anderson, 1955) B2b and B3a.

Topography. This pinewood is growing on undulating ground of hummocky moraines and hollows, but it spreads on to steep slopes towards the east. The general aspect is northerly. The range in altitude is from 300 to 750 ft. (90 to 225 m.), with scattered pine up to 1000 ft. (300 m.), while the birch reaches 1300 ft. (390 m.). The area is drained by the Greenfield Burn, the Allt Ladaidh, Allt Bolinn, and Allt Coire Bo Chailein, all flowing into either Loch Garry or the River Garry.

Geology and soils. The underlying rocks are Moine schists and gneisses. The whole area is mantled with glacial deposits – moraines, and fluvio-glacial sands and gravels – mainly derived from the underlying rocks, but containing also some granite and sandstone fragments. There is alluvium along the streams, and there are peat bogs at the south-west of the woodlands.

Under well stocked pine on the drier knolls, the soils are podsolised, but not strongly. Under more open pine where the drainage is impeded, the soils are gleyed with mottling in the B horizon, and some profiles showed a definite compacted horizon. Under the pine, the raw humus may be up to 3 in. (7·6 cm.) deep, but it is often shallower and may be absent. The peat bogs at the south-west are up to 7 ft. (2·1 m.) deep and eroded into hags.

THE FOREST

Tree species and larger shrubs. Since the pre-war fellings and the fire of 1942, birch has predominated in these woodlands. The birch consists of both the verrucose and pubescent species and intermediates. There are, however, groups of pure Scots pine up to an acre in extent, and there are also scattered old pine throughout the birchwoods and in the planted woodlands. Rowan is scattered throughout, and there is alder along the streams, while there are a few sessile oak principally among the birch and towards the west end of the forest. Juniper is not common and is usually of the bushy type.

Field layer. As in other western pinewoods, there is more bracken and *Molinia* than is usual in the eastern forests, and the latter species sometimes spreads on to the drier knolls. Under the better stocked pine, the typical communities, however, are still the *Vaccinium/Deschampsia/Hypnaceous* moss community No. 3 and the dry and moist *Calluna/Vaccinium/Deschampsia/*moss communities Nos. 5 and 6, but *Calluna/Molinia* No. 9 is common, and there are small areas of the *Deschampsia flexuosa/Hypnaceous* moss community No. 4, and the grass pinewood community No. 7. Under scattered pine, the communities are also Nos. 5, 6, and 9, with *Callunetum* No. 10 on the drier knolls, and *Calluna/Trichophorum* No. 11 and *Molinia/Trichophorum* No. 12 on the wetter areas. Where the birch predominates, the typical communities are the *Calluna*/grass/*Vaccinium* No. 13, and the grass/moss No. 14 communities with much bracken and *Molinia*. In wet places, there are patches of the *Molinia* flush No. 16, *Juncus communis* agg. No. 17, and *Juncus articulatus* flush No. 18. The most widespread bog community is *Eriophorum*/*Trichophorum*/*Sphagnum* No. 15, with local patches of the *Sphagnum* community No. 10. One eroded peat bog to the west of the woodlands is dominated by *Rhacomitrium lanuginosum*, a community not listed.

There are few of the more unusual species typical of pinewoods, but *Trientalis europaea* is common, and there are a few *Pyrola media*. *Tofieldia pusilla, Drosera intermedia,* and *Menyanthes trifoliata* are to be found in some of the bogs, and the orchids *Gymnadenia conopsea* and *G. bifolia* occur at the edges of the woodlands. There are many species typical of birchwoods such as *Primula vulgaris, Viola* spp., *Ajuga reptans* and *Ranunculus ficaria*.

Age structure. In view of the widespread fellings, little can be said about the age structure in this forest. The oldest tree found was 230 years old, but the majority of the older trees are between 130 and 200 years. One group had a mean age of 90 years and another of 120 years. There are a few pine between 20 and 80 years, and there is some young regeneration coming up in open places on dry knolls. Most of the birch is young, except to the south-west of the loch.

Growth and stocking. Of the surviving pine, the tallest measured was 65 ft. (19·5 m.) high, but the average is only between 40 and 50 ft. (12 and 15 m.). The maximum girth is 10 ft. (3 m.) and the average about 5 ft. (1·5 m.).

The stocking of the pine is very irregular. There are some well stocked groups at Doirean na h-Earba and at the south edge of Laddie Wood and in Coille Bolinn, but much of the surviving pine is scattered through the birch.

Fauna. Outside the Forestry Commission deer fence, there is grazing by red deer, sheep, and a few cattle, while there are roe deer throughout the woods. The wild cat is stated to be common in the district. The only birds that may be harmful to the pine are a few pairs of capercailzie, more black grouse, and, while crossbills have not been common in the native woods in recent years (Baxter, 1953), a small flock was observed in a Scots pine plantation at Invergarry in 1955.

The pine shoot beetle is common in the woods, chiefly *Myelophilus piniperda*, but *M. minor* is also present.

Natural regeneration. There has been little natural regeneration in recent years in these native pinewoods. Some is to be found, however, on the drier knolls and in the open amongst *Calluna*/*Molinia* community No. 9, with *Calluna* dominant and *Molinia* scattered thinly, in *Callunetum* No. 10, and in *Calluna*/*Vaccinium*/

Deschampsia/moss No. 5, but there are only small groups of seedlings and growth is slow even in the absence of grazing.

In 1933 the Forestry Commission carried out experiments on the direct sowing of a range of coniferous species, using different methods of soil cultivation. Good results were obtained with a number of species, but natural Scots pine seedlings were relatively few. In places, however, a good crop of birch and rowan was obtained (Macdonald, 1952).

BARISDALE

The Ordnance Survey Map spelling is Barrisdale, but in the eighteenth century the spelling was that now adopted.

FIG. 23. Barisdale

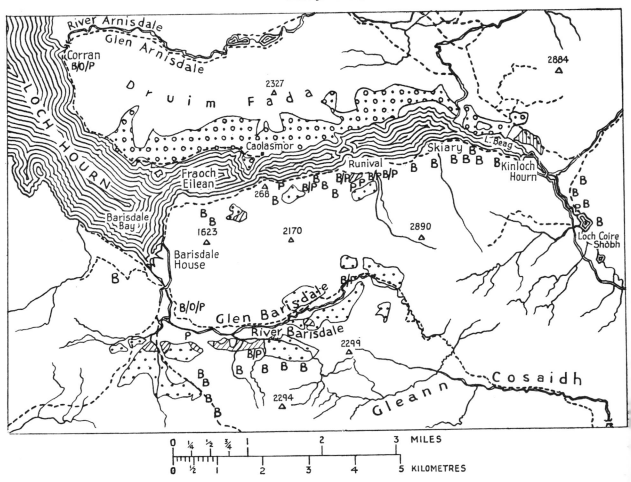

PLATE X

TOWER OF ESS WOOD, GLENTANAR

A plantation of Scots pine, mainly var. *horizontalis* Don, grown from seed collected from naturally regenerated pine in Glentanar Forest. The age is about 120 years, and the height about 60 ft. (18 m.). It is on an alluvial terrace at an altitude of 450-500 ft. (135-150 m.). This wood shows the potentialities of native pine on a favourable site when well tended.

Owners: Mrs M. F. Williams. There are scattered pine to the west and north-west of Barisdale on the Knoydart Estate which is owned by Col. O. Crossthwaite-Eyre, M.P., and on the north side of Loch Hourn belonging to Capt. H. Birkbeck and Capt. J. B. Kitson.

Location: Glenelg parish, Inverness-shire. Latitude, 57° 4' N.; Longitude, 5° 30' W. National Grid Reference 18 (NG)/890030. Ordnance Survey Maps: 1 in. to 1 mile, 41 (Scotland), 1947 edition; 6 in. to 1 mile, Inverness-shire 78 and 93, 1902 edition.

The principal pinewoods are on the south side of Glen Barisdale and two miles from Loch Hourn. They are the most inaccessible of any surviving native pine-wood. There are scattered pine along the south side of Loch Hourn between Skiary and Fraoch Eilean, and a few old trees in the gorge of the river running from Loch Coire Shubh into Loch Hourn at Kinloch Hourn. On the north side of Loch Hourn, there are woods of birch and oak with an occasional Scots pine (see Fig. 23).

HISTORY

These lands previously belonged to the Macdonells of Barisdale, the most famous or infamous of whom was the Barisdale at the time of the 1745 rising (Anderson, 1864; Lang, 1898). Nothing is known of the condition of the woods before that time, but the estates were forfeited, and there are a few references in the papers of the Commissioners for the Forfeited Estates (anon., 1745-84; anon., 1745-81). About 1774, a pinewood stretching westwards along Loch Hourn from Skiary was enclosed against grazing animals and the tenant compensated. This was successful in increasing the natural regeneration and led to similar measures at Loch Arkaig. This reference also shows that there was then a large pinewood where there are now only scattered trees. In Glen Barisdale, where the largest area of native pinewood has survived, there is a local tradition that there were fellings about the beginning of the last century, the logs being floated down the River Barisdale to a water-powered sawmill near Ambraigh Croft and sawn there, and the deals exported by sea. Near this croft there are still wide ditches which may have been used to bring the logs from the river and return the sawn timber to it. A cog wheel and other equipment has been found in the vicinity. It is believed that about this time or a little later there was a serious fire in these pine-woods, and there have been smaller fires in recent years. Red deer and roe deer have been numerous in this region since at least the beginning of the seventeenth century (Macfarlane, 1908), but the nature of the terrain makes it unlikely that the sheep population was ever high.

M

THE HABITAT

Climate.   Mean annual rainfall   110 in.   2794 mm.
            Temperature: Mean annual   45° F.   7·2° C.
                           January mean   37° F.   2·8° C.
                           July mean   55° F.   12·8° C.

Climatic sub-provinces (Anderson, 1955) B4b and C3a.

Topography. In Glen Barisdale, the pine trees are growing on steep, sometimes precipitous slopes, and some in rocky crevices. There are numerous streams tumbling down the hillsides to the River Barisdale. The altitudinal limits of the pinewoods are from sea-level to 1000 ft. (300 m.), with scattered trees up to 1250 ft. (375 m.), and the birch reaches 1800 ft. (540 m.). The surrounding steep-sided hills rise to 3083 ft. (925 m.) and provide good shelter from the south-westerly gales, but the scattered pine north and south of Loch Hourn are windswept.

Geology and soils. The underlying rocks are schists, rich in mica, and garnetiferous in places, belonging to the Moine Series (anon., 1948 *a* and *b*; Phemister, 1948). Rock outcrops and boulder screes are common. While a lobe of the Hourn glacier retreated up Glen Barisdale at the end of the Ice Age (Charlesworth, 1956), there is little morainic material covering the slopes, but at the higher elevations, about 1750 ft. (525 m.), there are perched blocks. There is stony alluvium along the River Barisdale.

The soils are unusually shallow, and there may be only a few inches of humus and dead mosses on the boulder screes, even under pine canopy. Amongst the rocks, there are deeper pockets of soil which are stained with humus and show little visible leaching. Even on the steep slopes, the drainage is only moderate, probably owing to the high rainfall, but there are no extensive peat bogs, except at the bottom of the valley.

THE FOREST

Tree species and larger shrubs. In the principal native wood in Glen Barisdale, both Scots pine and birch form relatively large, almost pure stands, and there is every gradation in their mixture. The birch is usually verrucose with some intermediates, and no true pubescent birch was found. The birch is often 40 ft. (12 m.) high, and there are pendulous variants. The Scots pine stands are on slopes with a northern aspect, with only scattered trees facing south, but the birchwoods are on both aspects. In the glen, there are some natural oaks which, somewhat unexpectedly, are all pedunculate. Rowan is common among both pine and birch and often attains 30 ft. (9 m.) in height, but no aspen was found. Along the streams, there are old alder trees some of which are dying of old age, with some *Prunus padus*. Small holly bushes are scattered through the woods in the glen, and this species is more abundant and vigorous in the woods north of Loch Hourn. Juniper sometimes attains 25 ft. (7·5 m.) in height and is of the bushy type.

Field layer. In common with other native pinewoods in the high rainfall regions of the west, *Molinia* is present in greater or less amounts in all communities. These are the same as in other native pinewoods of this Group, for example, Glengarry already described, but there are more species of grasses, *Vaccinium vitis-idaea* was not found, and the growth of *Sphagna* is more luxuriant.

Age structure. Borings showed that most of the trees were between 130 and 220 years old. There are occasional trees in the 80 to 120 year age class, and a few between 60 and 80, particularly in sheltered gullies and on rock faces where deer cannot reach them. Younger trees are rare and are confined to rock debris along rivers and below cliffs, with an occasional seedling on the bogs.

Growth and stocking. Considering the shallow and rocky nature of the soil, height growth is moderately good, the average being about 40 ft. (12.0 m.), except in full exposure to the north-west. Girths at breast height range up to 8 ft. 6 in. (2·6 m.), diameter increment after about 100 years often falling to 40 rings to the inch (16 per cm.).

Except where the slopes are very rocky, there are few open places in the wood, and the stocking in the pure stands of pine is moderately good for a native pinewood.

Fauna. There are red deer and a few sheep in the glen, but the better grazing in the birchwoods is probably preferred. There are a few wild cats, but no pine martens have been sent in recent years. Badgers are unusually common, the sets being often in rock crevices. There are no capercailzie or black grouse. Golden eagles are common in the nearby hills, and the kestrel feeds in or near the woods. The population of insectivorous birds is not large, but there are many species of duck and waders on Loch Hourn, and there is a large heronry of about a dozen nests on a small island.

Both *Myelophilus piniperda* and *M. minor* are in the woods, and cause a little damage.

Natural regeneration. Most of the old trees date from the end of the eighteenth century and beginning of the last, and may be the result of enclosure and the opening up of the woods by felling during that period. Today there are few seedlings, and these are restricted to open places on screes, cliffs, and bogs.

LOCH ARKAIG AND GLEN MALLIE

Owner: Cameron of Lochiel.

Location: The parish of Kilmallie, Inverness-shire. Latitude, 56° 58′ N.; Longitude, 5° 5′ W. National Grid Reference 27 (NN)/170875 to 27 (NN)/010910. Ordnance Survey Maps: 1 in. to 1 mile, 41 and 47 (Scotland), 1947 edition; 6 in. to 1 mile, Inverness-shire 109, 110, 125 and 126, 1902–03 edition.

The forest lies on the south side of Loch Arkaig and in Glen Mallie, to the north-west of Fort William (see Fig. 24).

HISTORY

There are a number of references in the early seventeenth century to the woods round Loch Arkaig, also called Argick, Argicke, Airgack, Airceig or Arkik – which should not be confused with the old place name Strath Arkeg on the east side of Loch Ness, now called Strath Errick (Blaeu, 1654). At that time a traveller, probably Timothy Pont, wrote as follows: "Loch Arkaig . . . upon the southsyd of the loch ther is a firrwood upon fourteen myles of lenth and upon the northsyd fair oaken wood" (Macfarlane, 1908). Early in that century, Crown surveyors, searching for timber suitable for naval purposes, reported that there were: "Firr-trees for masts in north-west Scotland upon the banks of Lough Argicke of such great height and thickness, that at the root they bear 28 handfuls about, and the bodies mounted to 90 foot of height they beare at that length 20 inches in Dia-

FIG. 24.   Loch Arkaig and Glen Mallie

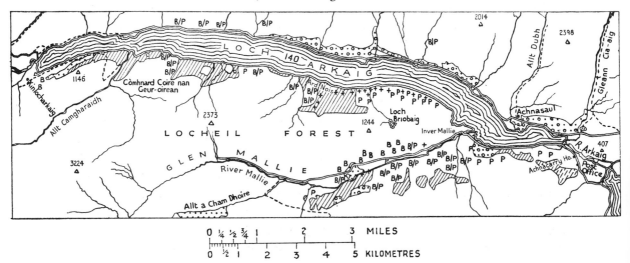

metre, as has been measured by some in commission, and so certified to his Majesty: and at this present growing upon the lands of the right worthy Knight Sir Alexander Hayes, his Maiesties principal Secretay for Scotland . . ." (Speed, 1611). For several centuries before that time, these lands had been in the possession of the Camerons of Lochiel, probably first as vassals of the Lords of the Isles, and from 1495 under charter from James IV. At the time of the above quotation, however, they had been forfeited to King James VI and I, following clan feuds, but were again in full possession of the Chief by 1624 (Cameron, 1892). The Chiefs of the Clan Cameron supported the Stewart cause both in 1715 and 1745, and on the latter occasion the estates were forfeited until 1784. The records of the Commissioners of the Forfeited Estates (anon., 1745-81) throw some light on the condition of the woods in the second half of the eighteenth century. In spite of earlier exploitation and lack of protection during the troublous times in the first half of that century, there appears to have been a good representation of age classes in the pinewoods; in a report of 1760 it is stated that there were 20,000 firs or 5000 tons fit for sale as well as young growing timber, and it was proposed to cut 300 tons per annum, estimated to yield £120 allowing for transport costs. In the following year, however, 9200 tons were offered for sale by public roup, the trees to be cut in seventeen years, and at a reserve price of 10s. per ton. Although all this timber was not sold, some was converted at a sawmill erected at Achnacarry and sold to shipwrights in Fort William, but the purchaser went bankrupt and fled the country. There was a further sale in 1768 to tacksmen, 200 tons to be cut per annum and at a price of 12s. per ton. It was also converted locally, and markets were sought on the Clyde and even in Ireland, but with limited success, and the logs were left lying too long in the woods where they "grew a blewish colour," which happens today in like circumstances. About this time there were many open places in the woodlands, particularly on the south shore of the loch, then called the Gusach, and young pine was being damaged by cattle, sheep, and goats belonging to the crofters. Proposals were made to enclose the pinewoods by dyke and ditch and this was done by 1777; there are still remains of these enclosures. Pine seed, probably of local origin, was sown both near the side of the loch, and, after the tall heather had been burnt, beyond the upper margin of the woods of the Gusach. A survey of these areas in 1781 showed that on dry sites the growth of the seedlings was promising, but in the wet places there were few trees, and they did not survive long (anon., 1745-81). The estate was restored to the Camerons in 1784. At that time the natural woods were stated to extend to 10,000 acres (2500 ha.), and one pine, the Queen of the Forest, was 18 ft. (5·4 m.) in girth at 3 ft. (0·9 m.) from the ground. Nevertheless, imported timber was already being used in the district because of the difficulties of extraction from the native woods (Sinclair, 1791-9), although a little later Telford reported that the timber from them was finer and more durable than the best of Baltic timber (Stirling-Maxwell, 1910). In the early decades of the last century, there were extensive fellings in the native pinewoods (anon., 1845), and later the number of sheep in this district increased greatly, while before the end of the century the preservation of red deer caused further damage to seedlings. At the beginning of this century, contemporary records and photographs show that there were many fine stands of clean trees over 60 ft. (18 m.) in height, and with girths of up to about 18 ft. (5·4 m.) at 5 ft. (1·5 m.) from the ground. At that time only blown trees were being removed for estate purposes from the more accessible parts of the forest, and it was found that trees that had lain for a long time and become covered with heather and moss often had sound heartwood. Seedlings sometimes came up and survived on the upturned roots of windblown trees, but elsewhere the dense herbage restricted natural regeneration, while red deer did serious damage by browsing. The first fellings for a long period, for other than local purposes, were carried out before the 1914-18 War by Souness and Speirs, timber merchants, of Edinburgh. Trees were felled in Glen Mallie, the logs dragged to the river side with the aid of a winding engine, floated down the river, and rafted along Loch Arkaig. The rafts were broken up at the entrance to the River Arkaig, down which the logs were floated to the sawmill at Bunarkaig by Loch Lochy. The timber was of high quality, but the firm could not get a price commensurate with the high cost of extraction, and the operations ceased in 1912. There were again fellings during the 1914-18 War, on this occasion by Messrs Rattray, timber merchants, of Perth (Mackenzie, 1956; Stirling-Maxwell, 1910). On 27 April 1942, a serious fire started during Commando training operations. The pine was either killed or damaged over an area of about 3,000 acres, both along the loch almost to the western limit of the woods, and up Glen Mallie except for the upper and western margins. It is interesting to note that trees with ridge bark proved to be more resistant to fire than the others. The damaged timber was sold and the salvage operations were not completed when this study was made.

THE HABITAT

Climate.   Mean annual rainfall   80–90 in.   2032–2286 mm.

Temperature: Mean annual   45° F.   7·2° C.

January mean   37° F.   2·8° C.

July mean   56° F.   13·3° C.

Climatic sub-provinces (Anderson, 1955) B3a and B4b.

Topography. The pinewoods are growing on undulating slopes on the south side of Loch Arkaig and on the southern side of Glen Mallie. The slopes are only moderate but become steep where there are outcrops of rock at the upper margins of the woods. The aspect is northerly. These pinewoods are growing at lower altitudes than those in the eastern groups, the range being from 140 (42 m.) to 1100 ft. (330 m.), with scattered trees up to 1400 ft. (420 m.). The woodlands are sheltered to the south by hills over 2000 ft. (600 m.) high, from which come numerous streams which flow into Loch Arkaig, the largest being the River Mallie. There is a road up the south shore to Inver Mallie, but at one point a boss of rock makes the transport of timber very difficult, hence the use of the loch for rafting at different times.

Geology and soils. This region consists of undifferentiated schists and gneisses of the Moine series (anon., 1948 *a* and *b*). In the closing phases of the Ice Age the Arkaig glacier retreated into the higher corries, and there was a glacier in Glen Mallie (Charlesworth, 1956). The parent material of the soils is, therefore, principally morainic and fluvio-glacial laid down during this period, and in places it forms typical hummocky moraine. Along the River Mallie there is alluvium. The material in the drifts consists of gneisses, schists including mica schist, and some granite, diorite, and quartzite.

The soils on knolls and ridges, where most of the pine groups are growing, are sands and gravels showing varying degrees of podsolisation, and there may be marked iron staining in the B horizon which in places amounts to a discontinuous iron pan. The raw humus layer is also variable, and is sometimes absent, but it may be up to 6 in. (15·2 cm.) deep. Locally the texture of the soils is heavier. Where the drainage is impeded, the soils become peaty and there are bogs in the hollows.

THE FOREST

Tree species and larger shrubs. As already mentioned, the native pinewoods are restricted to the north-facing, south side of the loch, while across it on the south-facing slopes there are natural broadleaved woods which earlier were dominated by oak, but now, after felling, also contain much birch, some alder, and rowan. Only sessile oak was found in these woods. They do not contain pine except for a few trees in some of the narrow valleys made by the streams.

In the pinewoods, the Scots pine may be pure over considerable areas, but it is often mixed with birch – verrucose, pubescent, and intermediate. Birch goes farther up the slopes than pine, and the westermost limit of the woodlands is pure birch scrub. There are a few sessile oak near the shore of the loch, alder along the

River Mallie and locally in the other woods, rowan, a few aspen, and holly scattered throughout. Hazel is rare in the pinewoods, but unexpectedly there are a few hawthorn bushes, *Crataegus monogyna*, both in Glen Mallie and near the shore. Juniper is not common and is usually stunted due to grazing.

Field layer. The communities in this forest are similar to those already described in other native pinewoods, but there is more *Molinia* and bracken and the latter may form almost pure societies, while there is less *Vaccinium vitis-idaea*. Under well stocked pine, *Vaccinium/Deschampsia/Hypnaceous* moss community No. 3 is again typical, and, under more open canopy, the dry and moist *Calluna/ Vaccinium/Deschampsia* communities Nos. 5 and 6 are to be found; but there is *Molinia* in both of these and particularly in the latter, which also has a well developed moss layer including cushions of *Sphagnum*. Where the field layer was burned in 1942, the ground is still being recolonised. Under scattered pine, the community is frequently *Callunetum* No. 10, but with some bracken and *Molinia*, and as the soils become moister it grades into *Calluna/Molinia* No. 9, with vigorous, tussocky *Molinia* and some *Myrica gale*. The tops of peaty knolls may be covered by *Calluna/Trichophorum* community No. 11, and their lower slopes by *Calluna/Vaccinum/Eriophorum/Sphagnum* No. 8. As the peat becomes deeper, the communities are *Molinia/Trichophorum* No. 12, *Molinia* flush No. 16, *Eriophorum/Trichophorum/Sphagnum* No. 15, and *Juncus communis* agg. flush No. 18. The first two of these are widespread throughout the woodlands, No. 18 local but frequent, and No. 15 local within the woodlands but widespread along their upper margins. There are also a few wet bogs with *Sphagnum* community No. 19. Where birch predominates, the communities are usually *Calluna/grass/ Vaccinium/*moss and grass/moss Nos. 13 and 14.

A number of the more characteristic species listed for other pinewoods were not found at Arkaig, such as *Goodyera repens* and *Listera cordata*. There are, however, *Pyrola minor*, *P. media* and *Trientalis europaea*. *Platanthera chlorantha*, *Polygonum viviparum*, and *Orchis maculata* are to be found in grassy communities, *Gymnadenia conopsea* on dry heathery knolls, and *Tofieldia pusilla* on peaty sites. An uncommon species for pinewoods is the ivy (*Hedera helix*). In the mixed pine and birch stands there are many species more typical of broadleaved woodlands, such as *Ajuga reptans*, *Ranunculus ficaria*, *Rhinanthus minor*, *Teucrium scorodonia*, *Lonicera periclymenum*, *Lysimachia nemorum*, *Prunella vulgaris*, and *Veronica chamaedrys*.

Age structure. The age of the oldest living tree, determined by borings, was between 320 and 330 years, while a ring count on the stump of a tree felled in 1951 gave 395 years, the greatest age found in any native pinewood. There are a number of scattered trees over 300 years old, but most are between 150 and 250 years. Trees under 150 years old are not numerous, and are usually to be found in small groups or individual trees. Young regeneration under 20 years old is found along the shores of the loch and occasionally near the River Mallie.

Growth and stocking. Most of the best trees have been felled or destroyed by the fire of 1942. The tallest surviving tree measured was 70 ft. (21 m.) high, but most of the older trees do not exceed 60 ft. (18 m.), and the average is about 45 ft. (13·5 m.). The largest girth measured was 12 ft. 6 in. (3·8 m.) and the average about 5 ft. (1·5 m.). The initial rate of height growth is slow, often only 3 ft. (0·9 m.) in the first ten years, and 10 ft. (3 m.) by 20 years. Thereafter it accelerates and 40 ft. (12 m.) may be reached in 60 years. The pattern of diameter increment is similar, slow growth for the first 20 years, increasing thereafter until about 90 years, during which period 10 to 15 rings per in. (4 to 6 per cm.) may be laid down, and thereafter there is a fall off to about 25 rings or more per in. (10 per cm.).

The stocking has been profoundly modified by fire and felling during the past 50 years, and there are large bare areas at the eastern end of the forest with only scattered pine and birch, while the lower slopes of Glen Mallie, for a distance of about two and a half miles, now carry trees killed by the fire. Farther west the woodlands are less damaged, although the fire reached Comhnard Coire nan Geur-oirean; beyond that point the woodlands are undamaged. Nevertheless, there are still well stocked groups and small stands of pine, for example on the upper slopes of Glen Mallie and at its west end, south-west of Achnacarry Post Office, and south-east of Ard Nois, west of Inver Mallie.

Fauna. The woods are open to grazing animals and there is some damage to young seedlings by red deer, sheep, and cattle. Roe deer, mountain hares, rabbits, and red squirrels do little harm. Evidence of the presence of badgers was seen, and small carnivores such as the wild cat are numerous. The evidence about the pine marten is conflicting, but it may be present. Harmful birds such as the capercailzie, the black grouse, and the crossbill are not numerous. The mixed pine and birch woodlands have a rich avifauna, with such species as the chaffinch, the green finch, the bullfinch, and the coal, blue, and long-tailed tits.

Myelophilus piniperda is doing considerable damage to both young and old trees, but the other common insect pests of pine are not important.

Natural regeneration. While many of the oldest trees felled during this century or still surviving date from the seventeenth century, most of the existing older trees came up during or after the exploitation in the following century, when measures were taken to limit grazing. Most of the recent regeneration is in open places near the loch and the seedlings are only sporadic. They originated before the fire of 1942 and excaped destruction. The drier knolls with little raw humus have few seedlings where the growth of the bracken is strong, but where there are the dry and moist *Calluna/Vaccinium/Deschampsia* communities Nos. 5 and 6, with only a little bracken, there may be some pine seedlings. Most of the regeneration, however, is on moist peaty soils covered with *Calluna/Molinia* community No. 9, and the trees are growing well when not grazed, but on the *Molinia* flush community No. 16 growth is poor. As usual there are a few stunted seedlings on bog communities, such as No. 15.

GLEN LOY

Owner: The Forestry Commission.

Location: The parish of Kilmallie, Inverness-shire. Latitude, 56° 55' N.; Longitude, 5° 8' W. National Grid Reference 27 (NN)/095840. Ordnance Survey Maps: 1 in. to 1 mile, 47 (Scotland), 1947 edition; 6 in. to 1 mile, Inverness-shire 125, 1902-03 edition.

The native pinewood, Choille Phuiteachan, is about four miles up Glen Loy, a tributary valley of the River Lochy, and only two miles south of Glen Mallie woodlands at Arkaig.

GENERAL DESCRIPTION

These lands previously belonged to the Camerons of Lochiel. Little is known about the past history of the pinewoods, except that there were fellings between 1746 and 1780 while they were under the management of the Commissioners of the Forfeited Estates (anon., 1745-81). The area was acquired by the Forestry Commission in 1931.

The climate is similar to that of Arkaig. The pinewood is on undulating, north facing slopes between 300 ft. (90 m.) and 1000 ft. (300 m.) above sea-level. The underlying rocks are schists and gneisses of the Moine series, mantled with morainic and fluvio-glacial deposits. Some of the sandy knolls are freely drained and podsolised with a shallow raw humus layer, but some are peat covered. The hollows are wet and peaty.

The native woodland consists of a mixture of pine and birch of both species and intermediates, with a few oak, alder along the streams, and an occasional rowan and holly. On peaty sites there are many willow bushes, mainly *Salix atrocinera* and *S. aurita*. The pinewood has now been planted with a range of coniferous species, including Scots pine of Glen Loy origin. The field layer communities are similar to those at Arkaig, but the growth of the *Molinia* is even more luxuriant, and *Myrica gale* forms taller bushes.

Most of the pine are over 100 years, and a few over 200 years old. There are scattered trees between 60 and 100 years, but the age class 20 to 60 is poorly represented. There are small groups of younger regeneration, principally on knolls with *Callunetum* No. 10 and *Calluna/Molinia* No. 9, and with a discontinuous raw humus layer, and most of the trees are growing vigorously. The Forestry Commission has carried out experiments on natural regeneration and sowing, but without much success (Macdonald, 1952). The pine are between 40 and 45 ft. high (12 to 13·5 m.).

GLEN NEVIS

Owner: The British Aluminium Company Ltd.

Location: The parish of Kilmallie, Inverness-shire. Latitude, 56° 47′ N.; Longitude, 5° W. National Grid Reference 27 (NN)/165684. Ordnance Survey Maps: 1 in. to 1 mile, 47 (Scotland), 1947 edition; 6 in. to 1 mile, Inverness-shire 161, 1902 edition.

The native pinewood is on both sides of Glen Nevis, between Polldubh and the Eas an Tuill gorge, five to six miles from Fort William.

GENERAL DESCRIPTION

Nothing is known about the past history of this wood, but by tradition it is a natural wood and no planting has ever been done in it.

The annual rainfall is over 100 in. (254 mm.). The woodland is on both sides of a steep-sided valley, drained by the swiftly flowing River Nevis, and between 300 ft. (90 m.) and 1000 ft. (300 m.) above sea-level. The underlying rocks on the south side are Dalradian Leven schists, and on the north granite (anon., 1948 *a* and *b*). The slopes are covered with glacial deposits containing schistose and granite debris and some limestone. On the south side of the valley the soils are loamy with little leaching, but peaty in places, and, on the north, the pockets of soil amongst the rocks are more leached, and the peat is over a foot deep (30·5 cm.) in the hollows.

The woodland is dominated by the birches, of both species and intermediates, and there are alder thickets along the river. The pine is scattered through the woodlands as individual trees and small groups. There are a few sessile oak, rowan, aspen, and holly throughout the woodlands, while the willows include *S. pentandra* which is unusual in a pinewood. The field layer communities where birch predominates are those with a high proportion of grasses, particularly

Molinia, such as Nos. 9, 13, and 16. The more typical pinewood communities, Nos. 3, 5, and 6, are only found under the pine. Some species of interest are *Melica nutans, Gymnadenia conopsea, G. bifolia,* and *Rhinanthus lochabrensis.*

Most of the pine are over 120 years old, but there are a few of younger ages, including a little recent regeneration, principally on eroded slopes. Most of the pine do not exceed 40 ft. (12 m.) in height.

ARDGOUR

Owners: Practically all the native pinewoods to be described are on the Conaglen Estate, the property of Michael Mason, Esq. There are a few scattered pine in Glen Scaddle and Glen Gour which belong to Miss Catriona Maclean of Ardgour.

Location: The parish of Ardgour, Argyllshire. Latitude, 56° 48′ N.; Longitude, 5° 21′ W. National Grid Reference 17 (NM)/960713. Ordnance Survey Maps: 1 in. to 1 mile, 47 (Scotland), 1947 edition; 6 in. to 1 mile, Argyllshire 4 S.E., 5 S.W. and S.E., 9 N.W. and N.E., 10, 11 S.W., N.W. and S.E., 19, 20 N.W. and S.W., and 29 N.W. and N.E., 1900 edition.

The pinewoods are in the valleys of a tract of mountainous country bounded by Loch Eil, Loch Linnhe, Glen Gour, and Loch Shiel. The most extensive pinewoods are on the south side of Cona Glen, and in the upper reaches of the South Garvan and the Callop Rivers. There are also small groups of pine or scattered trees in natural broadleaved tree communities in Gleann Sròn a' Chreagain, the head waters of Dubh Uisge, on the extreme south-east shore of Loch Shiel, at the south-west of the lower reaches of the Callop River, and at the western extremities of the woodlands in Glens Scaddle and Gour (see Fig. 25).

HISTORY

The earliest records of pinewoods in this region that have been found date from the first half of the seventeenth century (Macfarlane, 1908). At that time there were extensive pinewoods in Cona Glen and Glen Scaddle. The pine was already being exploited, and the timber was floated down the rivers to the sea, where both sawn timber and masts were loaded on to ships. The Macleans of Ardgour were already the owners of this extensive region, and it was recorded at the end of the eighteenth century in the first *Statistical Account* that there were about one thousand acres of firs, oak, and other species of timber on the lands of Ardgour. They continued in the possession of the Macleans until about 1860 when the lands north of Glen Scaddle, now known as the Conaglen estate, were sold to Lord Morton. From that time the numbers of red deer and sheep increased, but

Fig. 25. Ardgour

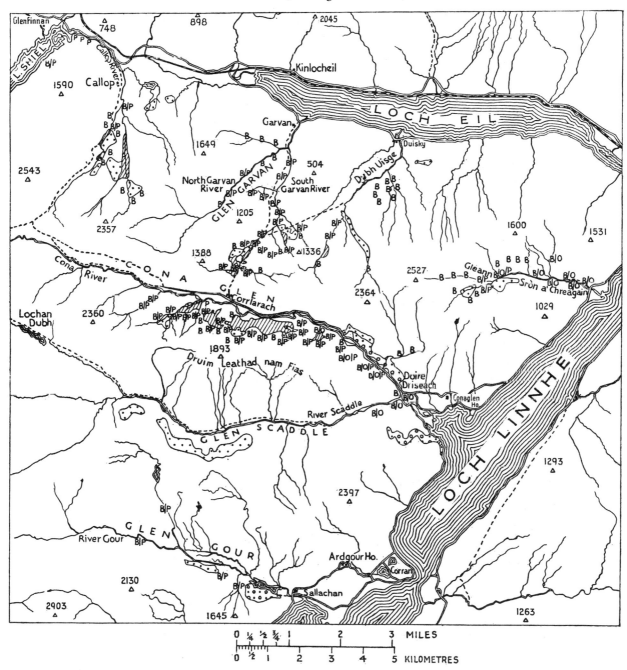

there has been practically no felling in the pinewoods for over a century. The Conaglen estate was purchased by Mr Michael Mason in 1952.

THE HABITAT

Climate. Mean annual rainfall   100 in.   2540 mm.
            Temperature: Mean annual   45° F.   7·2° C.
                            January mean   37° F.   2·8° C.
                            July mean   55° F.   12·8° C.
     Climatic sub-provinces (Anderson, 1955) C3b and C4a.

Topography. It is variable, ranging from gently undulating terrain to steep cliffs, but most of the pine is growing on moderate slopes. The pinewoods are at elevations between 200 and 1250 ft. (60 and 375 m.), but there are a few native pine below 100 ft. (30 m.), for example along the Callop River. The aspect of the woodlands is northerly.

Geology and soils. The rocks underlying the more important pinewoods are principally granulites of the Moine series on the whole felspathic, but there is a mass of intrusive gabbrodiorite above the pinewood in Cona Glen extending into Glen Scaddle, and there are thin bands of limestone and other ultrabasic rocks along the periphery of this intrusion (Drever, 1939, 1943; Phemister, 1948). The whole region is mantled with glacial deposits laid down principally in the closing phase of the Ice Age as the Eil, Cona, Scaddle, and Gour glaciers retreated up the valleys and into the corries (Charlesworth, 1956). The morainic material varies in depth in the different valleys. There is alluvium along the valley bottoms.

In the pinewoods, the soils are sandy, but the drainage is often poor and shallow peat frequently covers even the knolls. There is usually some degree of leaching. The peat is rarely deep within the woods, but at their margins it may be up to 5 ft. (1·5 m.) in depth.

THE FOREST

Tree species and larger shrubs. There are no areas of pure pine exceeding an acre (0·4 ha.) in extent, the woods being mainly a mixture of pine and birch. Most of the birches are intermediate between *B. pubescens* and *B. verrucosa*, tending to approach the former rather than the latter. There are oakwoods with some birch and ash along the shores of Loch Eil and Loch Linnhe. This community spreads up Gleann Sròn a' Chreagain and Cona Glen, and the oak mingles with the pine and birch farther up the glens (PL. IX.*a*), reaching an altitude of about 500 ft. (150 m.) on the south side of Cona Glen opposite Corrlarach. Most of the oak are *Quercus robur*. While there may have been some planting of oak on the lochsides, it is almost certain that the woodlands farther up the glens are natural, and are an interesting example of tension zones between oak, birch, and pine. The rivers are usually fringed with alder, while rowan is common throughout the pine and birchwoods, but aspen is rare. Juniper was not found, but there is holly under both pine and birch.

Field layer. *Molinia* is an important constituent of the vegetation, and *Calluna/ Molinia* No. 9 is one of the most widespread communities not only under more open pine and birch, but also in well stocked pine groups. Under the latter, however, there are patches of the more typical *Vaccinium/Deschampsia/Hypnaceous* moss No. 3, and dry and moist *Calluna/Vaccinium/Deschampsia/*moss Nos. 5 and 6. *Callunetum* No. 10 is uncommon and most of the knolls are covered with either *Calluna/Molinia* No. 9 or *Calluna/Trichophorum* No. 11. *Molinia* flush No. 16 covers large areas under scattered pine and birch and extends deep into the better stocked stands, the *Molinia* being usually dense, rank, and often tussocky in habit. Bracken is common in all these communities, particularly under tree canopy. The principal bog community is *Molinia/Trichophorum* No. 12 and not the more typical *Eriophorum/Trichophorum/Sphagnum* No. 15, but there are small areas of *Juncus communis* agg. No. 17 and *J. articulatus* No. 18. *Myrica gale* is common in most communities on wet sites. Where birch predominates, the field layer is either *Calluna/grass/Vaccinium/*moss No. 13 or grass/moss No. 14.

No unusual species were found, but it is of interest that, while there is a rich mountain flora above 2000 ft. (600 m.), it does not descend into the pinewoods, as, for example, into those of the Wester Ross Group. At South Garvan ivy is found on both pine and birch.

Age structure. Most of the Scots pine are over 140 years in age, the oldest tree, determined by a boring, being 210 and some may be still older. There are a few groups and scattered trees between 90 and 140 years, but younger trees are uncommon and are confined to the sides of streams and below cliffs.

Growth and stocking. The tallest pine measured was 70 ft. (21 m.), and the average in the better groups was 50 ft. (15 m.). The maximum girth found was 8 ft. (2·4 m.), and the average in good groups was about 7 ft. (2·1 m.). Diameter increment for the first ten years is slow, but thereafter until about 90 years it is moderately fast, six to eight rings to the inch (2·4 to 3·1 per cm.), after which it again becomes slow. There are some fine stems, particularly in South Garvan.

The stocking is irregular. While there are few close grown groups of pine, there are large tracts of mixed pine and birch that are well stocked, and, as already mentioned, with a sprinkling of oak on the lower slopes.

Fauna. Many animals graze within and around the pinewoods, including red and roe deer, sheep, and cattle, while there is a herd of about 100 feral goats which graze in summer on the high ground to the north-west of the region, and come into the Callop woods in the winter. Badgers are common, and there are both wild and feral cats, foxes, and other small carnivores. There may also be a few pine martens, but this requires confirmation. There are the usual avian predators including the golden eagle. A few black grouse and crossbills frequent the woods, but there are no capercailzie. There are many small insectivorous birds. The adder is commoner than in other western pinewoods.

The common insects of pine are present but are not doing any damage.

Natural regeneration. There is no current natural regeneration except for a few seedlings on disturbed soils in open places, such as on roadsides, river banks, and rocky sites, and they are generally grazed while still young.

PLATE XI

FOEMS OF JUNIPER

a) Rothiemurchus, columnar habit, height 13 ft. (3·9 m.).

b) Ballochbuie, bushy habit, height 5 ft. (1·5 m.), with a holly in the foreground.

CHAPTER 8

THE STRATH GLASS GROUP OF NATIVE PINEWOODS

I N THIS chapter are described four surviving native pinewoods in the tributary valleys of Strath Glass and in its upper reaches: Glen Strathfarrar, Glen Cannich, Glen Affric, and Guisachan including Cougie. From the fifteenth until the beginning of this century, this region, south of Strathfarrar, was part of the lands of the Chisholms. They supported the Stewart cause in 1715 and 1745 and their lands were forfeited to the Crown, being administered by the Commissioners appointed for that purpose, but a short time afterwards the property was purchased on behalf of the family and reverted to the Chisholms (Mackenzie, 1891). Strathfarrar has been Lovat property for several centuries.

A map in Blaeu's *Atlas* (1654), based on information collected probably in the early decades of the seventeenth century, shows woodlands in Strathfarrar, Glen Cannich, Glen Affric, Guisachan and Cougie. The information in the *Geographical Collections relating to Scotland* (Macfarlane, 1908) throws no light on these woodlands, but there is no doubt that they contained pine, because it is recorded that when Cromwell built the Citadel in Inverness between 1652 and 1657 the fir timber came from Strath Glass and the oak planks and beams from England (anon., 1886). Further light is shed on these woods by the information recorded on Avery's Map, dated 1725-30. In Glen Cannich, woods of pine and birch are shown on the south side of the glen near the west end of Loch Mullardoch to near Cannich, and farther east the woods were of birch. There were large, fine pine particularly on the south shores of Loch Mullardoch. There were also woods on the north side and those between Lochs Sealbhanach and Craskie were of pine and birch. In Glen Affric, the woods contained very large pine and birch on both the north and south sides of Lochs Affric and Beneveian (Beinn a' Mheard Loin), and again birchwoods at the lower altitudes towards Strath Glass. At the end of the eighteenth century, logs were being floated down the Rivers Cannich and Glass (Sinclair, 1791-9), and there was a sawmill above the Kilmorack Falls on the River Beauly which consisted of seven parallel saws driven by four wheels. Horses were used to carry the boards past the falls, from the foot of which they were again floated in rafts down the river to a place near Kirkhill (Robertson, 1808). In 1801 and 1810, tenants were cleared from Chisholm property in Strath Glass so that sheep runs could be formed, and many of the displaced clansmen crossed the Atlantic to settle in Cape Breton, Antogonish, and Glengarry in eastern Canada (Mackenzie, 1891). The expansion in the sheep population restricted natural regeneration, particularly of pine, and there was burning of the woodlands to improve the pasture, for example twelve miles of pine, birch and oak in Strathfarrar (Stuart, 1848). Later in the last century, the preservation of red deer became important in this tract of country. In recent years it has been the scene of hydro-electric developments which have led to felling in the woods and the raising of the levels in some of the lochs, while in some of the glens the Forestry Commission has begun planting and is extending this work. There was a serious fire after the last war in the woodlands south-east of Loch Mullardoch in Glen Cannich which killed the pine, and these trees have been felled.

GLEN AFFRIC

Owner: The Forestry Commission. It was acquired in 1951.

Location: The parish of Kilmorack, Inverness-shire. Latitude, 57° 15′ N. Longitude, 4° 50′ to 5° 4′ W. National Grid Reference 28 (NH)/145225 to 28 (NH)/300285. Ordnance Survey Maps: 1 in. to 1 mile, 36 and 37 (Scotland), 1947 edition; 6 in. to 1 mile, Inverness-shire 27, 37, 38, 39 and 51, 1904 edition.

The woodlands stretch westwards from Strath Glass on both sides of Glen Affric from the Badger Falls in the east to within a mile from the western end of Loch Affric (see Fig. 26). Since the study was made, hydro-electric developments have led to the raising of the level of Loch Beneveian by twenty feet (6 m.), and some trees have been felled along the shores.

HISTORY

See introduction to this chapter.

THE HABITAT

Climate.   Mean annual rainfall   70 in.   1778 mm.
           Temperature: Mean annual   43° F.   6·1° C.
                          January mean   35° F.   1·7° C.
                          July mean   54° F.   12·2° C.
        Climatic sub-province (Anderson, 1955) B3a and B4b.

Topography. The woodlands are in a valley running E.N.E. and W.S.W. which is relatively broad with moderate, hummocky slopes above Lochs Beneveian and Affric, becoming steeper to the east. Swiftly moving streams tumble down the slopes into the river and lochs. While there are many pine on the north side of the valley, particularly on the north shore of Loch Affric and to the northeast of Loch Beneveian, most of the woods with pine in them are on the south side and with a northerly aspect. The range in altitude of the woods is from 600 to 1500 ft. above sea-level (180 to 450 m.), with a few scattered trees up to 1700 ft. (510 m.). While there is little difference in the absolute limit reached by the pine and birch, the latter often forms the upper fringe. The valley is encircled and sheltered on the north and west by hills over 2000 ft. high (600 m.).

Geology and soils. The underlying rocks belong to the Moine series. The district has not yet been surveyed by the Geological Survey, but observations

FIG. 26. Glen Affric, Guisachan and Cougie

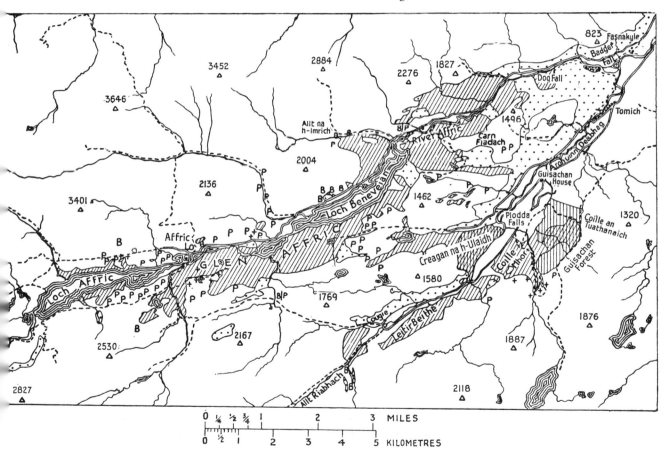

show that the rocks are much foliated schists, including soft mica schist, and gneisses. The slopes are mantled with glacial drifts which often form characteristic hummocky moraines. These consist of sand and gravel, with fragments of both schist and gneiss and often with micaceous material. Alluvium is restricted to the banks of the river, and in places there is some boulder clay at the bottom of the valley.

Many of the better stocked stands of pine are growing on knolls with deep, well drained, sandy and gravelly soils, often covered with a deep layer of litter and raw humus and with a definite leached horizon. As the drainage deteriorates on flatter ground, the depth of peat increases, and the scattered pine become more and more stunted. Within the woods and beyond their margins there are treeless and badly aerated bogs.

THE FOREST

Tree species and larger shrubs. As in other western woodlands there is a varying proportion of Scots pine and birch (PL. VIII.*a*). There are almost pure pine stands on the south-east shore of Loch Affric, and, until it was felled recently, there was a similar stand near the new hydro-electric dam. Elsewhere, the pine is in groups or single trees amongst the birch which is generally much younger than the pine and appears to have spread in recent decades. At the eastern end of the glen, there are extensive areas of pure birch of greater age, and two oaks were found there, both intermediate in characteristics between pedunculate and sessile. There are also considerable tracts of scattered pine with little or no birch. The birch consists both of *Betula verrucosa* and *B. pubescens*, but the former tends to predominate and there are also intermediates. There is alder and a little *Salix atrocinerea* along the streams, and the latter is growing also on some of the bogs. Rowan is common, particularly in the birchwoods. Juniper is rare; some is of the columnar form.

Field layer. Under the better stocked pine stands and groups, the communities are moist moss No. 2, *Vaccinium*/*Deschampsia*/*Hypnaceous* moss No. 3, and the dry and moist *Calluna*/*Vaccinium*/*Deschampsia* moss Nos. 5 and 6, the mosses, including *Sphagnum*, being luxuriant and sometimes in cushions, particularly in No. 6. The latter community is also found under more open pine but sometimes with few *Vaccinium* spp., and the community tends towards *Callunetum* No. 10. Under scattered pine, *Calluna*/*Trichophorum* No. 11 sometimes caps the knolls, with *Calluna*/*Molinia* No. 9 on their slopes, and *Calluna*/*Vaccinium*/*Eriophorum*/*Sphagnum* No. 8 as the drainage deteriorates. As the peat increases in depth and trees become few, the typical communities are *Molinia*/*Trichophorum* No. 12, *Molinia* flush No. 16, *Eriophorum/Trichophorum/Sphagnum* bog No. 15, with *Sphagnum* spp. bog No. 19, and *Juncus communis* agg. flush No. 17. Where birch predominates, communities Nos. 3, 5, and 6 are also found with increasing amounts of *Molinia* as the soils become wetter, but on the better loams *Calluna/grass/Vaccinium/moss* No. 13 and grass/moss No. 14 are typical.

Among the less common plants, there is a little *Pyrola media* and *P. minor*. A number of mountain species, such as *Saxifraga oppositifolia* and *Lycopodium alpinum*, extend down into the open pinewoods beside Loch Affric at an altitude of 800 ft. (240 m.). The woodlands, particularly south-east of Achagate, have a rich moss flora which includes *Antitrichia curtipendula*, *Hookeria lucens*, and *Hedwigia ciliata* which have not been found in other native pinewoods.

Age structure. The woods are uneven-aged by groups. There are few very old trees but many over about 140. The predominant age class, however, is between 80 and 140 years. There are a few groups between 40 and 10 years, for example on upturned roots, and some current regeneration.

Growth and stocking. The height of the pine ranges up to 60 ft. (18 m.), but the mean of the older trees is about 45 ft. (13·5 m.). The maximum measured girth was 8 ft. (2·4 m.) and the mean about 5 ft. (1·5 m.).

The stocking is irregular. The stands of pine, particularly north and south of Loch Affric, are well stocked, and the groups of pine in the open irregularly stocked woods of birch and pine are also dense. At the other extreme there are large areas of scattered pine. The woodlands dominated by birch are generally well stocked.

Fauna. On the Affric estate, extending to about 30,000 acres (12,000 ha.), there were about 1200 red deer, 24 roe deer, about 100 cattle, and 300 sheep in 1951-2, according to the head keeper. Many of these animals graze in the woods during the winter. There are wild cats and foxes and a few badgers, but pine martens have not been seen for many years. The usual avian predators frequent the woods, especially buzzards. There are a few capercailzie and some black grouse, as well as many small insectivorous birds.

Myelophilus piniperda is doing some damage to the pine.

Natural regeneration. There are a few pine seedlings in open places, particularly beside streams and on upturned stumps, in communities rich in *Calluna*, such as Nos. 6, 9, 10, and 11. They are generally healthy but grazed. There is also young regeneration on bogs, particularly in *Eriophorum/Trichophorum/Sphagnum* community No. 15. These trees are yellow and stunted in appearance and do not survive for long, no doubt due to the conditions of poor aeration already mentioned.

GLEN CANNICH

Owners: The Forestry Commission, east of Lubguish Croft on the River
   Cannich. The North of Scotland Hydro-Electric Board west thereof.
   Since the study was made the Board has sold the land to various owners.
Location: The parish of Kilmorack, Inverness-shire east of Allt Taige and Allt
   Lùb nam Meann which flow into Loch Mullardoch. The parish of Kintail,
   Ross and Cromarty west of these streams. Latitude, 57° 20′ to 57° 22′ N.;
   Longitude, 4° 49′ to 5° 3′ W. National Grid Reference 28 (NH)/160300
   to 28 (NH)/312325. Ordnance Survey Maps: 1 in. to 1 mile, 36 and 37
   (Scotland), 1947 edition; 6 in. to 1 mile, Inverness-shire 26 and 27, and
   Ross and Cromarty 120, 1904 edition.

The pinewoods are principally on the south side of Glen Cannich from near
Strath Glass on the east to almost the west end of Loch Mullardoch. On the
north side, there is a pine stand one to one and and a half miles (1·6 to 2·4 km.)
up the Liatrie Burn, and a few scattered trees farther east. They must be the
descendants of the trees in the extensive woodlands that were growing there at
the beginning of the eighteenth century (Avery, 1725-30). Since the study was
made, the level of Loch Mullardoch has been raised from 705 ft. (212 m.) to
817 ft. (245 m.) above sea-level for hydro-electric purposes, and the area of the

FIG. 27.   Glen Cannich

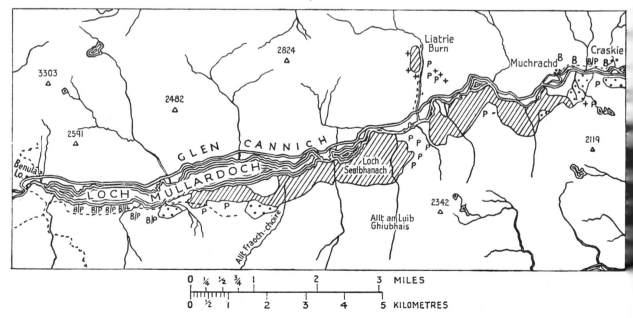

wood on the south side of the loch has been correspondingly reduced from that shown on the map (see Fig. 27).

(see Fig. 27)

HISTORY

See introduction to this chapter.

THE HABITAT

Climate. Mean annual rainfall 70 in. 1778 mm.

Temperature: Mean annual 43° F. 6·1° C.

January mean 35° F. 1·7° C.

July mean 54° F. 12·2° C.

Climatic sub-province (Anderson, 1955) B3a.

Topography. Glen Cannich runs more or less east and west. The lower slopes are only moderately steep but they become steeper at the higher altitudes, and they are less regularly hummocky than in Glen Affric, except south of Loch Mullardoch. As already mentioned, most of the surviving woodlands are on the south side of the glen and thus have a northerly aspect; their range in altitude is from 500 to 1500 ft. (150 to 450 m.), with a few scattered pine up to 1700 ft. (510 m.). On both sides of the glen, there are sheltering hills rising from 2000 to 3000 ft. (600 to 900 m.) above sea-level.

Geology and soils. The underlying rocks are of the Moine series. The schists are less micaceous than in Glen Affric and there are pelitic gneisses. The slopes are covered with moraines over 20 ft. (6 m.) deep in places, and there is some boulder clay in the valley bottoms, and alluvium along the streams (anon., 1913).

The parent material of the soils is mainly sands and gravels derived from the schists and gneisses, The knolls and ridges on which the best pine are growing are freely drained, and the soils show podsolisation. In the hollows and flatter ground, the soils are wet and peaty, but the extent of bog is less than in Glen Affric.

THE FOREST

Tree species and larger shrubs. At the eastern end of the glen, birch is the principal species, and there are only scattered pine amongst it. West of the point where the public road crosses the River Cannich to the north side, pine dominates the woods but there are still small groups of birch. There are both *Betula verrucosa* and *B. pubescens* as well as intermediates in the woodlands, with an occasional rowan, while alder fringes the streams. The shrubs consist of a few holly bushes, and low, scrubby juniper.

Field layer. The communities are the same as in Glen Affric.

Of the less common species there are a few plants of *Moneses uniflora* as well as *Pyrola media* and *P. minor*, and one or two colonies of *Saxifraga oppositifolia*. *Arctous alpina* was found with *Arctostaphylos uva-ursi* on rocky knolls covered with *Calluna*. Of the mosses there is much *Rhacomitrium lanuginosum* on rocky sites throughout the woods.

Age structure. Most of the pine are between 90 and 150 years old. The oldest trees found were 180 years but there may be still older trees. There are some groups of trees between 40 and 90 years, with a few still younger.

Growth and stocking. Some of the pine are well grown and clean with heights up to 70 ft. (21 m.), and the average is about 45 ft. (13·5 m.). The maximum girth at breast height is 7 ft. (2·1 m.), and the average about 4 ft. (1·2 m.).

Some of the stands in which pine predominates are well stocked and in places dense. In most of the woodlands where pine is mixed with birch, the stocking is irregular but with some well stocked groups. As already mentioned, fire has damaged the woodlands south of Loch Mullardoch.

Fauna. There are many red deer, a few roe, and also sheep in or near the woodlands. The other fauna, including the insect pests, is the same as in Glen Affric.

Natural regeneration. There has been a little more regeneration during the past few years than in Glen Affric. The seedlings, never numerous, come up in open places at the margins of the woods, and amongst *Callunetum* No. 10, and also in communities Nos. 9, 11, and 15. There are also pine seedlings on the *Rhacomitrium*-rich sites already mentioned. The seedlings grow best in the dry *Callunetum* and poorest in the wet and bog communities. When they grow above the *Calluna*, they are almost always grazed so that few develop into trees.

GLEN STRATHFARRAR

Owner: The Lord Lovat.

Location: The parish of Kilmorack, Inverness-shire. Latitude, 57° 24′ to 57° 25′ N.; Longitude, 4° 43′ to 5° 3′ W. National Grid Reference 28 (NH)/170373 to 28 (NH)/370390. Ordnance Survey Maps: 1 in. to 1 mile, 36 and 37 (Scotland), 1947 edition; 6 in. to 1 mile, Inverness-shire 7, 15, 16 and 17, 1903-04 editions.

The woodlands stretch westwards along Glen Strathfarrar from Struy Bridge in Strath Glass, and those considered to be genuinely native are between Culligran Falls in the east and Uisge Misgeach in the west, with scattered trees on the south shores of Loch Monar. There are four principal native woodlands: Culligran Wood, a birchwood with a few groups of pine it in; Coille Gharbh, predominantly of pine; Inchvuilt Wood, consisting of birch and pine, some of the latter having been felled in recent years; and Uisge Misgeach, with birch and pine (see Fig. 28).

The old woodland at Struy at the mouth of the glen has been considered to be a native pinewood. It contains well grown and regularly stocked Scots pine about 130 years old with a few European larch of similar age. Morphologically the pine are of native type. The field layer communities, however, are not typical of a native pinewood, being rich in herb species such as *Mercurialis perennis*, *Prunella vulgaris*, and *Ranunculus ficaria*, and this along with the presence of larch suggests that it is a planted wood and that the site previously carried broadleaved species.

HISTORY

See introduction to this chapter.

THE HABITAT

Climate.   Mean annual rainfall   70 in.   1778 mm.
               Temperature: Mean annual   43° F.   6·1° C.
                             January mean   35° F.   1·7° C.
                             July mean   54° F.   12·2° C.
               Climatic sub-provinces (Anderson, 1955) B2b and B3a.

Topography. West of Culligran Falls, the River Farrar meanders through alluvial flats which extend as far as Broulin Lodge. The woodlands are growing on moderate slopes, sometimes steep, and the terrain is broken and rocky in places. The range in altitude is 250 to 1450 ft. (75 to 435 m.), and woodlands in which pine predominates have a northerly aspect. The valley is sheltered by hills to the

FIG. 28.   Glen Strathfarrar

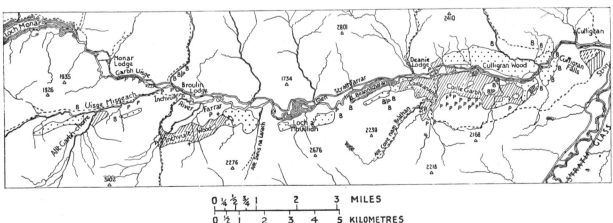

north, west and south, culminating in Sgurr na Lapaich, 3773 ft. (1132 m.) high.

Geology and soils. The underlying rocks are a complex of Moine siliceous granulites and mica schists together with hornblende gneiss; there are some thin bands of marble and other rocks rich in lime and magnesia at their margins (anon., 1913*b*; Phemister, 1948). These more basic rocks, although the area of their outcrop is small, have probably influenced the glacial parent material of the soils and may explain in part the amount of birch in some of the woods. The slopes are covered with moraines, hummocky at the lower elevations, laid down as the Farrar–Monar glacier retreated at the end of the Ice Age (Charlesworth, 1956).

The soils on knolls and ridges where the better pine are growing are well drained sands and gravels, often with a deep litter and humus layer, but not usually strongly podsolised. Elsewhere, there is often a covering of peat, usually not more than a foot deep (·3 m.) where there are trees, but deeper in clearings and at the margins of the woodlands.

THE FOREST

Tree species and larger shrubs. In Coille Gharbh, Scots pine is the principal species in most of the woodlands, but sometimes fringed with birch (PL. VIII.*b*), and there are birch stands at both the eastern and western extremities. In Inchvuilt, the pattern was similar until the felling of some of the pine after the last war, and it is now a varying mixture of pine and birch by groups. In both these woods some small areas have been damaged recently by fire. Culligran Wood is principally of birch with pine stands at its south-west boundary and scattered groups elsewhere. The birch consists of *Betula verrucosa*, *B. pubescens*, and intermediates. There are a few pedunculate oak beside the river. There is more aspen than is usual for a Scottish native woodland; as elsewhere rowan is frequent, and there is alder along the streams. The shrubs include holly and juniper, which are commoner under birch than pine.

Field layer. The communities associated with the pine and birch are the same as in Glen Affric, but the extent of the bog communities is less, although the *Juncus communis* agg. community No. 17 covers considerable areas of marshy land along the river.

The less common species include *Pyrola media*, *Moneses uniflora*, *Trientalis europaea*, and *Lycopodium annotinum*, and there is more *Goodyera repens* than in other northern and western pinewoods.

Age structure. As in other forests, the age structure is irregular and the greatest range in age of the pine is in Coille Gharbh. The maximum age in this woodland is about 300 years and most of the trees are between 140 and 200 years old. There are groups between 60 and 140 years but very few young trees. In Inchvuilt, the maximum age is about 200 years and most are over 130.

Growth and stocking. The average growth of the pine is good, particularly in Coille Gharbh, but there are no outstandingly good groups as in Cannich. In the former, the maximum height is about 60 ft. (18 m.) and the average about 45 ft. (13·5 m.), the heights being about 5 ft. (1·5 m.) less in the other woods. The maximum girth attained is about 8 ft. (2·4 m.) and the average about 6 ft. (1·8 m.). Diameter growth is slow for the first thirty to forty years, over 20 rings to the inch (8 per cm.), then increasing to eight or nine rings (3·1 to 3·5 per cm.) until about 110 years, after which it decreases.

Coille Gharbh is moderately well stocked, mostly over 50 per cent. canopy, with still better stocked groups (PL. VIII.*b*), but there are only scattered pine on the peat-covered depression round Loch an Airidh Fhraoich. The stocking in Inchvuilt was similar before the recent felling which has left considerable gaps.

Fauna. There are red deer and a few roe as well as some cattle and a large sheep stock in the woods and on the adjoining hills. The fauna, including the insect pests, is similar to that in Glen Affric.

Natural regeneration. There are scattered pine seedlings on margins and under open pinewood, principally amongst the dry and moist *Calluna/Vaccinium/Deschampsia*/moss communities Nos. 5 and 6, *Calluna/Trichophorum* No. 11 and *Calluna/Molinia* No. 9, and also on the treeless bogs. On all sites, most of the seedlings are grazed before they reach two feet (·6 m.) in height.

GUISACHAN AND COUGIE

Owners: The Guisachan estate was acquired by the Forestry Commission in 1935. It includes the two principal native pinewoods, Coille an Tuathanaich and Coille Mhòr, and also the eastern part of Coille na h-Ulaidh and the north-eastern part of Lcitir Beithe. The Cougie estate is owned by Lt.-Col. A. H. Wilkie. On it are the remainders of the two last-named woods and those to the south-west.

Location: The parish of Kintarlity and Convinth, Inverness-shire. Latitude, 57° 15′ to 57° 16′ N.; Longitude, 4° 49′ to 4° 56′ W. National Grid Reference 28 (NH)/230200 to 28 (NH)/298235. Ordnance Survey Maps: 1 in. to 1 mile, 36 and 37 (Scotland), 1947 edition; 6 in. to 1 mile, Inverness-shire 39, 51 and 52, 1904 edition.

The woodlands are in the valley of Amhuinn Deabhag at the south-west extremity of Strath Glass, and two and a half to six miles (4·0 to 9·6 km.) south-west of the village of Tomich (see Fig. 26.)

HISTORY

See introduction to this chapter.

Since 1948 the Forestry Commission has done planting in the open places of Coille an Tuathanaich and on its margins, using species other than Scots pine. The natural regeneration of Scots pine west of Plodda Falls, now up to about 50 years old, may be in part from older Scots pine trees above the Falls. These pine, mixed with larch and other conifers, were almost certainly planted.

THE HABITAT

Climate.	Mean annual rainfall		50 in.	1270 mm.
	Temperature:	Mean annual	43° F.	6·1° C.
		January mean	35° F.	1·7° C.
		July mean	54° F.	12·2° C.

Climatic sub-province (Anderson, 1955) B2b.

Topography. The pinewoods are growing in the valleys of the Amhuinn Deabhag and its tributaries. The slopes are undulating, but there is a deep gorge in Coille Mhòr cut by Eas Socach. The range in altitude of the woods is from 700 to 1400 ft. (210 to 420 m.), and the aspects are principally from north-east to north-west.

Geology and soils. The Moine series rocks have not yet been surveyed by the Geological Survey, but observations show that they are schists and gneisses as in Glen Affric. The lower slopes are covered with deep moraines which are shallower and more stony higher up.

The soils are similar to those in Glen Affric.

THE FOREST

Tree species and larger shrubs. The woodlands are a mixture of pine and birch. Over large areas the mixture is intimate, but there are tracts, often of considerable extent, where each species is almost pure, the largest pure pine stands being in Coille Mhòr. The birches consist of both *Betula verrucosa* and *B. pubescens* and many intermediates. The other broadleaved species are alder along the streams, and rowan throughout the woods. Juniper is only common in Cougie and is usually heavily grazed. As already mentioned, there has been considerable recent planting in Coille an Tuathanaich.

Field layer. The communities are the same as in Glen Affric, but there are fewer unusual species.

Age structure. Most of the trees are over 130 years old and the oldest, sometimes over 200 years, are in Coille Mhòr and Leitir Beithe. Younger trees are few and are to be found principally at the south-west corner of Coille Mhòr and west of Plodda Falls, where there is also some young regeneration.

Growth and stocking. The tallest pine are about 60 ft. (18 m.) in height, and the average about 45 ft. (13·5 m.). The largest girth found was over 11 ft. (3·3 m.), and the average is about 4 ft. (1·2 m.).

Some of the pure pine groups and stands are dense, and the parts of the woodlands that are mixed are moderately well stocked.

Fauna. Shortly after acquiring Guisachan, the Forestry Commission erected a deer fence to enclose their land, although deer could still come into Creagan na h-Ulaidh until recently from across the river. Since that time, therefore, grazing has been restricted. There is a large sheep stock, as well as red deer, in the Cougie Woods. The fauna, including insect pests, is similar to that in Glen Affric.

Natural regeneration. There has been a certain amount of natural regeneration of pine in recent times at Guisachan. The area west of Plodda Falls has been mentioned already where there are some quite dense patches of pine regeneration of varying ages up to 50 years, but the parent trees are probably planted. It has come up on podsolised sands and gravels with up to 6 in. (15·2 cm.) of litter and raw humus and amongst *Calluna/Vaccinium/Deschampsia/*moss community No. 5, and *Callunetum* No. 10. During the past ten years scattered seedlings came up beyond the south margin of Coille Mhòr, principally on *Callunetum* No. 10, but these were burned. The regeneration suffers little from grazing at Guisachan.

CHAPTER 9

THE WESTER ROSS GROUP OF NATIVE PINEWOODS

THERE ARE four native pinewoods in this group, Loch Maree, Coulin, Achnashellach, and Shieldaig. All are relatively near each other in a region with a marked oceanic climate and a high rainfall, Shieldaig being on a sea loch. Scots pine when planted under such conditions often shows poor growth and tends to lose its needles after one or two years, hence it is of interest that the native pine has not only survived but has remained healthy through successful generations.

The surviving native pinewoods are small in area, and they are usually surrounded by extensive tracts of climatic peat moorland, dominated either by *Eriophorum* or *Trichophorum*. The present pinewoods were almost certainly more extensive in earlier historical times, for example they probably stretched from Loch Maree towards Achnashellach, while the southern shores of Upper Loch Torridon may have been partly pine forest.

In this region there are still natural birchwoods, with or without oak, for example on the north shores of Loch Maree and at Talladale on its south side, and it is known that these woodlands were more extensive over three centuries ago.

LOCH MAREE

Owner: Major C. Greig of Grudie. The islands on Loch Maree belong to various owners including the Forestry Commission. Since the date of the survey, the Nature Conservancy has acquired land at the south-east of Loch Maree, including the principal native pinewood, the whole forming the Beinn Eighe Nature Reserve.

Location: The parish of Gairloch, Ross and Cromarty. Latitude, 57° 37' to 57° 42' N.; Longitude, 5° 21' to 5° 32' W. National Grid Reference 28 (NH)/010609 to 18 (NG)/897735. Ordnance Survey Maps: 1 in. to 1 mile, 26 (Scotland), 1947 edition; 6 in. to 1 mile, Ross and Cromarty, 58, 70 and 71, 1905 edition.

The most important pinewood is Coille na Glas-leitire at the south-east end of

FIG. 29. Loch Maree

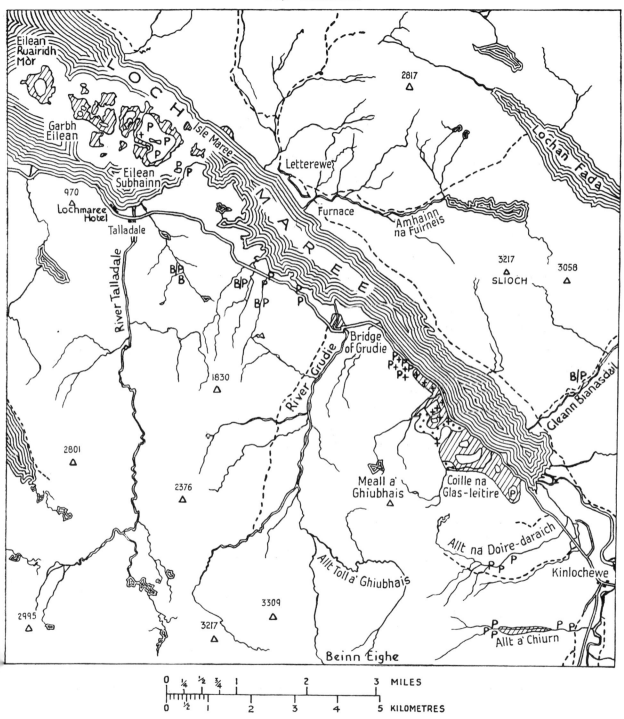

Loch Maree, and there are scattered pine trees along the south shore as far as Talladale. There are also some native pine along Allt na Doire-daraich, a side valley south-west of the loch, and in Allt a' Chiurn south of Kinlochewe. Native Scots pine are growing on most of the twenty-four islands, the largest woods being on Eilean Sùbhainn, Garbh Eilean, and Eilean Ruairidh Mòr. There is also a small group of pine on the rocky north shore about one mile north-west of Letterewe, and an occasional tree in Gleann Bianasdail (see Fig. 29).

HISTORY

The lands in the neighbourhood of Loch Maree belonged to the Mackenzies of Gairloch from early times; there is a record of a grant from the Crown to Hector Roy Mackenzie in 1494 (Dixon, 1886). The earliest known reference to the woods at Loch Maree only date, however, from about 1600, when a traveller, probably Timothy Pont, described this district, some of his information being used in the preparation of Blaeu's *Atlas*. He called Loch Maree "fresh Loch Ewe" or the "inner Loch Ewe" to distinguish it from the salt water Loch Ewe which is connected with Loch Maree by the River Ewe. At that time, there were dense and extensive woods along the south shore of Loch Maree, consisting of pine, birch, oak, ash, aspen, elm, and holly, described as some of the best woods in the west of Scotland, and already known at that time as Glas-leitire. In some places there were: "fair and beautifull fyrrs [pines] of 60, 70 and 80 foot of good and serviceable timmer for masts and raes, in other places ar great plentie of excellent great oakes, whaer may sawing out planks of 4 sumtyms 5 foot broad" (Blaeu, 1654; Macfarlane, 1908). The Letterewe woods on the north side of the loch, now mainly of birch, with a few oak, were formerly much more extensive, and supplied the wood for some of the earliest large-scale iron works in the Highlands. About 1607, Sir George Hay, who later became High Chancellor of Scotland and Earl of Kinnoull, obtained the woods of Letterewe from Mackenzie of Kintail to provide charcoal for the smelting of iron. There may have been an iron mill at Fasagh near the mouth of Gleann Bianasdail before that time, but Hay erected large works at Furnace on the north side of the loch and probably also near Talladale on the south shore, while a little later another mill was built at the "Red Smiddy" on the River Ewe. Experienced workers were brought from the north of England. Particularly at Furnace, operations were on a large scale, and continued for about sixty years. A wide range of different articles were made, including cannon, and the whole of Scotland was supplied from this source at that time (*Acts of Parliament*, VOL. IV, p. 515; Dixon, 1886; Macadam, 1887). Probably birch and oak were the principal species used for the production of

PLATE XII

INTERESTING SPECIES IN NATIVE PINEWOODS

a) *Goodyera repens.*

b) *Ramischia (Pyrola) secunda.*

c) *Saxifraga aizoides.*

d) *Lycopodium annotinum.*

charcoal, but this work and the increased population no doubt resulted in heavy demands on the local pinewoods. The first reference to the pine on the islands of Loch Maree was in the first *Statistical Account* at the end of the eighteenth century, and pine has persisted on them and from time to time has regenerated. The largest island, Eilean Sùbhainn, is unusual, because there is a small loch on it which in turn has a little island. There was once an old Scots pine on it, and there is a tradition that fairies assembled under this tree. To turn back to natural history, however, the osprey nested at one time in its crown (Dixon, 1886; Mackenzie, 1922). Most of the pine on this island were destroyed by fire during the 1939-45 War. Queen Victoria (1884) visited Loch Maree in 1877 and referred to the Scots pine "twisted with head and stem like a stone-pine." In a report on the Forests of Ross-shire in 1885 (Gunn, 1885), the bluish tinge of the needles of the native pine on the south shore of the loch was commented upon, and at that time cones were collected from these trees and plants raised in a home nursery. Natural oak as well as birch were then growing in the Letterewe woods on the north side of the loch as well as at Talladale on the south. After the 1914-18 War, the Forestry Commission acquired land at the northern end of the loch, including the island Ruairidh Mor. There was felling in Coille na Glas-leitire during the 1939-45 War, but, on the evidence of Blaeu's *Atlas* (1654), its present boundaries are similar to what they were three hundred years ago.

THE HABITAT

Climate.	Mean annual rainfall:		
	Coille na Glas-leitire	70-80 in.	1778-2032 mm.
	The islands	60 in.	1524 mm.
Temperature:	Mean annual	45° F.	7·2° C.
	January mean	38° F.	3·3° C.
	July mean	56° F.	13·3° C.

Climatic sub-province (Anderson, 1955) B3a.

Topography. The pinewood of Coille na Glas-leitire is on moderately steep slopes rising from 32 ft. (9·6 m.) on the shores of Loch Maree to the cliffs at about 1250 ft. (375 m.) on Meall a' Ghiubhais, which means the rounded hill of the pine. The wood is divided by a narrow gorge and the aspect is north-easterly. The islands are gently undulating, and, although their altitude is low, they are exposed to the north-west.

Geology and soils. Glas-leitire is on Lower Cambrian basal quartzite and pipe-rock, the latter named from its worm-casts. The edges of the woodland spread on to pre-Cambrian Torridonian sandstone of the Applecross Group which also

o

forms the islands (Phemister, 1948). The underlying rocks are covered with morainic material which is only deep on the lower slopes and with peat bogs.

The soils on the more freely drained knolls and ridges are sands and gravels, often dark coloured, and in places heavily leached; there may be a compacted layer in the B horizon. A large part of the wood is poorly drained and covered with peat of varying depth, culminating in deep bogs, some convex and already described by Tansley (1949).

THE FOREST

Tree species and larger shrubs. In Glas-leitire, there is much birch associated with the pine, particularly in the centre of the wood (PL. III), but pine predominates in the southerly third of the wood, where there was felling in the last war, and on the lower slopes towards the northern end of the wood. Most of the birch are intermediate between verrucose and pubescent, but the majority have more verrucose than pubescent characters. There are a few oak in this wood, both pedunculate and sessile, and also intermediates. Alder is found along the streams and in the wetter birchwoods, rowan varies in amount from occasional to frequent, but aspen is rare. There is some holly and a few stunted juniper bushes. It is interesting to find *Salix herbacea* on wet screes. There are scattered pine east of Talladale, but the woods there consist mainly of oak and birch. Near the road the oak may have been planted, but the upper part of the wood appears to be semi-natural and consists of both species and intermediates. On the islands, Scots pine is the principal species; there is little birch, but more holly and juniper than in Glas-leitire, the juniper sometimes attaining 15 ft. (4·5 m.) in height.

Field layer. The communities are similar to those already described for the woodlands in the Great Glen Group, *Molinia* being a prominent constituent, but there is more *Nardus stricta* than usual. Under pine of varying stocking, there are small patches of *Vaccinium/Deschampsia/Hypnaceous* moss community No. 3, the dry and moist *Calluna/Vaccinium/Deschampsia/*moss communities Nos. 5 and 6, the latter with a well developed moss layer including *Sphagnum* spp., and *Calluna/ Molinia* No. 9 which spreads even on to knolls. Locally there is a little bracken in these communities. Under more open woodland and with decreasing natural drainage, the following communities are found: *Callunetum* No. 10 with an unusually deep moss layer and some bracken; moist *Calluna/Vaccinium/Erio- phorum/Sphagnum* No. 8; *Calluna/Trichophorum* No. 11; and *Molinia/Trichophorum* No. 12. In the open and under scattered pine, there are a number of flush and bog communities, such as *Molinia* flush No. 16, *Juncus communis* agg. flush No. 17, and *Eriophorum/Trichophorum/Sphagnum* No. 15, with local pools of *Sphagnum* No. 19.

Where birch predominates, in addition to communities Nos. 6, 8, 9 and 16 mentioned above, there are also *Calluna/grass/Vaccinium/*moss No. 13, and grass/moss No. 14.

Ivy (*Hedera helix*) is growing on some birch trees and on an occasional pine, while honeysuckle (*Lonicera periclymenum*) sometimes encircles the roots of the former. There are *Sedum* spp. on the rocks of the islands, and the uncommon *Arctous alpina* is found on the rocky cliffs at the upper limit of Glas-leitire. In the upper slopes of Allt a' Chiurn, there are *Rubus chamaemorus*, *Saxifraga stellaris*, and *Listera cordata*.

Age structure. Many of the older trees in Glas-leitire were felled in the last war, but there are still a number ranging in age up to 210 years. The predominant age class is 100 to 150 years, and there are also groups between 80 and 100; but there are few trees between 60 and 80. There are many stunted trees on shallow peat which may not exceed 15 ft. (4·5 m.) in height, although they are between 20 and 60 years old. Regeneration up to about 20 years old is common in places.

Growth and stocking. The maximum height of the pine is about 65 ft. (19·5 m.), and the average is about 50 ft. (15 m.); the greatest and average girths at breast height are 8 ft. (2·4 m.) and 5 ft. (1·5 m.) respectively. Increment borings showed that diameter growth was very slow initially and sometimes for a period up to 60 years, followed by an increase to about 10 to 15 rings per in. (4 to 6 rings per cm.) until growth again decreased in old age.

The stocking in Glas-leitire is very irregular, due partly to the different proportions of pine and birch, and partly because of felling during the past twenty years. At the north and south ends of the wood where most of the pine are to be found, the stocking varies from scattered trees to well stocked groups. In the centre of the woodland, there are individual pine and small stands in a matrix of birch (PL. III). On the islands, the pine is often restricted to a belt near the shore, the interior usually being boggy.

Fauna. Red deer and roe have been numerous in this region for centuries. The former frequent the islands, and there are also a few feral goats on Eilean Sùbhainn. There has been some grazing by sheep in Coille Glas-leitire. The wild cat is to be found in the neighbourhood, and a keeper stated in 1950 that there were also pine martens. There are no capercailzie, but black grouse have been troublesome from time to time, and there are usually crossbills in the woods.

The pine shoot beetle (*Myelophilus piniperda*) is common and has done some damage to pine up to 20 ft. (6 m.) high. The pine sawfly (*Diprion pini*) defoliated many of the old pine in 1951, but was rare in 1953.

Natural regeneration. There has been more natural regeneration at Glas-leitire during the past 50 to 60 years than in any other western native pinewood, particularly on the lower slopes at the northern end of the wood. The source of the seed was old and still surviving, scattered pine, and the seedlings came up on irregular patches amongst them. Although most of these trees are now about 40 to 60 years old, there is a range in age, and regeneration is still taking place. In recent years at least, it has come up amongst *Callunetum* No. 10, with rank but open *Calluna* and a thick layer of mosses including *Sphagnum*, and *Calluna/Molinia* No. 9, the *Molinia* sometimes being dominant. These communities are growing on peat up to about one foot (0·3 m.) deep often on sloping ground, and there is probably a regular flow of water through the peat which may help aeration. Nevertheless on such sites it is not surprising that many of the pine have become stunted as they grow older, and there is some evidence of grazing damage both in the past and in the pre-

FIG. 30. Coulin

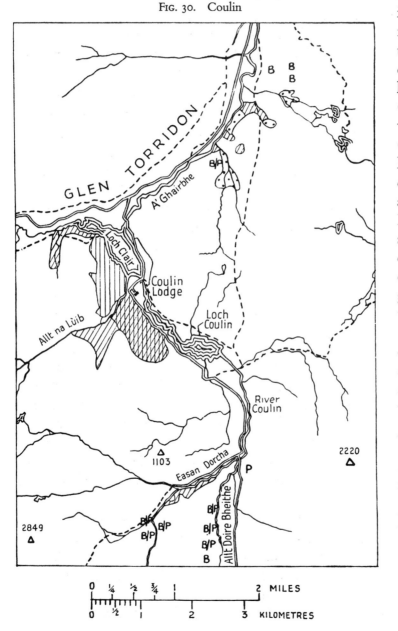

sent. There are also some pine seedlings on the bog communities already mentioned, but they rarely attain any size. On the islands there is little successful regeneration, partly because of the extent of the bog communities, and partly due to damage by grazing.

COULIN

Owner: The executors of the late Capt. Michael D. H. Wills.

Location: The parishes of Gairloch and Lochcarron, Ross and Cromarty. Latitude, 57° 32′ N.; Longitude, 5° 21′ W. National Grid Reference 18 (NG)/995557. Ordnance Survey Maps: 1 in. to 1 mile, 26 (Scotland), 1947 edition; 6 in. to 1 mile, Ross and Cromarty 82, 83 and 94, 1905 edition.

The native pinewoods to be described under Coulin are on three different sites. First, in the upper reaches of Allt na Luib which flows into Loch Clair and at the north-west end of the loch, with scattered pine amongst planted trees and natural birch on the slopes above that loch and Loch Coulin. Secondly, on the south side of Easan Dorcha, a tributary of the River Coulin. The third is one to two and a half miles south of Kinlochewe on the east side of A' Ghairbh, a tributary of the Kinlochewe River (see Fig. 30). These woods lie between those at Loch Maree in the north and Achnashellach in the south.

HISTORY

What is now known as the Coulin Estate was part of the lands of Kinlochewe which belonged to different branches of the Mackenzie family from at least the sixteenth century (Dixon, 1886). Lord Elphinstone acquired Coulin about 1881 and built the lodge, using pine timber for the staircase and other woodwork from native trees growing on the south shore of Loch Clair. There were many fine old pine in this wood at that time, and the age of those felled averaged 250 years (Mackenzie, 1922). Between 1890 and 1896, part of the woodland west of Coulin Lodge was fenced and planted principally with Scots pine. Unfortunately much of this plantation was on wet boggy land and most of the trees died. Some of the old pine in the neighbourhood of Coulin Lodge show marks of resin tapping; resin was used mixed with butter and tobacco juice for smearing sheep before the days of sheep dips.

THE HABITAT

Climate.	Mean annual rainfall	90 in.	2286 mm.
	Temperature: Mean annual	44° F.	6·7° C.
	January mean	37° F.	2·8° C.
	July mean	55° F.	12·8° C.

Climatic sub-province (Anderson, 1955) B3a and B4a.

Topography. The woods at Lochs Clair and Coulin are growing on moderate, undulating slopes except at the north-west of Loch Clair where the pine are in a gorge. The aspect is mainly northerly, and the range of altitude is from 300 to 1000 ft. (90 to 300 m.). At Easan Dorcha, the pine are on moderately steep river banks facing north-west and between 400 and 850 ft. (120 and 255 m.) above sea-level. The gently undulating slopes at A' Ghairbh also have a north-westerly aspect and the altitude is from 200 to 700 ft. (60 to 210 m.).

Geology and soils. The pinewoods are growing on successive narrow bands of Cambrian pipe-rock and basal quartzite, Torridonian sandstone, Lewisian gneiss, and Moine schists and gneisses (anon., 1913*b*), the rocks from these formations being mingled in the overlying glacial deposits, but the predominance of schistose material at A' Ghairbh is reflected in the more fertile soils. The morainic and other glacial deposits are relatively deep on all three sites, and, in the bottoms of the valleys, have been resorted by stream action.

The natural drainage is poor in these woods, and there are numerous peat bogs which merge into blanket bogs at the upper margins of the woods. The better stands of pine are restricted to the drier knolls and steeper slopes, where the soils are often bouldery and of light texture, but in places there is boulder clay. There is frequently a deep layer of living and dead mosses, followed by a thick deposit of raw humus, and locally a marked leached horizon. As the natural drainage deteriorates and there is a covering of peat, the soils become gleyed with mottling, and there may be a compaction layer. On such soils the pine becomes more open, growth is poor, and the trees are slowly dying.

THE FOREST

Tree species and larger shrubs. All the woodlands consist of a mixture of Scots pine and birch in all gradations from pure birch to groups of pure pine. There is more verrucose than pubescent birch, but intermediates predominate. There are rowan scattered throughout the woods, and alder along the streams, but neither aspen nor oak were found in the native pinewoods. There is an occasional holly, a few bushy type juniper, and some clumps of *Salix aurita* and *S. atrocinerea* along the streams.

Field layer. There is the same range of communities as at Loch Maree, but at Loch Clair the bog communities are relatively more extensive, and at A' Ghairbh less common.

There are a few interesting species at the upper altitudinal limits of the pinewoods, such as *Listera cordata* and *Rubus chamaemorus*, while one plant of *Salix repens* was found in the upper reaches of Allt na Luib. In the mixed birch and pine woods at A' Ghairbh, there is a number of species more typical of birch-woods, including ivy, honeysuckle, *Primula vulgaris*, and *Lysimachia nemorum*.

Age structure. Most of the surviving Scots pine are over 130 years old, and one stump of a tree felled during the past ten years had 205 annual rings. There are a few groups between 60 and 100 years surrounding the parents, but younger trees are uncommon, and there are only scattered seedlings under ten years old.

Growth and stocking. The average height of the pine is about 40 ft. (12 m.) and some trees reach 60 ft. (18 m.). The maximum and average girths at breast height are 8 ft. 6 in. (2·6 m.) and 5 ft. (1·5 m.) respectively.

The stocking is very irregular from scattered trees to well stocked groups both of pine and birch.

Fauna. Except in the fenced area near Coulin Lodge, the woodlands are grazed by red and roe deer, Highland cattle, and sheep. The other fauna is similar to that at Loch Maree.

Natural regeneration. There is very little recent regeneration, and only along paths, streams, and eroded banks, and on peat bogs. Most of it is unhealthy and browsed. There are some pine seedlings east of Coulin Lodge which have originated from planted pine.

ACHNASHELLACH

Owner: The Forestry Commission.

Location: The parish of Lochcarron, Ross and Cromarty. Latitude, 57° 28′ N.; Longitude, 5° 17′ W. National Grid Reference 28 (NH)/035470. Ordnance Survey Maps: 1 in. to 1 mile, 26 and 36 (Scotland), 1947 edition; 6 in. to 1 mile, Ross and Cromarty 94 and 105, 1905 edition.

The native pinewoods lie on the south side of the valley of the River Carron, east of Loch Dùghaill. There are three separate woodlands: in the valley of Allt Coire Leiridh, with scattered trees in the Golden Valley; in the deer sanctuary of Coire a' Bhàinidh; and at Sloc Mor in the valley of Allt a' Chonais. There are also many scattered native pine in conifer plantations half a mile west of Sloc Mor (see Fig. 31).

HISTORY

Achnashellach was formerly part of the lands and estate of Applecross and Strathcarron and was owned by the Mackenzie family until 1854. Thereafter, it belonged for short periods to different owners, until it was purchased in 1921 by the Forestry Commission. No early references to the native pinewoods have been found.

THE HABITAT

Climate.   Mean annual rainfall   90 in.   2286 mm.
             Temperature: Mean annual   44° F.   6·7° C.
                           January mean   37° F.   2·8° C.
                           July mean   55° F.   12·8° C.
Climatic sub-province (Anderson, 1955) B3a.

Topography. The native pine are growing on undulating slopes, locally steep, and occasionally scarred by deep gorges and gullies. The aspect varies but is generally northerly, and the pine is between 200 and 900 ft. (60 and 270 m.), with scattered trees up to 1100 ft. (330 m.).

Geology and soils. The underlying rocks are mainly siliceous granulites of the Moine series. The slopes are mantled with morainic material, laid down by the Carron glacier as it retreated up the tributary valleys at the end of the Ice Age, and by boulder clay (anon., 1913b; Charlesworth, 1956; Phemister, 1948). There are extensive peat bogs at the edges of the pinewoods, and smaller bogs within them.

The stony morainic soil is usually covered by a deep layer of litter and raw

FIG. 31.   Achnashellach

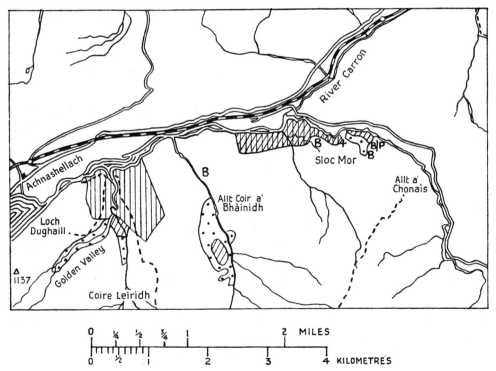

humus or shallow peat and it is often slightly leached. The natural drainage is on the whole better than at Coulin and Loch Maree, because the slopes tend to be steeper.

THE FOREST

Tree species and larger shrubs. The pine forms pure groups and small stands, often amongst birch, but sometimes they are in intimate mixture. Rowan is common, alder fringes some of the streams, and there is an occasional holly.

Field layer. Under the few well stocked stands of pine there are moist moss No. 2, *Vaccinium/Deschampsia/Hypnaceous* moss No. 3, often with some *Molinia* and bracken, the dry and moist *Calluna/Vaccinium/Deschampsia/* moss Nos. 5 and 6, and *Deschampsia flexuosa/Hypnaceous* moss No. 4, the different communities reflecting minor variations in stocking and natural drainage. As the proportion of birch increases, and particularly in the deer sanctuary, the field layer contains more pasture grasses, and the above communities grade into *Calluna/grass/Vaccinium/*moss No. 13 and grass/moss No. 14. Under the more open woodlands which are usually also wetter, there is *Calluna/Molinia* No. 9, while *Molinia/Trichophorum* No. 12 and *Calluna/Trichophorum* No. 11 may spread in from the margins, and *Callunetum* No. 10 is to be found on drier sites in the deer sanctuary. In open places both within the woodlands and at their margins, there are many flushes of *Molinia* No. 16, a few of *Juncus communis* agg. No. 17, and an occasional bog with *Eriophorum/Trichophorum/Sphagnum* No. 15.

There are few unusual species, but *Arctous alpina* is to be found on rocks at the upper limit of the scattered pine in Sloc Mor, and *Saxifraga aizoides* is growing nearby on wet rocks and gravel (PL. XII.c).

Age structure. Most of the trees are over 130 years old, and some, on the evidence of recently felled stumps, are about 200 years. There are a few scattered trees in the wood that are between 80 and 130 years, and only an occasional younger tree.

Growth and stocking. There are a number of unusually well grown pine, particularly in Sloc Mor, with heights up to 65 ft. (19·5 m.), and an average of about 50 ft. (15 m.). The maximum girth at breast height is 10 ft. (3·0 m.), the average in the better groups being about 5 ft. (1·5 m.).

Fauna. The deer sanctuary is unfenced, but the other two woods are partly enclosed, the unenclosed parts being subject to grazing by deer and sheep. The wild cat and the pine marten are commoner than in any other native pinewood. There are a few badgers, principally in the birchwoods. Neither capercailzie nor black grouse were seen; it is said that the latter were common about 1940. The remaining avifauna is similar to that in other western woodlands.

There is a little damage by *Myelophilus piniperda*.

Natural regeneration. There are a few seedlings in open places, both at the edges of the woods and within them, often by streams and on eroded banks, and usually growing amongst *Calluna/Molinia* No. 9 and *Molinia* flush No. 16. In Sloc Mor, while there are a few seedlings within the enclosure, there are none outside it.

SHIELDAIG

Owner: A. Greg, Esq.

Location: The parish of Applecross, Ross and Cromarty. Latitude, 57° 31′ N.; Longitude, 5° 37′ W. National Grid Reference 18 (NG)/820524. Ordnance Survey Maps: 1 in. to 1 mile, 25 (Scotland), 1947 edition; 6 in. to 1 mile, Ross and Cromarty, 91 and 92, 1905 edition.

The native pinewoods are in the vicinity of Shieldaig on the upper reaches of Loch Torridon, a sea loch. The principal woodland, called Coille Creag-loch, is situated between Loch Shieldaig and Loch Dùghaill, south of Shieldaig village, and there are scattered pine on the shores of Òb Mheallaidh to the east of the village, and also on the shores of Loch Shieldaig to the west (see Fig. 32).

HISTORY

In the first *Statistical Account of Scotland*, written in the closing decades of the eighteenth century, the parish minister of Applecross recorded that there were some natural woodlands of Scots pine, birch, and hazel in the parish. At that time the lands belonged to the Mackenzies. Fifty years later, in the second *Statistical Account*, there is a definite reference to a "good fir wood at Shieldaig, producing timber fit for boats, vessels and buildings." About 1870, the woodlands were fenced, partly to keep the red deer from invading the crofts, and partly to keep cattle and sheep out of the woodlands (Murray, 1956). In 1932, the then owner, Mr C. W. Murray, sold some of the larger pine to W. M. Carmichael, timber merchant, who erected a sawmill in the woodland south of Shieldaig, and the sawn timber was despatched by sea, a temporary pier being built. At that time there were two fires which destroyed much young natural regeneration (Murray, 1956). Since then there has been practically no felling.

THE HABITAT

Climate.   Mean annual rainfall   60 in.   1524 mm.

            Temperature: Mean annual   44° F.   6·7° C.

                             January mean   37° F.   2·8° C.

                             July mean   55° F.   12·8° C.

            Climatic sub-province (Anderson, 1955) B4a and C3a.

Topography. The wood south of Shieldaig is growing on very steep, almost cliff-like slopes that become less steep towards the bottom of the valley. The ground is strewn with boulders and the terrain is very rocky. In the woodland east of Shieldaig, the slopes are also steep, but that to the west is on undulating ground. The woodlands lie between sea-level and about 1000 ft. (300 m.), the principal one having a south-westerly aspect, and the others northerly.

Geology and soils. The principal and western woodlands are on pre-Cambrian Torridonian sandstone, and the woodland to the east on the still older Lewisian gneiss. There is little evidence of glacial deposits on the steep rocky slopes, but in the principal woodland and that to the west, there are sandy deposits near the bottom of the valleys.

On the upper slopes, the soils are thin with frequent outcrops of rock, but they are deeper at the lower altitudes. The soils, particularly on the knolls, are sandy in texture, have a raw humus covering from 1 to 3 in. (2·5 to 7·6 cm.) in depth, and show a variable amount of leaching. Soils derived from Torridonian sandstone are usually infertile.

THE FOREST

Tree species and larger shrubs. The woodland south of Shieldaig is principally Scots pine with only a little birch, but the other two are predominantly birch with only scattered pine. Most of the birch are verrucose and no typical *pubescens* was seen, although there are many intermediates. There are a

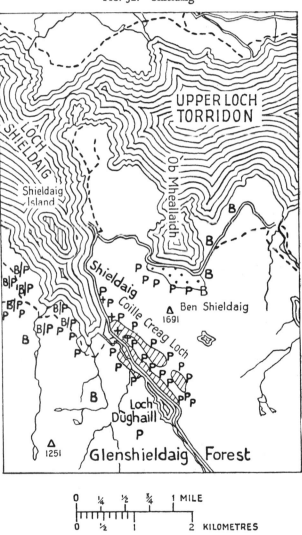

FIG. 32. Shieldaig

number of oak even under the pine; most of them are young and only about 15 ft. (4·5 m.) high, but a few are twice that height. Some are definitely pedunculate, others sessile, and the remainder intermediates. There are rowan scattered throughout the woods, and alder along the streams. A striking feature is the abundance of holly bushes usually only 4 to 6 ft. (1·2 to 1·8 m.) high, but sometimes reaching 15 ft. (4·5 m.) and very vigorous in growth. No juniper was seen.

Field layer. As in other western pinewoods, *Molinia* is a distinctive constituent of the communities, but is less abundant and luxuriant than in those with higher rainfall or less steep slopes. Bracken is frequent but not vigorous. *Deschampsia flexousa* is relatively scarce, and *Vaccinium vitis-idaea* was not found. The variations in tree stocking are reflected in rapid changes in the field layer communities. In well stocked groups of pine on freely drained slopes and knolls, the communities are *Vaccinium/Deschampsia/Hypnaceous* moss No. 3, the moist *Calluna/Vaccinium/Deschampsia/*moss No. 6, and a very little of the dry variant No. 5. In more open places *Callunetum* No. 10 is to be found, but *Calluna/Molinia* No. 9 is commoner, with some *Calluna/Trichophorum* No. 11 under scattered pine. There are also small areas of *Molinia/Trichophorum* No. 12, *Molinia* flush No. 16, *Juncus communis* agg. No. 17, and *Eriophorum/Trichophorum/Sphagnum* No. 15.

The flora is not rich but along streams and associated with pine and a little birch and oak, there is *Teucrium scorodonia*, while honeysuckle and ivy festoon pine as well as birch.

Age structure. In the pinewood south of Shieldaig, the trees range in age up to over 200 years, but most of the crop is relatively young, from 60 to 90 years old. Natural regeneration under 15 years is relatively abundant along the road and on the lower slopes.

Growth and stocking. On alluvium at the north-west corner of the principal woodland, there are well grown pine up to 70 ft. (21·0 m.) high, and the average of the older trees is about 50 ft. (15 m.). The younger trees about 60 to 90 years old are about 30 ft. (9 m.) in height, but lower down the growth is poorer due probably to past damage from the pine shoot beetle and from the extraction of timber. The maximum girth at breast height is about 8 ft. (2·4 m.).

In the principal pinewoods, there are well stocked stands of younger trees on the upper slopes, and there is a small, dense stand of older trees near the river. Elsewhere in this woodland the stocking is irregular, with large, almost bare areas, while in the other two woodlands there are only scattered, older pine amongst the birch.

Fauna. There are red deer, roe, and sheep in the woodlands, which cause considerable damage by browsing to pine regeneration up to five feet high.

There are wild cats in the vicinity but no pine martens. Capercailzie and black grouse are absent from this region.

There is some damage by *Myelophilus piniperda*.

Natural regeneration. There was a considerable amount of natural regeneration, 60 to 90 years ago, on the rocky, upper slopes of the principal pinewood, following the exclusion of sheep and cattle, and the population of red deer does not appear to have been high at that time. As already mentioned, young regeneration is now coming up on slopes and knolls in the main woodland, principally amongst communities Nos. 5, 6, and 10, where the raw humus layer is 1 to 3 in. (2·5 to 7·6 cm.) deep and continuous. The seedlings are now getting above the *Calluna*, but are usually damaged by grazing. It would appear, therefore, that with protection it would be possible to get good natural regeneration, probably because of the relatively infertile nature of the soil and the consequent reduced competition from the field layer communities.

CHAPTER 10

THE NORTHERN GROUP OF NATIVE PINEWOODS

IN THIS chapter are described the northernmost native pinewoods in Scotland, namely Amat, Rhidorroch, Glen Einig, and Strath Vaich. Amat, Einig, and Vaich are almost equidistant from the seas on the east and west, while Rhidorroch is near the western seaboard.

In addition to these woodlands which are considered to be genuine native pinewoods, there are some others regarded as such by local tradition, and they have been studied. First, there are groups of Scots pine on the islands and shore of Loch Assynt (N.G.R. 29 (NC)/212250), on the road from Inchnadamph to Lochinver in Sutherlandshire and at a latitude of 58° 10′. If these are genuine native pine communities, they would be the most northerly surviving in Scotland. The trees could be of native origin morphologically, and one would not expect that planting would be done on these rocky islands. On the other hand, the trees are less than a hundred years old and there are no older parent trees in the vicinity, while the available historical accounts, such as that for the parish of Assynt in the first *Statistical Account*, only mentions natural birch. Secondly, there is a pinewood on the southern slopes of Sròn na Croiche (N.G.R. 29 (NC)/458107) in the parish of Creich, on the north side of Strath Oykell about a mile west of the junction of that strath with Glen Cassley and at a latitude of 57° 59′ N. The pine in this woodland are similar morphologically to those in native pinewoods and are now over 150 years old with girths up to 12 ft. (3·6 m.) at breast height. This woodland has been considered to be a native pinewood in recent times, but in Macfarlane's *Geographical Collections relating to Scotland* (1908) there is a categorical statement "there are no firrs in the parish" (Creich). This statement was probably written about 1726. Later that century it was recorded in the *Statistical Account* that there were natural woods of oak and birch in this parish, but the only reference to pine was to extensive plantations, particularly at Rosehall near Sròn na Croiche. This pinewood is likely, therefore, to be a survivor of eighteenth-century planting. Thirdly, there are a few pine over 150 years old at Leckmelm (N.G.R. 28 (NH)/168908), between Ullapool and Lael on the north shore of

Loch Broom on the western seaboard of Ross and Cromarty, which are the survivors of a wood of about an acre in extent, irregularly stocked with old pine, which was felled about 1953. This has been considered to be a native pinewood (Innes-Will, 1948), but there is a lack of positive evidence. The heartwood of these trees is of a yellow colour not at all characteristic of native pine of this age. Moreover, no historical references to this woodland have been found, although there is a record in 1651 of standing, old, but dead pine on the south side of Little Loch Broom not far distant (Cromarty, 1710). Because of these doubts these woods are not described further.

Blaeu's *Atlas* (1654), which was based on reports of travellers, such as Timothy Pont, Robert Gordon and others, writing about 1600, shows forests farther north than those already mentioned. The farthest north were in the district of Strath Naver, Sutherland, where there were extensive woodlands on both sides of Lochs Loyal and Craggie and in Strath More south of Loch Hope. Farther south and also to the east, there were woodlands in Glen Cassley, south-west of Loch Shin, which at that time were called Dirry Meanach Forest, and also north and south of the valley of the Brora River, also in Sutherland. In the west of that county, there were woodlands in Coygach and north of Loch Assynt. These earlier travellers give no information about the species of trees in these woodlands, but there is reference to this in the writings of some eighteenth-century travellers, such as Pennant (1771) and Lightfoot (1777), and a little in the first *Statistical Account*. At that time there was some pine in Glen Cassley and also in Coygach, but the woodlands appear to have been principally of birch with perhaps some oak in the valleys. Roy (1793) also refers to birch in Coygach.

One of the earliest uses to which these woodlands were put, other than to provide for the needs of the local inhabitants, was the production of charcoal for the smelting of iron. In Timothy Pont's map of Strath Naver in Blaeu's *Atlas* (1654), such sites are marked. Probably oak and birch were used for this purpose because pine made a less useful charcoal (Walker, 1808).

AMAT

Owners: Amat Wood is owned by Lt.-Col. V. H. Holt, the scattered pine south and south-west of it by Mr Maclean of Glencalvie, and those west and south-west of Alladale Lodge by Lady Ross of Balnagown.

Location: The parish of Kincardine, Ross and Cromarty. Latitude, 57° 50′ to 57° 53′ N.; Longitude, 4° 34′ to 4° 44′ W. National Grid Reference 28 (NH)/460855. Ordnance Survey Maps: 1 in. to 1 mile, 20 (Scotland),

1947 edition; 6 in. to 1 mile, Ross and Cromarty 24 and 25, 1905 and
1907 editions respectively.

Amat Wood, the principal native pinewood, lies at the western extremity of
Strath Carron, at the confluence of the River Carron and the Black Water. There
are also the following small groups and scattered pine: on Cnoc nan Sac to the
east; in Abhainn Coir' a' Mhalagain, a tributary valley of Glen Calvie, to the
south; at the north-eastern end of Gleann Mor to the south-west; along both
sides of the Alladale River; and in An Sgaothach to the west (see Fig. 33).

HISTORY

In a sixteenth-century manuscript, a traveller, believed to be Timothy Pont,
writes: "The head of Strath Carron is 30 myl fra Tayne south south west [mar-
ginal note corrects to W.N.W.] . . . 2 myl thence Amad, a myl thence Amad na
heglisse with gryt firr woods." At that time, therefore, Amat Wood was principally pine. About half a century later, another traveller, probably Robert Gordon
of Straloch, described Strath Carron as a tract for the most part wooded, and

FIG. 33. Amat

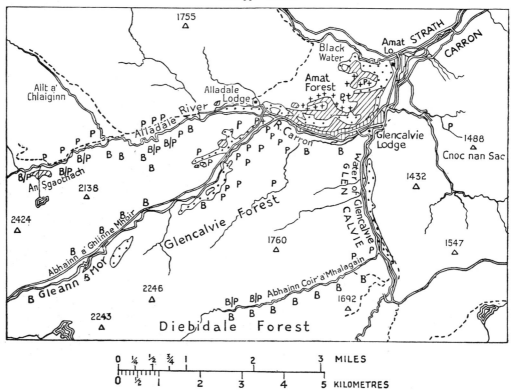

PLATE XIII

FOUR HABIT TYPES OF MATURE SCOTS PINE IN
NATIVE WOODS (see CHAPTER 13)

a) var. *horizontalis* Don (centre
    tree), Black Wood of Rannoch.

b) f. *ascensa* Carlisle, Black Wood
    of Rannoch.

c) f. *fastigiata* Carrière (centre tree),
    Black Wood of Rannoch.

d) f. *condensata* Fries, Glen Feshie.

clothed with particularly tall firs, supplying neighbouring and distant places with timber (Macfarlane, 1908). Blaeu (1654) shows extensive woods on both sides of Strath Carron from the Firth of Dornoch to beyond Amat, and in Diebidale to the south. James Robertson (1767), while making a survey of the flora of the Highlands for the Commissioners of the Forfeited Estates, recorded: "In a glen at Dybdol [Diebidale] and in Glenmore [Gleann Mor], there is a considerable quantity of natural fir and birch. The fir is the finest I have seen in Scotland. One tree rearing a straight uninterrupted trunk to the height of 30 or 40 feet measures in circumference $8\frac{1}{2}$ feet. The stump of another measured $3\frac{3}{4}$ feet in diameter. The timber of these trees is as red and good as any brought from Norway." There is a local tradition that until about a hundred years ago there was a large pinewood in Diebidale which supplied timber both for local building and other uses and for export, the timber being carried by ponies along a rough hill track via Strath Rusdale to the Cromarty Firth. In the Amat district, it was the custom until about eighty years ago for young people leaving the glen to be provided with a "fir chest" made from local pine timber. At the end of the last century, Scots pine was planted in a strip along the River Carron to the south of Amat Wood, and a little later a deer fence was erected round it and the natural Amat Wood. There was some felling of the native pine in Amat during the 1914-18 War, but little since that time. During the past ten years, fire swept through the woods in An Sgaothach and in an area south of the junction of Alladale and Gleann Mor.

THE HABITAT

Climate. Mean annual rainfall 50 in. 1270 mm.
Temperature: Mean annual 44° F. 6·7° C.
January mean 36° F. 2·2° C.
July mean 55° F. 12·8° C.
Climatic sub-province (Anderson, 1955) B1a and B2b.

Topography. This is a region of rounded hills and some of the pine are growing on their exposed shoulders. The slopes in Amat Wood are undulating and only moderately steep, but in the other woods often steeper. The aspect is variable but mainly southerly, although some of the pinewoods with that aspect are in the shadow of higher hills. The altitudinal upper limit of both the pine and birch is the same, and the range in the different woods is from 300 ft. (90 m.) to 1250 ft. (375 m.).

Geology and soils. The underlying rocks belong to the Moine series, and are mainly siliceous granulites with a more micaceous band running north-west to

P

south-east across the junction of Gleann Mor and Alladale (anon., 1912; anon., 1925; anon., 1948b; Phemister, 1948). The slopes are covered with deep glacial deposits laid down at the end of the Ice Age when the Carron glacier split into smaller glaciers in the tributary valleys (Charlesworth, 1956). There is stony alluvium along the rivers, particularly at the western end of Alladale. There are extensive peat bogs towards and beyond the upper limits of the woodlands and particularly at the north-west corner of Amat Wood.

The soils are variable from shallow, stony soils at the western end of Alladale to deep peat in Amat Wood. On its upper slopes, there are rocky or sandy knolls forming islands in the peat. There is usually a deep layer of raw humus on these knolls, and the soil is often strongly leached. On the lower slopes, there are peaty loams with little leaching, but with impeded drainage and mottling, and birch is growing on such soils.

THE FOREST

Tree species and larger shrubs. There is a considerable area of almost pure Scots pine towards the upper limit of Amat Wood and a smaller one in An Sgaothach, but elsewhere there is a mixture of pine and birch. Some of the birch is definitely *verrucosa* and a few *pubescens*, but most are intermediate. There is rowan throughout the woods, while alder is growing beside the streams. In Amat Wood, there is an occasional holly and a few juniper.

Field layer. In the best stocked pine stands in Amat Wood, the typical community is *Vaccinium/Deschampsia/Hypnaceous* moss No. 3, with small areas of dry and moist moss Nos. 1 and 2. Where the canopy is less complete, there are the dry and moist *Calluna/Vaccinium/Deschampsia/*moss communities Nos. 5 and 6, the former often containing much *Empetrum nigrum*, and the latter a little *Eriophorum vaginatum* where the pine stands are merging into bog. In communities Nos. 3, 5, and 6, there is more bracken than is typical. Under scattered pine on the drier ridges and rocky knolls there are small areas of *Callunetum* No. 10. In places between the knolls, there are large tracts of stunted pine growing on wet peaty ground covered with *Calluna/Molinia* No. 9 and patches of *Molinia* flush No. 16, the *Molinia* seldom being tussocky, and, as they grade into bog communities, *Eriophorum* and *Trichophorum* increase, and there are zones of *Calluna/Vaccinium/Eriophorum/Sphagnum* No. 8. Both in clearings with stunted pine and at the margins of the wood, there are *Calluna/Trichophorum* No. 11 and *Molinia/Trichophorum* No. 12. The typical community on the bogs is *Eriophorum/Trichophorum/Sphagnum* No. 15, often with *Trichophorum* dominant, but with more *Calluna* than usual, and there are also patches of *Juncus communis* agg. flush No. 17, with small pools of

Sphagnum No. 19. As the birch increases, the field layer becomes *Calluna*/grass/
Vaccinium/moss No. 13, and under pure birch grass/moss No. 14, together with
the flush communities already described.

There are few species of special interest, but there is some *Goodyera repens* (PL.
XII.*a*).

Age structure. There is a wide range of age classes in Amat Wood. The Scots
pine in the more open stands are usually over 140 years old and a few are more
than 200 years. The trees in the denser groups are younger, about 100 to 130 years,
with a few older parent trees amongst them. The scattered pine at the upper edge
of this woodland that show blasting by wind are between 70 and 140 years old;
and there are a few small stands, here and there, in the 20 to 70 years age class,
while on bogs some of the stunted pine, only a few feet high, are probably about
the same age. Seedlings under 20 years old are relatively common. In the other
woodlands the trees are mostly over 120 years old, except in the surviving stand
at An Sgaothach where they are younger.

Growth and stocking. The tallest pine measured in Amat Wood was 60 ft.
(18 m.) high, but the average of the older trees is only about 45 ft. (13·5 m.).
Some of the old, branchy trees have large girths, one being 12 ft. (3·6 m.) at breast
height, and one of its branches had a girth of 7 ft. (2·1 m.) above the swelling
where it left the stem. The range in girth, even in the better stocked groups, is
wide – from 3 ft. (0·9 m.) to 8 ft. (2·4 m.), and the average of the old trees is about
5 ft. (1·5 m.).

The stocking is irregular. On the upper slopes of Amat Wood, there are small
pure stands of pine that are well stocked and contain good timber, forming islands
in the bogs on which there are only scattered, stunted trees. Lower down the
slopes, there are fewer groups of pine and an increasing amount of birch, with
considerable areas of almost pure birch. The other woods contain only scattered,
bushy-crowned pine, but at the north-east end of Gleann Mor there are some
dense groups of twisted and gnarled trees at about 1100 ft. (330 m.) altitude, and
one group of well grown small trees in An Sgaothach which survived the fire in
Alladale.

Fauna. In this instance the red deer are fenced into the wood, and there are
also a few roe and Japanese sika deer that have become naturalised in this district,
but there are no sheep within the deer fence. Both wild cats and pine martens
were seen in the woods, and red squirrels although present are not doing damage.
Capercailzie, black grouse, and crossbills are uncommon but have been seen
during most years.

Myelophilus piniperda is doing considerable damage to pine in the pole stage.

Natural regeneration. There has been more natural regeneration in Amat Wood during the past 80 years than in any other northern native pinewood and in most western pinewoods. It is to be found principally on knolls and peat bogs on the upper slopes. On the former, while the growth is slow and only 30 ft. (9 m.) may be attained in 80 years, the trees are of good form and some of the groups are well stocked, but on the bogs the trees are stunted or even prostrate. Regeneration is still continuing in open places, particularly in field communities Nos. 9 and 11, and there is also some in Nos. 8, 12, 15, and 19. Most of the regeneration under 6 ft. (1·8 m.) high is grazed by red deer. Outside the deer fence where there is also grazing by sheep, surviving regeneration is rare.

RHIDORROCH

Owners: The woods in Glen Achall belong to John A. Ingleby, Esq., and those south of Loch Achall to Lt.-Col. Charles Rose.

Location: The parish of Loch Broom, Ross and Cromarty. Latitude, 57° 54 N.; Longitude, 4° 58' W. National Grid Reference 28 (NH)/235933. Ordnance Survey Maps: 1 in. to 1 mile, 20 (Scotland), 1947 edition; 6 in. to 1 mile, Ross and Cromarty, 14, 15 and 23.

Most of the native pinewoods are in the glen between Loch Achall and Loch an Daimh, east of Ullapool (see Fig. 34).

FIG. 34. Rhidorroch

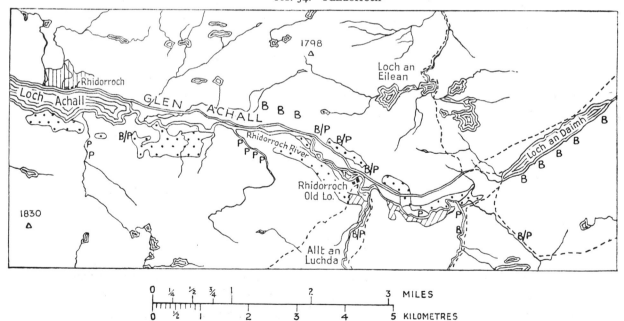

HISTORY

These lands belonged to the MacLeods of Coygach until the seventeenth century, when they passed to George, first Earl of Cromarty, when he married the MacLeod heiress. About 1725, he sold pine from Achichall, almost certainly Achall, for £1600 (Lang, 1898). Pennant (1771) later in that century also makes reference to pinewoods in Coygach. As far as is known there has been little felling in these woods for a long period.

THE HABITAT

Climate. Mean annual rainfall   60 in.   1524 mm.
       Temperature: Mean annual   44° F.   6·7° C.
                   January mean   37° F.   2·8° C.
                   July mean   54° F.   12·2° C.
      Climatic sub-province (Anderson, 1955) B2b and B3a.

Topography. The principal pinewood on the south side of Glen Achall is on gently undulating slopes scarred by deep and narrow gorges formed by streams cutting through the flaggy rocks. On the north side, there are scattered pine on steep slopes rising to cliffs. The pine in the birchwoods south of Loch Achall are on undulating ground. The range in altitude is from 300 to 750 ft. (90 to 225 m.) and the aspect is northerly except for some trees on south-facing screes and cliffs.

Geology and soils. The underlying rocks are siliceous granulites of the Moine series (anon., 1948b; Phemister, 1948). There is also evidence of minor basic intrusions in the neighbourhood, for example about a mile (1·6 km.) west of Loch Achall where the lime-loving *Asplenium viride* was found on an outcrop, and also on the south side of Glen Achall. The slopes are covered with glacial drift laid down as the Douchary glacier retreated at the end of the Ice Age (Charlesworth, 1956). The drifts are generally over 20 ft. (6 m.) deep on the lower slopes, becoming shallower farther up, and are generally sandy and gravelly. The bottom of the valley is filled with alluvium.

The sandy soils are covered with a shallow layer of litter and raw humus and show podsolisation, but the drainage is often poor and peat may spread even on to the knolls.

THE FOREST

Tree species and larger shrubs. In this forest, birch is a more important species than the pine, but the latter predominates to the south of Rhidorroch Old Lodge and farther up the glen to the east. Most of the birch are intermediate in characters between *B. verrucosa* and *B. pubescens*. There is rowan scattered throughout the woodlands and alder fringes the streams, while there is an occasional holly.

Field layer. In the small groups of well stocked pine, the typical *Vaccinium/ Deschampsia/Hypnaceous* moss community No. 3 is found as well as the dry and moist *Calluna/Vaccinium/Deschampsia/*moss Nos. 5 and 6, No. 5 often having much *Empetrum nigrum* as at Amat, and No. 6 some *Molinia*. Both these communities and also *Calluna/Trichophorum* No. 11 are also growing on knolls under scattered trees, but under open woods on such sites *Calluna/Molinia* No. 9 is more characteristic, and on wetter ground *Molinia* flush No. 16. On peat up to about 2 ft. (·6 m.) deep, *Molinia/Trichophorum* No. 12 is found, and on deeper peat *Eriophorum/Trichophorum/Sphagnum* No. 15. In the woods dominated by birch, community No. 9 is also to be found, but the more characteristic communities are the grass/moss No. 14 and *Calluna*/grass/*Vaccinium*/moss No. 13.

Of the more unusual species, *Saxifraga aizoides* (PL. XII.c) is common on wet gravels within the woods, and there is an occasional plant of *S. oppositifolia* at their upper limits.

Age structure. Most of the pine are over 140 years old, but there are a few groups between 80 and 140 years and some still younger on the steep river gorges and cliffs.

Growth and stocking. There are a few trees over 50 ft. (15 m.) in height, and the average in the better groups is 40 to 45 ft. (12 to 13·5 m.). The maximum girth measured was 8 ft. (2·4 m.), and the average about 5 ft. (1·5 m.).

The stocking is irregular. There is a well stocked stand of pine south of Rhidorroch Old Lodge with some belts along the rivers, but elsewhere the pine is scattered throughout the birchwoods.

Fauna. There is grazing in the woodlands by red and roe deer, sheep, and cattle. Pine martens are common, and there are a few wild cats, and an occasional badger. There are black grouse and one or two capercailzie.

There is a considerable population of *Myelophilus piniperda*.

Natural regeneration. There are some pine seedlings under five years old in communities Nos. 6, 9, and 11, but they are badly grazed. A few young pine growing on the sides of gorges out of the reach of grazing animals have attained heights up to 15 ft. (4·5 m.).

GLEN EINIG

Owner: Lady Ross of Balnagown.
Location: The parish of Kincardine, Ross and Cromarty. Latitude, 57° 57′ N.; Longitude, 4° 46′ W. National Grid Reference 28 (NH)/365988. Ord-

nance Survey Maps: 1 in. to 1 mile, 20 (Scotland), 1947 edition; 6 in. to
1 mile, Ross and Cromarty 10 and 16, editions 1905 and 1906 respectively.

This native pinewood in Glen Einig is one to two miles south-west of Oykell
Bridge. It is about eight miles north-west of Amat and the same distance north-
east of Rhidorroch.

GENERAL DESCRIPTION

Nothing is definitely known about the past history of this wood, but the earlier
references to pinewoods in Coygach, already mentioned for Rhidorroch, probably included it. It is of interest that some of the old pine show recent slashing by
tinkers for "candle fir" or kindling.

The annual rainfall is 50 in. (1270 mm.). The pine is growing on undulating
ground between 130 and 520 ft. (39 and 156 m.) above sea-level, and the general
aspect is north-westerly, most of the pine being on the south side of the valley.
The underlying rocks are siliceous granulites of the Moine series, and there is a
lamprophyre dyke in the wood (anon., 1925; Phemister, 1948). The slopes are
covered by moraines with a little boulder clay in places (anon., 1925). The soils
are light in texture and on the knolls are podsolised, with a layer up to 3 in. (7·6
cm.) deep of litter and raw humus merging into peat in the hollows; the peat is
deep beyond the upper limits of the woodlands.

This wood consists mainly of birch, intermediate in character between verrucose and pubescent. There are, however, three groups of pine on the south side
of the river, one at the north-east and two in the valley of Allt nan Càisean, with
scattered trees elsewhere including the north side of the river. There are a few
oaks which show characters intermediate between sessile and pedunculate, alder
along the streams, rowan, and a few holly. The field layer communities are the
same as at Rhidorroch, but, as there are fewer pine, the communities associated
with pine, such as Nos. 3, 5, and 6, cover smaller areas and the birchwood communities are more extensive. Most of the pine are over 120 years old and the
oldest over 180. They range up to 60 ft. (18 m.) in height, but at the upper limits
they are stunted due principally to exposure. The maximum girth measured was
over 8 ft. (2·4 m.). The woods are open to grazing by deer, including Sika deer,
sheep, and a few cattle, and the other fauna is the same as at Rhidorroch. There
is very little current natural regeneration.

STRATH VAICH

Owner: Commander A. M. Williams.

Location: The parish of Contin, Ross and Cromarty. Latitude, 57° 45′ N.;
Longitude, 4° 47′ W. National Grid Reference 28 (NH)/345770. Ordnance Survey Maps: 1 in. to 1 mile, 27 (Scotland), 1947 edition; 6 in. to
1 mile, Ross and Cromarty, 50, 1905 edition.

This small woodland is at the northern end of Strath Vaich between the
tributary streams Allt Beithe and Allt Glas Toll Mòr and 11 miles N.N.W. of
Garve.

GENERAL DESCRIPTION

In one of the maps in Blaeu's *Atlas* (1654), there are trees shown near the site of
this woodland, but the species is not known and no written records have been
found, although it is of interest that farther down the glen there is a place name,
Druimean Giubhais, the ridge of the pines. The existing trees and associated field
layer communities suggest that it is a native wood and it is included, therefore,
although its status is not certain.

The annual rainfall is 70 in. (1778 mm.). The pinewood is on a moderate
slope at an altitude of 850 to 1300 ft. (255 to 390 m.) above sea-level; it is on the
western side of the glen and has an east to north-east aspect. The underlying rocks
are siliceous and sometimes distinctly micaceous schists of the Moine series (anon.,
1912), and they are covered with morainic drift, with alluvium along the river.
The pine is growing on well drained podsolised soil of light texture, but the
natural drainage is poor in the vicinity.

The pinewood has only a few birch and rowan scattered through it, with an
occasional stunted juniper. To the south, there are birchwoods both on the east
and west sides of the glen. The stocking of the pine, while irregular, is about 40
per cent. of full canopy, and the principal field layer community is *Vaccinium/
Deschampsia/Hypnaceous* moss No. 3, with *Listera cordata* and the white and pink-
flowered forms of *Trientalis europaea*, but with little or no *Calluna vulgaris*. Most
of the pine are over 150 years old, and the heights range up to 50 ft. (15 m.). Deer,
cattle, and sheep graze in the woodland and there is no natural regeneration.

CHAPTER 11

THE SOUTHERN GROUP OF NATIVE PINEWOODS

THIS GROUP consists of the southern and western woodlands east of Loch Linnhe and the Firth of Lorne. All are relatively small remnants and those considered to be genuinely native and also of some extent are: The Black Mount woodlands, consisting of Tulla, Crannach, and Fuar; Glen Orchy; Tyndrum; and Glen Falloch.

In this region, there are also smaller groups and scattered old trees of pine that are believed to be native in origin and natural: a few old trees at Coire Giubhsachain about two miles south of Ballachulish (N.G.R. 27 (NN)/065583); some old pine along the river about seven miles up Glen Etive (N.G.R. 27 (NN)/210513, a few pine in the lower reaches of Allt Mheuran a tributary valley of the same glen (N.G.R. 27 (NN)/141455), and scattered pine above a birch and oak woodland north of Barrs on the west side of Loch Etive (N.G.R. 27 (NN)/083410); and a few trees along the river and in a birchwood in Glen Strae, north-east of Loch Awe (N.G.R. 27 (NN)/170315). All these trees are morphologically the same as the native pine. There is some historical evidence of pine in the Loch Etive district in the eighteenth century (anon., 1845), and there are place names there, as well as Coire Giubhsachain mentioned above, and in the neighbourhood of the pine in Glen Strae, that have the Gaelic word for pine, *gius* or *giubhas*, in some form. While this latter evidence is not conclusive, it is almost certain that these trees are the survivors or descendants of earlier native pinewoods, but as these pine are so few in number they do not constitute definite communities and they are not described below.

There are also in this region small pinewoods and scattered pine which are almost certainly of Scottish origin and have been considered to be genuinely native and natural, but the balance of evidence suggests that they are either planted or natural regeneration from planted trees. They are at the following places: on the slopes north of Creagan on Loch Creran (N.G.R. 17 (NM)/980450); on the islands of Loch Awe (N.G.R. 27 (NN)/098242); north of Creggans on Loch Fyne (N.G.R. 27 (NN)/090030); on the Dunans Estate in Cowal (N.G.R. 26 (NS)/

045915); and at Rowardennan on Loch Lomond (N.G.R. 26 (NS)/358996).

No historical references have been found to native pinewoods before the eighteenth century in the region covered by this Group. In this instance, the maps in Blaeu's *Atlas* (1654) throw little light on the woodlands; the seventeenth-century writings on which these maps were based rarely mention woodlands, and when they do so they only speak of oak and birch. It is known also that Sir Duncan Campbell of Glenurquhay (Glenorchy) sowed and planted pine as well as oak and birch at Glenorchy and elsewhere in this district as early as 1613 and 1614 (anon., 1855). It is recorded, however, that this early afforestation was in parks, hence probably on low ground and not in the woodlands described in this chapter. In the middle of the eighteenth century, Pennant (1771) refers to a small pinewood on the side of Loch Tulla, and a little later the parish minister of Glenorchy and Inishail writes in the first *Statistical Account* as follows: "The higher parts of the parish abounded once with forests of the largest and best firs; but these were cut down about 60 years ago by a company of adventurers from Ireland, with little benefit to themselves, and less to the noble proprietor of the county. There are still some tracts of natural firs in Glenochray: a good deal of oak mixed with ash, birch and alder." Also towards the end of the eighteenth century, James Robertson (1799) states that there had been a considerable tract of natural fir near Tyndrum but only a "few gleanings" remained at the time when he wrote. There is little further information about the early exploitation of these woodlands, except for the production of charcoal for the smelting of iron. Iron smelting was carried out at Bonawe on Loch Etive from 1730 to 1866 (Macadam, 1887). Oak, pine, birch, and hazel from the shores of Loch Leven to the north were used as fuel (Robertson, 1771), as well as timber from Glen Kinglass near by. It is not known what species of trees were taken from the latter site, but there are references to pine as well as oak in this glen in earlier times (anon., 1845).

The limited historical evidence, as well as the surviving semi-natural woodlands, indicate that most of the natural woods in this region were broadleaved communities of oak, birch, and other species, and while the native pinewoods which have persisted to the present day were more extensive, and some that existed have almost or completely disappeared, the pinewoods were even less numerous and extensive in the past in this part of Scotland than in the regions already described.

THE BLACK MOUNT WOODS

Owner: Major Philip Fleming.

Location: **The parish of Glen Orchy and Inishail, Argyllshire.**

	Crannach	Loch Tulla	Gleann Fuar
Latitude N.	56° 34′	56° 32′	56° 31′
Longitude W.	4° 40′	4° 47′	4° 51′
National Grid Reference	27 (NN)/350455	27 (NN)/285418	27 (NN)/245394

Ordnance Survey Maps: 1 in. to 1 mile, 54 and 55 (Scotland), 1947 edition; 6 in. to 1 mile, Argyllshire 61 N.E., S.E., 76 N.E., and 77 N.W., 1900 edition.

These woodlands lie south of Rannoch Muir, and about twelve to twenty miles (19 to 32 km.) west of the Glen Lyon pinewoods described in Chapter 12. The Crannach Wood is about three miles up the valley of the Water of Tulla, the

FIG. 35.   The Black Mount Woods

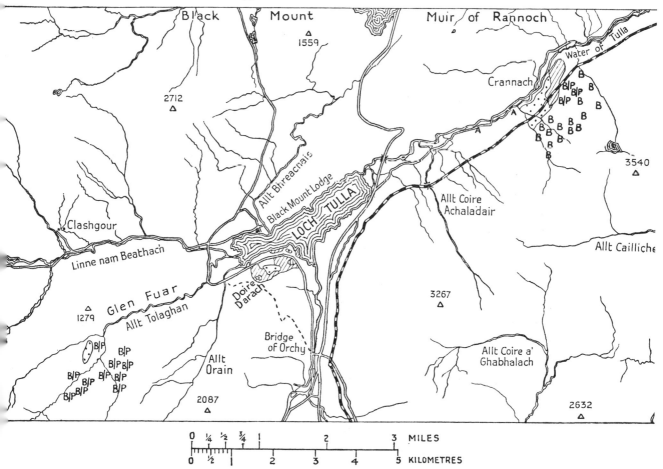

Tulla Wood on the south shore of Loch Tulla, and the Fuar Wood in the glen of that name south-west of the loch (see Fig. 35).

It is of interest that on the Ordnance Survey maps Tulla Wood is called Doire Darach, which means in Gaelic the thicket of oak. There is now no natural or semi-natural oak in or in the immediate vicinity of this woodland, but there may have been in the past, although, as already mentioned, Pennant referred to this pinewood over two hundred years ago.

HISTORY

See introduction to this chapter.

THE HABITAT

Climate.	Mean annual rainfall	80 in.	2032 mm.
	Temperature: Mean annual	45° F.	7·2° C.
	January mean	37° F.	2·8° C.
	July mean	55° F.	12·8° C.

Climatic sub-province (Anderson, 1955) B3a and B4c.

Topography. All three woodlands are on undulating slopes with a north-westerly aspect, but with different altitudinal limits. The pine at Crannach is from 650 to 1200 ft. (195 to 360 m.) above sea-level with a birchwood above it, Tulla 600 to 950 ft. (180 to 285 m.), and Fuar 700 to 1300 ft. (210 to 390 m.).

Geology and soils. The underlying rocks in all three woodlands are granulites of the Moine series, either flaggy gneisses as in Crannach or quartzose schists as in Fuar. The southern edge of the granite mass of the Muir of Rannoch comes into the northern edge of Crannach (anon., 1923). The slopes on which the woodlands are growing are covered with moraines and other glacial deposits, often cut through by subsequent stream action. There are also faint strand lines cutting into the general morainic cover of the hillsides, for example in Crannach Wood, which are considered to be caused by an ice-dammed lake. There are alluvial terraces along the Water of Tulla (anon., 1923; Charlesworth, 1956).

On the freely drained morainic knolls and ridges on which the best stocked pine is growing, the soils are sandy and gravelly and contain much granitic material. Profiles showed depths of litter and raw humus up to 6 in. (15·2 cm.) and sometimes marked podsolisation. In the hollows between these knolls and at the margins of the woods, there is peat over one foot (30·5 cm.) deep, and sometimes much deeper, which is steadily encroaching on to the hummocks. These peat areas are either treeless or have only scattered trees.

THE FOREST

Tree species and larger shrubs. As in other native woodlands, there is both Scots pine and birch but the proportions vary. In Crannach, the middle part of the woodland along each side of the railway is predominantly pine. Towards the river, birch is the principal species with only an occasional pine, while above 1200 ft. (360 m.) there is pure birch which here reaches 1900 ft. (570 m.). Most of Tulla Wood is Scots pine with little birch, but the latter species forms several pure stands, one of considerable extent in the middle of the wood. At Fuar, there are scattered pine with only an occasional birch, except that there are small pure groups of that species amongst the pine at the north-east end of the woodland, and there is a birchwood on the slopes west of Allt Tolaghan. Most of the birch are intermediates between *B. verrucosa* and *B. pubescens*. In all the woodlands, there is an occasional rowan with some alder along the rivers and the loch. A few juniper were seen in Tulla Wood, one 14 ft. (4.2 m.) high, and also a few dwarf holly. There are a few fenced plots of planted trees of various species along the road at Tulla.

Field layer. Under the better stocked pine in all the woods, the principal communities are *Vaccinium/Deschampsia/Hypnaceous* moss No. 3, dry and moist *Calluna/Vaccinium/Deschampsia/*moss Nos. 5 and 6, and, at Crannach, there are more *Empetrum nigrum* and bracken than usual, and also small areas of *Deschampsia flexuosa/Hypnaceous* moss No. 4. As the pine becomes more open and the soils peat-covered, the communities are *Calluna/Molinia* No. 9, *Calluna/Trichophorum* No. 11, *Molinia/Trichophorum* No. 12, and *Molinia* flush No. 16; Nos. 9 and 16 sometimes spread on to the knolls under the better stocked pine. On the deeper and often treeless bogs, the most important communities, in addition to Nos. 12 and 16, are *Eriophorum/Trichophorum/Sphagnum* No. 15, *Juncus communis* agg. No. 17, *Juncus articulatus* flush No. 18, and *Sphagnum* spp. No. 19. Where birch predominates, the usual communities are *Calluna/grass/Vaccinium/*moss No. 13 and grass/moss No. 14, but in Fuar Nos. 3, 5, and 6 are to be found, and in all these birchwood communities bracken is an important constituent.

Age structure. In all three woodlands, most of the pine are over 120 years old, and some are much older. There are occasional younger trees, most at Crannach where natural regeneration has come up on the railway banks since the railway was completed in 1894. There would have been more but for destruction by fire.

Growth and stocking. The maximum height is about 60 ft. (18 m.), and the average 45 ft. (13.5 m.), except in Fuar where it is less. The maximum and average girths are 8 ft. (2.4 m.) and 5 ft. 6 in. (1.7 m.) respectively. The younger trees at Crannach attain about 15 ft. (4·5 m.) in height in 20 years.

At Crannach and Tulla, the pure pine groups and stands are moderately well stocked, but where the pine is mixed with birch, the woodlands are irregular in stocking and rather open. Fuar is a derelict woodland, the result either of earlier felling or burning, and the stocking is open with little birch. There has been damage by fire in recent years at the north end of Crannach Wood.

Fauna. The woodlands are open to grazing by red deer, roe deer, and sheep, the first named being numerous, and these woodlands are the only shelter available in winter for miles around. The usual predators, including the wild cat, are present. Black grouse were seen and there are records of capercailzie, although we did not see any.

The insect pests of pine are doing little damage.

Natural regeneration. There is very little current regeneration in the pinewoods, only an occasional seedling in open places, and it is almost always grazed before it attains any size. As already mentioned, however, there is a certain amount of natural regeneration on the railway embankments in Crannach Wood, and the trees that escape damage by fire grow vigorously, being partly protected against grazing by the railway fencing. As mentioned by Fraser Darling (1947), the proprietor of Tulla Wood about 1938 enclosed by a deer and rabbit fence a plot of about half an acre in extent adjoining a mature pine stand, and screefed the soil; some pine seedlings have since come up.

GLEN ORCHY

Owner: Capt. R. A. Oldham.

Location: The parish of Glenorchy and Inishail, Argyllshire. Latitude, 56° 29′ and 56° 27′ N.; Longitude, 4° 51′ and 4° 53′ W. National Grid Reference 27 (NN)/250360 and 27 (NN)/226328. Ordnance Survey Maps: 1 in. to 1 mile 54 (Scotland), 1947 edition; 6 in. to 1 mile, Argyllshire 90 N.E., S.E. and S.W., 1900 edition.

There are two pinewoods situated between Bridge of Orchy and Dalmally, the first in the valley of Allt Coire Bhiocair to the north and the second in the valley of Allt Broighleachan to the south; these streams are western tributaries of the River Orchy. The first is about two miles south of Fuar, one of the Black Mount Woods already described, and the second about four miles east of the pine in Glen Strae mentioned in the introduction to this chapter (see Fig. 36).

HISTORY

See introduction to this chapter.

THE HABITAT

Climate.   Mean annual rainfall   90 in.   2286 mm.
             Temperature: Mean annual   46° F.   7·8° C.
                           January mean   38° F.   3·3° C.
                           July mean   56° F.   13·3° C.
Climatic sub-province (Anderson, 1955) B4c.

Topography. Both woodlands are on moderately steep, hummocky slopes scarred by deep declivities cut by the streams. The aspect is northerly, and the range in altitude in the northern woodland is from 600 to 900 ft. (180 to 270 m.), and in the southern 350 to 850 ft. (105 to 255 m.), with a few scattered pine up to 950 ft. (285 m.), and birch up to 1000 ft (300 m.).

Geology and soils. The underlying rocks are granulitic quartzose schists of the Moine series, and in Allt Broighleachan mica schists and an intrusion of kentallenite (anon., 1923; Hill 1905). The slopes are covered with moraines which contain fragments of the local rocks including mica schist and granite.

There are podsols with up to six inches of litter and raw humus on the more freely drained knolls,

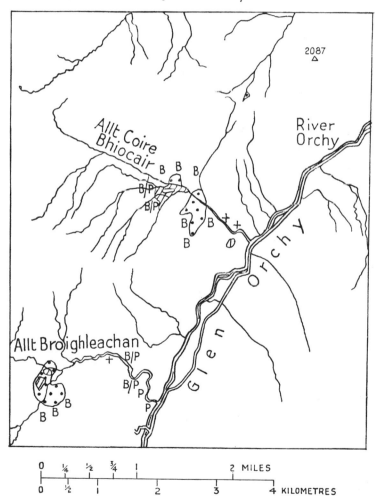

FIG. 36.   Glen Orchy

but sometimes there is a compaction layer at a depth of over a foot (30·5 cm.) with evidence of gleying. There are patches of brown forest soils in Allt Broighleachan on the mica-rich parent material, on which a mixture of pine and birch is growing. In the hollows there is peat generally over a foot (30·5) deep.

THE FOREST

Tree species and larger shrubs. In the two woodlands, there is a mixture of pine and birch, the pine being both in groups, sometimes almost half an acre (·2 ha.) in extent particularly in the valley of Allt Broighleachan, and as single trees. There is both *Betula verrucosa* and *B. pubescens* as well as intermediates. In the southernmost of the two woodlands, there are a few oak, with predominantly sessile characters, and in the northern some aspen up to 40 ft. (12 m.) high. In both woods there is a little alder, rowan and holly, but no juniper was seen.

Field layer. As in other woodlands there are communities Nos. 3, 5, and 6 under the better stocked pine, but in Allt Coire Bhiocair where birch predominates their extent is small and they grade into *Deschampsia flexuosa/Hypnaceous* moss No. 4 and grass/moss No. 14, often with much bracken. As the soils become progressively wetter and the peat becomes deeper, the important communities are Nos. 9, 11, 12, 15, 16, 18, and 19.

Age structure. In Allt Broighleachan, there are some pine trees over 200 years old, and in both woodlands most are over 130. There are occasional trees under 100 years, but very few under 30.

Growth and stocking. The tallest trees, up to 75 ft. (22·5 m.), are in the southern woodland; and the average is about 50 ft. (15 m.), but less in the northern woodland. One short-boled tree in Allt Broighleachan is 15 ft. (4·5 m.) in girth at breast height, and the average in both woods is about 5 ft. (1·5 m.).

The stocking is more irregular than usual, but there are some well stocked groups in the southern wood, as well as only scattered trees.

Fauna. It is similar to that in the Black Mount Woods.

Natural regeneration. There is very little natural regeneration, only an occasional seedling on disturbed soils on river banks and on bogs.

TYNDRUM

Owner: Edward Lowes, Esq.

Location: The parish of Killin, Perthshire. Latitude, 56° 25′ N.; Longitude, 4° 43′ W. National Grid Reference 27 (NN)/330280. Ordnance Survey Maps: 1 in. to 1 mile, 62 (Scotland), 1945 edition; 6 in. to 1 mile, Perthshire 77 S.E., 78 S.W., 89 N.E., and 90 N.W., 1900-01 editions.

PLATE XIV

THREE HABIT TYPES OF MATURE SCOTS PINE IN NATIVE WOODS (see CHAPTER 13)

a) var. *pendula* Caspary, Rowardennan.

b) umbrella-shaped crown (Habit type, No. 9), Glen Mallie, Loch Arkaig.

c) bushy crown (Habit type No. 10), surrounded by progeny with straight stems and normal crowns, hence this habit type is not due solely to genetic factors, Glen Feshie.

This native pinewood known as Coille Coire Chuilc is in the fork of the River Coninish and Allt Gleann Achrioch, one and a half to two miles south of Tyndrum in Strath Fillan (see Fig. 37).

HISTORY

See introduction to this chapter.

THE HABITAT

Climate.

Mean annual rainfall		90 in.	2286 mm.
Temperature:	Mean annual	44° F.	6·7° C.
	January mean	36° F.	2·2° C.
	July mean	55° F.	12·8° C.

Climatic sub-provinces (Anderson, 1955) B4c.

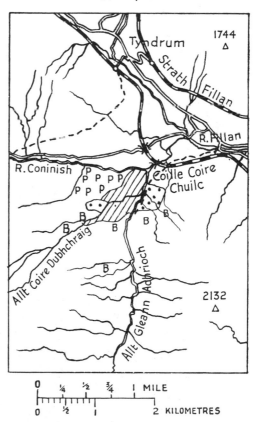

FIG. 37. Tyndrum

Topography. The pine is growing on gently undulating slopes drained by streams tributary to the River Fillan which rise on the hills to the south and west, including Beinn Laoigh, 3708 ft. (1112 m.) above sea-level. The aspects are north to north-east and the limits in altitude of the pine are 650 and 1200 ft. (195 to 360 m.), with scattered birch to 1400 ft. (420 m.).

Geology and soils. The underlying rocks form a complex pattern. Most of the woodland is on quartzose mica schists of the Dalradian series, but there is a band of limestone at the southern margin of the woodland, and intrusions of basic rocks both immediately north and south of it (anon., 1948*b*).

The slopes are covered with morainic and other glacial material laid down by the retreating Fillan glacier

Q

at the end of the Ice Age (Charlesworth, 1956). The drifts contain mainly schists and quartzose rocks and a little granite, but also limestone fragments.

North of Allt Coire Dubhchraig, the soils on the knolls and ridges are sandy and gravelly, with a relatively deep layer of litter and raw humus, and are weakly podsolised. Between them the hollows are peat covered. On the east and south margins of the woodland, the soils are stony, loamy brown forest soils, probably the result of the limestone parent material, and they tend to be peaty in the wet hollows; birch is the principal species on such soils.

Tree species and larger shrubs. This woodland consists mainly of Scots pine, and the birch is only scattered through it in open places, but there are birch stands on the east and south margins as already mentioned. The birches are principally intermediate in character between the two species. As usual there is alder along the streams and rowan scattered through the woodlands. There is some holly and it is of interest that there is a little dwarf hazel beside the rivers.

Field layer. In the part of the woodland north of Allt Coire Dubhchraig, the communities are the same as those already described for Glen Orchy; there is a considerable area under scattered pine where *Calluna* is dominant, but it is not a typical *Callunetum* in that there is a thick layer of actively growing *Sphagna* and other moisture-loving mosses. On the east and south margins of the woodland near the limestone band where there are brown forest soils, the birchwoods have grassy communities and there is a comparatively rich herb flora, including *Achillea millefolium*, *Bellis perennis*, *Lysimachia nemorum*, *Prunella vulgaris*, and *Viola riviniana*.

Age structure. There are only one or two very old trees in this wood but most are over 120 years. Although few in number, there is some representation of younger ages from current regeneration upwards, both as single trees and as small groups.

Growth and stocking. The maximum height is only 50 ft. (15 m.) and the average 35 ft. (10·5 m.). The rate of height growth is slow and only 20 ft. (6 m.) may be attained in 50 years. The maximum girth measured was 9 ft. (2·7 m.) and the average about 5 ft. (1·5 m.). This is an irregularly stocked and open woodland, with a few well stocked but small groups of pine, and the trees have short boles and bushy crowns. At the north-west corner of the woodland, there are only scattered pine, and at the east and south margins irregularly stocked birch.

Fauna. It is similar to that described for the Black Mount Woods. For such a high rainfall district, there is an unusual number of large anthills made by *Formica rufa*.

Natural regeneration. There are only scattered seedlings under ten years old in open places along the streams and on bogs; they are almost always grazed.

GLEN FALLOCH

Owner: Edward Lowes, Esq.

Location: The parish of Killin, Perthshire. Latitude, 56° 22' N.; Longitude, 4° 39' W. National Grid Reference 27 (NN)/367233. Ordnance Survey Maps: 1 in. to 1 mile, 62 (Scotland), 1945 edition; 6 in. to 1 mile, Perthshire, 90 S.W., 1901 edition.

This is not a pinewood community but only scattered trees on the south-east of Glen Falloch, two miles south-west of Crianlarich. Morphologically they are similar to native pine. No early historical information has been found about these trees, but they have been considered to be native and natural (Balfour, 1932). If so, they constitute the southern limit in Scotland.

GENERAL DESCRIPTION

The climate is similar to that of Tyndrum, but the rainfall is only about 75 in. (1905 mm.). The trees are growing on undulating slopes facing north-west and between 500 (150 m.) and 700 ft. (210 m.) above sea-level. The underlying rocks are the same as at Tyndrum, but the limestone is farther away from the pine (anon., 1948), and the soils are podsolised or peat covered.

There are only scattered pine; the field layer communities are, therefore, not characteristic of pinewoods, being grass moorland. The trees are over 130 years old and the maximum height is about 45 ft. (13·5 m.). There is no natural regeneration.

CHAPTER 12

EARLY STUDIES OF THE VARIATIONS IN SCOTS PINE IN SCOTLAND

NOMENCLATURE

THE INDIGENOUS Scots pine of Scotland is regarded by many authorities (Beissner, 1909, 1930; Clapham, 1952; Dallimore, 1954; Elwes, 1908; Gilbert-Carter, 1936; Rehder, 1940) as a geographical variety or race of the species, *Pinus silvestris* L. It is generally referred to as *Pinus silvestris* L. var. *scotica* Schott (Beissner), but there is a number of synonyms:

Pinus scotica Willdenow (Schott, 1907),
Pinus horizontalis (Don, 1814),
Pinus silvestris L. var. *horizontalis* (Don, 1814),
Pinis silvestris L. var. *horizontalis*, Willdenow (Gordon, 1858),
Pinus silvestris rubra Grigor (Gilchrist, 1871; Gordon, 1858),
Pinus silvestris montana Sang (Loudon), (Gordon, 1858; Loudon, 1855, 1883),
Pinus silvestris montana hort. (Gordon, 1858).

It has also been given a number of common names in Scotland, such as: Scots fir, Highland pine, horizontal Scotch pine, Speyside pine, Mar pine, red Scotch pine (Grigor, 1868; Loudon, 1838). Where the word "fir" is used in the older British, literature, it means Scots pine.

EARLY DESCRIPTIONS

In 1871, Gilchrist (1871) described the typical native Scots pine of Scotland as a tree 60 to 80 ft. (18 to 24 m.) high, bearing horizontal branches which tended to hang downwards at the tip. Its timber was red, the bark smooth and light coloured, the buds blunt and ovate, and the leaves stiff, twisted, 1 to $3\frac{1}{2}$ in. (2·5 to 8·9 cm.) long, pale green or glaucous with serrulate edges. The male flowers were yellowish, and the comparatively smooth female cones were 2 to 3 in. (5·1 to 7·6 cm.) long and 1 to $1\frac{1}{2}$ in. (2·5 to 3·8 cm.) wide, with black seeds, and reddish seed wings. This early description agrees more or less with that of later authorities, except that the cones and leaves were longer.

The more recent descriptions of *P. silvestris* L. var. *scotica* Schott by Elwes and Henry (1908), and Dallimore and Jackson (1954) state that the tree has short (3·8 cm.) glaucous leaves and short (3·8 cm.) symmetrical cones, the cone scale apophysis being flat at the cone base and at its apex tending to be pyramidal. Rehder's (1940) description is similar, the leaves and cones being 3·5 cm. long. These compare with 2·5 to 10·2 cm. for the leaves and 2·54 to 7·62 cm. for the cones in the species as a whole.

The Controversy concerning the Quality of Scots Pine Timber

According to Loudon (1838), Scots pine began to be used in plantations in various parts of Britain in the seventeenth century. It is possible that some of the seed may have been imported, but, as already mentioned, there was a lively trade in pine seed from the Highlands of Scotland from at least the beginning of the eighteenth century, and kilns were used for its extraction (Haddington, 1765). When these plantations were felled in the middle of that century, the timber was found to be inferior to that of the Highland pinewoods and of the Baltic. Scots pine fell into disfavour as a plantation tree, the prejudice reaching its peak from 1790 to 1810, and some writers went as far as to say that Scots pine was useless as an economic species. For example, Marshal (1785) stated: "Scotch fir . . . should be invariably excluded from every soil and situation in which any other timber tree can be made to flourish . . . In better soils, and in milder situations, the wood of Scotch fir is worth little. . . . We therefore now discard it entirely from all useful plantations."

The controversy which ensued was concerned with discovering whether this poor timber was due to differences in the inherent nature of the trees, or to factors of age, cultivation, and environment. At this period, plantations of Scots pine were grown on a very short rotation of 25 to 30 years, and some maintained that the reason for the poor timber of these plantations was that the trees were felled before the wood had time to mature (Louden, 1838). It was a number of years before Scots pine returned to favour as a plantation tree.

Under the stimulus of this controversy, landowners, nurserymen, and travellers began to take note of the timber variations in Scots pine. Before the end of the eighteenth century, Pennant (1771) observed that the native Scots pine in the vicinity of Braemar, Aberdeenshire, had very resinous, heavy, dark red timber. More than a century later, Ablett (1880) also said that Scots pine in the Highlands of Scotland had hard resinous wood. James Farquharson (1775) observed in 1775 that on his estates in Scotland there were marked timber differences in the Scots pine, and attributed these differences to site factors: "It is generally believed that there are two kinds of Fir-trees the produce of Scotland, viz. the red or resinous large trees, of a fine grain and hard solid wood; the other a white wooded Fir, with a smaller proportion of resin in it, of a coarser grain, and a soft spongy nature, never comes to such a size and is much more liable to decay. At first appearance this would readily denote two distinct species, but I am convinced that all the trees in Scotland, under the denomination of Scotch Fir, are the same; and that the differences of the quality of the wood and the size of the trees, is entirely owing to the circumstances, such as climate, the situation and the soil they may grow in. . . . I believe the climate has . . . a great share in forming the nature of the best wood, which I account for in the following manner; the most mountainous parts of the Highlands, particularly the northerly hanging situations, where these fine Fir trees are, have a much shorter time of vegetation than a southerly exposure, or the lower open countries, being shaded by high hills from the rays of the sun, even at midday for months together; so that, with regard to other vegetables, nature visibly continues longer in a torpid state than in other places of the same latitude. This dead state of nature for so long a time yearly, appears to me to be necessary to form the strength and health of this species of timber."

This viewpoint, although supported later in 1881 by McLaren and McCorquodale (1881), was not generally accepted. The Edinburgh nurseryman, William Boutcher (1775) believed that the timber differences could not be attributed only to site and age factors: "It has been an old dispute, which still subsists, whether there are more sorts than one of the Scots pine or Fir, and 'tis commonly asserted, that the differences we see in the wood when cut down and polished, is owing only to the age of the tree, or the quality of the soil in which it grew; but this assertion I am obliged to believe is not just, and proceeds from want of sufficient observation, as I have seen many Fir trees cut down of an equal age in the same spot, where some were white and spongy, others red and hard, which appears to me evident, that there are two distinct species of them."

Although few people would consider that this evidence justified the subdivision into two species, it suggests intra-specific genetic differences. Boutcher's observation is supported by the Earl of Haddington (1765) who stated in 1760 that in the Scots pine plantations on his estates, although the trees were even-aged and growing in uniform conditions, the timber differences between individual trees were quite definite. In such conditions this variation could not be attributed to site and age factors. In his studies of the pinewoods of Speyside, Grigor (1868, 1881) noted that where woods of native Scots pine and those raised from imported pine seed respectively stood side by side in identical conditions, the timber of the native Scots pine was far superior to the imported "degenerate" type. The native pine produced red resinous timber on a wide range of sites, and on trees both of slow and rapid growth. While there is no doubt that site, age, and rate of growth influence the timber of the Scots pine, these early observations suggest that the differences in the timber of the heterogenous populations of Scots pine in Scottish plantations are at least in part genotypic, that of the native Scottish pine being characteristically hard, red, and resinous. While the present investigations have confirmed this, the subject has not been studied in detail.

At the beginning of the nineteenth century, landowners were greatly concerned at the deterioration of the Scots pine in Scotland, and it gradually came to be accepted that this was due largely to the planting of unsuitable types. By virtue of these earlier general researches, and later thanks to the work of George Don (1814), the superiority of the native pine was realised, and the Highland Society of Scotland offered premiums in the early decades of the last century for the greatest collections of Scots pine seed from the best native pinewoods in Scotland, provided that all the seeds were sold and sown (Ablett, 1880). The largest collections were made by Messrs. Grigor & Co., nurserymen of Forres, a firm which took particular interest in Scots pine, and extensive plantations were formed from these seeds by landowners. It was from this time that Scots pine gradually began to return to favour as a plantation tree, and it became generally accepted that it was necessary to plant the native race, a fact later forgotten.

VARIATION IN THE HABIT AND OTHER CHARACTERISTICS OF SCOTS PINE

While this early work had considerable influence on the choice of strain of Scots pine, it was concerned principally with timber differences. The first significant work on the general characters of Scottish pine was carried out by George Don (1814) between 1810 and 1814. He noted that in Scots pine plantations in the vicinity of Forfar, although the trees were of similar age and grew in more or less uniform conditions, some trees grew more rapidly than others and exhibited differences in habit, bark and cone characters. Don described four distinct "varieties" of Scots pine in these woods:

> *Variety No. 1.* The common Scots pine. The branches form a pyramidal head and the bark is very rugged. The leaves are dark green, marginate and only a little glaucous on the underside. The elongated cones taper to a point and are produced very freely. Altogether an inferior type of tree, being short-lived, and soon developing a stunted appearance.

> *Variety No. 2.* A well defined variety. The branches are markedly horizontal, tending to bend downwards near the trunk. The bark is less rugged than in Variety No. 1. The leaves are broader and serrulated, but are not marginate, and have a distinctive light glaucous colour. The cones are thicker, less pointed, and smoother. It is tolerant of a

wide range of soils and sites, is a more hardy tree, grows freely, and quickly attains considerable size.

Variety No. 3. A distinctive variety with serrulated leaves of an even lighter colour than variety No. 2, having a light glaucous to silvery tint. The branches form a pyramidal head as in Variety No. 1, but the cones are very distinct, bearing blunt "prickles"[1] which are bent backwards. It is a good type of tree.

Variety No. 4. A scarce variety with the leaves curled or twisted and much shorter than those of the other varieties.

Don tentatively proposed that Variety No. 2, with horizontal branches, should receive specific status, and suggested the term *Pinus horizontalis*. This suggestion, however, did not receive general acceptance. The varieties were later given varietal names (Selby, 1842): Variety No. 1, var. *vulgaris* Don; Variety No. 2, var. *horizontalis* Don (PL. XIII.*a*); Variety No. 3, var. *uncinata* Don; Variety No. 4, var. *tortuosa* Don. The plantations examined by Don were not composed entirely of native Scottish pine, but he conjectured that "the fir woods which formerly abounded in every part of Scotland and the trees of which arrived at a great size, had been of this variety (Variety No. 2) or species (*Pinus horizontalis*)." This point of view was supported by Grigor's (1831) observation in 1831 that the Scots pine of the native pinewoods of Abernethy (Inverness-shire) included a type of pine with very durable timber and horizontal branches, closely resembling var. *horizontalis* Don.

Loudon (1838) compared the native Scottish or Highland pine with that grown in the plantations of the Lowlands of Scotland. He stated that the Highland pine outlives many generations of the common cultivated Lowland pine and ultimately attains a greater size. The former is a robust, shaggy tree. Compared with the Lowland pine it grows to a greater girth in crowded woodlands when young, attains a greater size on wet sites, and produces redder, harder, more durable, and inflammable timber. It bears fewer fertile cones, and these are smaller and less elongated than those of the Lowland type. The quality of the soil did not appear to affect to any great extent the external morphology of the native pine.

Comparatively little work has been done on the morphology of the native Scottish pine in the last fifty years. Two broad types of native pine, however, were noted by Mr Gilbert Brown (Guillebaud, 1933), the factor of the Seafield Estates, in the native pinewoods of the Spey Valley, Inverness-shire. One type had drooping branches and another had sturdy, horizontal branches with drooping tips. The crowns flattened out at an early age and both types appeared to be

[1] Don probably refers to the cone scale apophysis rather than the minute prickle or mucro borne upon the umbo.

resistant to snow damage. In both types also, the dead branches were persistent and dense stands of forty to fifty-year-old pine carried branches almost to ground level; the needles were short and persisted four to five years; on the older trees the bark units were very large and of a dull colour. Guillebaud (1933) pointed out that in Curr Wood (by Dulnan Bridge, Inverness-shire), a sub-spontaneous pinewood which originated from parents of reputed native origin, 10 per cent. of the pines have red stems with the thin bark persisting almost to the foot of the trees. These thin-barked trees are apparently much cleaner than stems with thicker bark, and frequently have narrower crowns.

The Forestry Commission has carried out provenance trials with Scots pine from the various native pinewoods in Scotland. These trials only date, however, from about 1936 and it is still too early to draw any general conclusions, but there is some indication that the pine from Glen Moriston has comparatively straight stems, fine branches and good silvicultural form compared with those of Loch Maree and Abernethy. The Loch Maree trees are described as often, but not consistently, coarse, and the Abernethy trees as variable (Edwards, 1953).

The early observations described above are of particular interest in that they are some of the first studies of morphological variation in a coniferous species in any country. It is only to be expected that Scots pine with its wide distribution, great economic value, and bewildering variability should attract attention, and more work has since been carried out on its variations than on any other conifer.

CHAPTER 13

THE HABIT OF SCOTS PINE

B Y HABIT is meant such characteristics of the crown of a tree as angle of branching, length and thickness of the branches, arrangement of foliage, and also such stem characters as influence the crown, for example the tendency for the stem to persist to the apex of the crown or the reverse. For convenience, dwarf and other unusual forms of Scots pine are discussed in this chapter also.

Unlike many conifers, Scots pine is not markedly monopodial in its growth, for example compared with spruce, but within the species there are variations in this tendency, On the other hand, the conditions under which it grows and particularly the degree of competition influence the form of its crown. The reaction between these two forces produces a great variety of habit forms, and, as this is of silvicultural importance, it is not surprising that it should have been studied, and endeavours made to assess the respective roles of genetic constitution and environmental conditions. The variations have been studied in provenance trials since Vilmorin first started them at Les Barres in France. While tentative conclusions have been reached by this method of approach (Brown, 1878; Vilmorin, 1862), these are long term investigations, and light can be thrown on this problem immediately by studies in the native pinewoods.

It is more or less generally accepted that the Scots pine has at least two contrasting habit types, the narrow or spire-like crown and the broad or rounded crown. These appear to be genetically controlled, although this is not yet beyond all doubt.

PREVIOUS WORK

THE BROAD AND NARROW CROWN TYPES, THEIR CHARACTERISTICS AND DISTRIBUTION IN EUROPE

Broad and narrow Scots pine crown variants have been recorded and studied in Sweden, Germany, France and various parts of the Alps.

The early studies of the pine in Sweden indicated that var. (ssp.) *lapponica* Fries in North Sweden and Lapland, had a characteristic narrow, pointed crown reaching low down a straight stem, with relatively short, slender branches (Lindquist, 1935-8; Sylven, 1916). In contrast the Scots pine of the middle and southern regions of Sweden, sometimes called var. *septentrionalis* Schott (1907), had a rather broader crown and heavier branches, persisting only a short way down the stem (Sylven, 1916). Recent investigations, however, have shown that there is reason to believe that the difference in the habit of Scots pine in the northern and southern pine regions of Sweden is not as clear-cut as earlier workers believed. In the north there are both broad and narrow crown variants, with many intermediate types, and Lindquist (1935) found that the true narrow crowned type was by no means as common in the north as was generally supposed. Similarly, in the more southerly pine regions not all the Scots pine are broad crowned, and Lindquist found in these woods a narrow crown form closely resembling that of the north. In the same region, Nordmark (1950) states that the narrow crown and the associated better stem form are most common in the eastern, and the broader crown types in the western regions with their higher rainfall, heavier soils, and more severe competition from other species.

Pinus silvestris L. var. *rigensis* Loudon, in Latvia, although similar to var. *lapponica* Fries, has a slightly narrower crown. The stem is described as being exceptionally tall, straight and cylindrical (Elwes, 1908; Rehder, 1940), and was once in great demand for the masts of ships (Loudon, 1838).

In Germany and neighbouring countries, the narrow crown type predominates in northern, eastern, and mountain localities, and the broad crown in southern, western and lowland regions (Grosse, 1932; Kienitz, 1911; Meyer, 1944; Münch, 1924). Grosse (1932) distinguished two habit types, the "rundkiefer," or round Scots pine, and the "spitzkiefer," or spire-like Scots pine. In the Prussian forests, the two types grow in the same stands, so that the difference in the crown form is not due only to site factors. The "rundkiefer" forms a broad, rounded crown early in life, with a forked stem and coarse branches. It may attain a height of 117 ft. (35 m.), and a girth of up to 13 ft. 5 in. (4 m.). It is common throughout eastern Prussia, but is least common in the extreme east. In contrast, the "spitzkiefer" has a more or less narrow, pyramidal, acute crown extending one to two thirds down the stem even in close canopy, with fine, thin, and short branches. This variety attains a height of 143 ft. (43 m.), but does not exceed 9 ft. 2 in. (2·79 m.) in girth. It is most common in the extreme east of Prussia and at the higher elevations. Variations in the form of the crown of the so-called "noble race" of Scots pine in Germany were recorded by Seitz (1929-38). He distinguished three forms: an extremely narrow crown with persistent stem, a conical dense crown with a persistent stem, and a flattened crown with a branchy stem. He correlated these crown forms with different bark types and regarded them as distinct races. Many other authorities have considered the question of Scots pine crown variation in Germany, the majority recognising broad and narrow crown differences. Münch (1924), for example, in his detailed work on pine races in Germany, noted a narrow crowned mountain type of Scots pine, the "hohenkiefer" (Rubner, 1957), very different in appearance to the pine of the lowland regions at a similar latitude.

Broad and narrow crowned Scots pine have also been distinguished in the pine forests of France. In the Vosges, for example, the Scots pine at the higher elevations has a pointed, conical crown two to three times as long as it is wide, and a columnar tendency. The stem is characteristically straight and the branches short, slender, and horizontal. Self cleaning of these trees is good, and they can withstand snow, a certain amount of shade, and a high tree density. In contrast, the Scots pine of the nearby plains, even when transplanted and grown in the mountains, has a tendency to form a crooked stem and a rounded irregular crown which is wider than it is long. In open situations this type of tree develops an "umbrella" habit. The branches are long, thick, and fastigiate, with a tendency to spread laterally, and self cleaning is poor. This type is liable to damage by snow and needs more light for survival (anon., 1941a; François, 1947). These variations provide an example of different habit types at the same latitude but at different elevations.

A similar range of crown forms is found in Switzerland and the neighbouring Alps. In the warmer Swiss lowlands, there are both broad and narrow crowned Scots pine, but, at the higher elevations, the broad crown types become less common. It has been suggested that this may be due to the effects of natural selection by snow, the broad crowned types being unable to withstand snow to the same extent as the narrower crowns (Engler, 1913). An example of the mountain type of Scots pine in this region is *P. silvestris* L. var. *engadinensis* Heer (1862), which occurs at high elevations in the Engadine Alps, eastern Switzerland, and the Tyrol. It is a small tree, from 30 to 50 ft. (9 to 15 m.) high, with a very slender crown (Rubner, 1934), and branches that persist low down the stem almost to ground level (Beissner, 1891). When the tree is old it frequently assumes an "umbrella" shaped crown. The general appearance of this variety is like that of var. *lapponica* Fries, and some workers regard it as the same "race" (Beissner, 1891, 1909; Christ, 1907; Willkomm, 1887), but Rubner (1934) is probably correct in his statement that the two varieties are distinct but parallel types.

It may be seen from these descriptions that in most regions the narrow crown form is associated with the following characteristics: a straight stem comparatively free from forking; short slender branches reaching low down the stem; a resistance to snow damage; and a tolerance of low light intensities. On the other hand, the broad crown variant has the opposite characteristics. Silviculturally, the narrow crowned pine is the more desirable type owing to its straight stem and its tolerance of heavy stocking (Lindquist, 1935-8). The broad crown type predominates in the south and west of Europe, and the narrow crowns are most common in the north and east. At the same latitudes, narrow crown types are commoner at the higher elevations, and the broader predominate in the lowlands. Both types are to be found throughout the range of the species but vary in their frequency; the populations are, therefore, mixed.

THE GENETICS OF CROWN FORM VARIANTS

The question whether or no the different crown forms are genetically controlled has been a subject of heated controversy, particularly in Sweden and Germany. In Sweden, Lindquist (1935-8) found the broad crown type in close as well as open stands, and the narrow in open places where the tree had ample room for lateral development. He concluded, therefore, that the crown form was inherent, although admitting the importance of the effect of environment. Wretlind (1936), however, has pointed out that the condition of the canopy competition may have varied during the growth of the trees. Hickel (1914) and Rubner (1934) have stated that the narrow crown characteristic is transmitted from parent to progeny, but Langlet (1937), while recognising the importance of heredity, expressed the view that environment dominated genetic factors in this instance. Meyer (1939) found a correlation between the increment in length of the main axis of Scots pine and the rounding off of the crown over long periods. If this increment is great, that of the side branches diminishes after some years, and the crown becomes pointed and regular. If, however, the axis increment is small, due to drought or disease, the increment of the side branches becomes and remains large in proportion to that of the main axis, and the crown rounds off. If the tree recovers after a long period of slow growth, and the increment of the main axis increases while that of the lateral branches decreases, it is possible for a pointed regular crown to be formed above an older bushy crown. Meyer's principal point, therefore, is that crown form can be influenced by rate of growth.

THE ANGLE OF BRANCHING OF SCOTS PINE

The variations in the angle of the branch relative to the main axis have been used by some workers in attempts to classify the numerous habit variants of Scots pine (Brown, 1878; Vilmorin, 1862). The most obvious branch angle types are the ascending, fastigiate, horizontal, and pendulous variants. Ascending and fastigiate types include such named forms as f. (v.) *fastigiata* Carrière (1867), f. *condensata* Fries (1890), f. (v.) *pyramidalis* (Elwes and Henry, 1908), and f. (v.) *watereri* Beissner (1930) (see pp. 238 and 239). Horizontal branch types occur in Scotland, for example var. *horizontalis* Don (1814) (see pp. 232 and 240-241), and in the Vosges (anon., 1941). Pendulous branch types have been recorded on the continent of Europe, and are generally called f. *pendula* Caspary (1866), the "Trauerkiefer" or Weeping Scots pine (anon., 1932; Beissner, 1891, 1930; Dallimore, 1954; Elwes, 1908; Hippel, 1866; Tubeuf, 1897; Veitch, 1891, 1900).

The effect of environment and competition upon the angle of branching in Scots pine has not been studied in detail.

UNUSUAL CROWN FORMS AND HABIT TYPES OF MINOR SILVICULTURAL IMPORTANCE

The following forms have been described.

f. *condensata* Fries (Arnborg). The "Kvastall," "Busktall," Mop pine, or Bushy pine.

This ususual habit type of Scots pine has a dense, bushy, ovate or pyramidal crown which spreads out and becomes mop-like in old age. The crown consists of a large number of strongly fastigiate stem-like branches. In youth there is generally no definite main axis, but, as the tree grows older, the erect stem-like branches become closely applied and even fused to form a "stem" which gradually increases in length (PL. XIII.*d*). The tree bears small cones and cone production is poor (Arnborg, 1941, 1946*a*, 1946*b*; Fries, 1890). It occurs principally in eastern middle Sweden. Arnborg found that the characters of branchiness and absence of a definite main stem were reproduced in the progeny, so it would appear that the tree is a distinct genotype. He regards f. *condensata* Fries as quite distinct from other fastigiate types such as f. (v.) *fastigiata* Carrière (1867) and f. (v.) *pyramidalis* (Elwes and Henry) (Beissner, 1898; Elwes, 1906).

f. (v.) *fastigiata* Carrière.

This type of Scots pine is 50 to 60 ft. (15 to 18 m.) high and has a spire-like or columnar crown form with erect, strictly fastigiate branches (PL. XIII.*c*). It is found in Norway and Finland, and differs from f. *condensata* Fries in having a definite main stem and narrow crown (anon., 1932; Bean, 1951; Beissner, 1891; Carrière, 1867).

f. (v.) *pyramidalis* (Elwes and Henry).

A fastigiate type of Scots pine with a pyramidal crown; this variant is sometimes regarded as the same as f. (v.) *fastigiata* Carrière and f. *watereri* Beissner (anon., 1932; Beissner, 1891, 1909, 1930; Elwes, 1908; Grozdov, 1945).

f. *watereri* Beissner.

This type has a semi-dwarf habit with ascending branches, a broadly columnar crown form, dense foliage, and steel blue leaves (anon., 1932; Rehder, 1940). It is sometimes regarded as synonymous with f. (v.) *fastigiata* Carrière.

f. (v.) *virgata* Caspary. The "Schlangenkiefer," "Rutenkiefer," or "Ormtall."

This peculiar habit type has the branches of the first order distributed in very irregular whorls. No branches of the second order are produced for several years, but later the tree may branch to the sixth order in the lower parts of the crown. Only the outermost branchlets bear leaves, giving the tree a very singular appearance (Beissner, 1891, 1930; Caspary, 1882-3; Elwes, 1908; Lindquist, 1943; Schwerin, 1906; Sylven, 1910; Tubeuf, 1897; Veitch, 1900). It has been recorded in France, Prussia, and Sweden, but is, on the whole, uncommon and only found as single trees.

DWARF FORMS OF SCOTS PINE

Scots pine exhibits a great many dwarf forms, some of which may be inherent. In many instances, however, the dwarfing is due to adverse site factors, and, when the trees are grown under better conditions, they adopt a more normal habit. The more constant dwarf forms have achieved popularity in horticulture, and have been given a great many different names, many of which are synonymous (Hornibrook, 1923, 1938).

The two most common dwarf habit variants in the wild state are f. (v.) *nana* Carrière (1867) and f. (v.) *globosa* hort. (Dallimore) (1954), sometimes collectively called f. (v.) *globosa nana* hort. (Beissner, 1930) or f. (v.) *pygmaea* hort. (Beissner, 1891, 1909).

> f. (v.) *nana* Carrière. A 20 in. (50 cm.) high bush with a rounded or globose crown, and numerous short, erect branches. The leaves are short, $1\frac{1}{4}$ in. (3·2 cm.) long, straight, and glaucous (anon., 1932; Bean, 1951; Carrière, 1867; Dallimore, 1954; Rehder, 1940).
>
> f. (v.) *globosa* (Dallimore) (1954). A dense rounded shrub, with leaves 1 in. (2·5 cm.) long and cones about $\frac{3}{4}$ in. (1·9 cm.) long. Not quite as dwarf as f. (v.) *nana* Carrière.

Other dwarf types found in nature are the prostrate f. *katakeimenos* Graebner (1899) of the Baltic coast, Sweden, and North Russia; f. (v.) *turfosa* Woerlein, a shrub 1·7 to 6·7 ft. (0·5 to 2·0 m.) high, with a flat crown and many small cones (Beissner, 1930; Woerlein, 1893), growing in bogs in N.W. Germany, and on the Baltic coast, and elsewhere.

THE VARIATIONS IN THE HABIT OF THE NATIVE SCOTS PINE OF SCOTLAND

In any natural pinewood where the trees are uneven-aged and the stocking is irregular, there are, inevitably, a great number of habit variants which are undoubtedly due to these causes. For example, dense stocking restricts crown development, and the trees in such a wood will have narrower crowns than those in an open wood, and young trees tend to have more conical and pointed crowns than older. There are, however, certain habit variants that cannot be directly attributed to the environment, as, for example, when a broad-crowned tree occurs in a very dense stand of even-aged pine. In such instances, where a certain habit has developed in spite of, and not because of, the environmental factors, it seems very probable that the habit is, at least to some extent, genetically controlled, although this assumption can only be proved by long term progeny trials. The principal Scots pine habit variants in the Scottish native pinewoods which appear to be genotypic are as follows, the descriptions referring to mature trees, about 140 years old, unless otherwise stated:

I. HABIT TYPES WITH HORIZONTAL BRANCHES

In this category, there are two main types, a narrow-crowned type, crown diameter 10 to 16 ft. (3·0 to 4·8 m.), and a broad-crowned type, crown diameter more than 16 ft. (4·8 m.).

Habit type No. 1. Narrow-crowned Scots pine with horizontal branches

Crown form	Cylindric to cylindric-conic, very regular, with or without a definite leader, maximum crown diameter 16 ft. (4·8 m.).
Stem	Persistent and straight.
Angle of branching	Horizontal in the middle third of the crown, tending to ascend at the top of the crown and frequently pendulous at the base.
Branch diameter	Fine branches, seldom more than 3 in. (7·6 cm.) in diameter.
Branch persistence	On trees under 60 years old, persistent on isolated trees, variable in close canopy, with good branch cleaning in older trees.
Foliage density	Sparse to moderately dense.
General appearance	A symmetrical tree with a straight stem and a cylindrical crown, consisting of fine horizontal branches with rather sparse foliage. The crown generally has an "open" appearance (PL. XIII.*a*).

This type is *Pinus silvestris* L. var. *horizontalis* Don (see p. 232). Its general habit and particularly its fine branching and usually straight stem makes it desirable from the silvicultural point of view.

It is found both as isolated trees and in close stands, but competition in the

PLATE XV

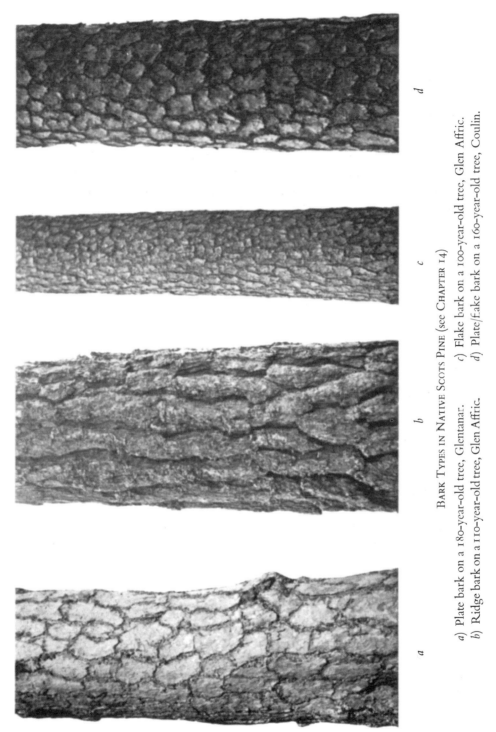

BARK TYPES IN NATIVE SCOTS PINE (see CHAPTER 14)

a) Plate bark on a 180-year-old tree, Glentanar.
b) Ridge bark on a 110-year-old tree, Glen Affric.
c) Flake bark on a 100-year-old tree, Glen Affric.
d) Plate/fake bark on a 160-year-old tree, Coulin.

latter tends to cause the branches to ascend. Individual trees differ in their capacity for retaining the horizontal branch angle. At forest margins, whilst some trees have horizontal branches on the fully lighted side of the crown and ascending branches on the shaded side, others retain the horizontal branch angle on both sides of the crown. In extreme cases, trees retain their horizontal branch angle in dense woods where the crown is shaded on all sides and subjected to intense competition, although this is by no means common. Where horizontal branches occur on an isolated tree, such a tree might have developed ascending branches if grown in a dense stand, and all that can be said is that such a tree has at least a slight tendency to the habit of var. *horizontalis* Don.

The diameter of the crown of var. *horizontalis* Don varies to some extent with the canopy density, and the very narrow crowns with maximum crown diameters of 12 ft. (3·6 m.) or less are mainly confined to dense stands, but in rare instances they are to be found on forest margins with ample room to spread their branches.

The available evidence is, therefore, that the habit of var. *horizontalis* Don is genotypic.

Habit type No. 2. Broad-crowned Scots pine with horizontal branches

Crown form	Cylindric to dome-shaped, tending to be irregular, with or without a leader, maximum diameter more than 16 ft. (4·8 m.).
Stem	Moderately persistent, tending to be crooked.
Angle of branching	Horizontal in the middle third of the crown, variable at the base and ascending at the top.
Branch diameter	Coarse, generally more than 3 in. (7·6 cm.).
Branch persistence	Persistent both in well stocked stands and in isolated trees of all ages.
Foliage density	Moderately dense.
General appearance	A symmetrical but coarse branchy tree with thick horizontal branches.

This type retains its broad crown and coarse horizontal branches even in close stands and is probably genetically controlled. It is similar in its angle of branching to the true var. *horizontalis* Don, but has a wider crown, less persistent stem and coarse persistent branches. Silviculturally it is not a good type and much inferior to var. *horizontalis* Don.

II. HABIT TYPES WITH ASCENDING BRANCHES

The trees of this group possess branches which have not the extreme upward tendency of the fastigiate types, but which nevertheless tend to ascend. There are two variants, the relatively narrow crowned and the very broad crowned.

R

Habit type No. 3. Narrow crowned Scots pine with ascending branches

Crown form	Cylindric to cylindric-conic, with or without a definite leader, frequently irregular, diameter 10 to 20 ft. (3 to 6 m.).
Stem	Persistent to moderately persistent, straightness variable.
Angle of branching	Ascending in the upper two thirds of the crown. Sometimes tending to the horizontal or even pendulous at the base of the crown.
Branch diameter	Generally coarse branches, but sometimes less than 3 in. (7·6 cm.) in diameter.
Branch persistence	Persistent in isolated trees of all ages.
Foliage density	Moderately dense to dense.
General appearance	A tree with an irregular crown of variable form, with coarse ascending branches reaching low down the stem and with rather dense foliage.

In this characteristic type (PL. XIII.*b*) the branches ascend even in isolated trees where the branches have free access to light and cannot owe their angle to the influence of light and competition. In dense stands, many trees adopt this habit, but their branch angle may then be due to competition for light. It is probable that isolated trees with this habit are distinct genotypes. This is supported by the fact that trees of this type are commonly found standing side by side with trees of Habit type No. 1 of the same age and under the same conditions of site.

This habit variant is very common in the native pinewoods, and, because of its importance and apparent genetic nature, it is suggested that it should be given the name *Pinus silvestris* L. f. *ascensa* to distinguish it from the fastigiate forms f. *condensata* Fries and f. *fastigiata* Carrière, and from the pyramidal pine with ascending branches, f. *pyramidalis* (Elwes and Henry). The term f. *ascensa* only applies to a habit variant of Scots pine which is genetically controlled and is *not* a separate variety possessing correlated morphological characters.

Habit type No. 4. Very broad crowned Scots pine with ascending branches

In the native woods, Scots pine trees are to be found which have ascending branches like f. *ascensa* (*loc. cit.*) but with very wide pyramidal or dome-shaped crowns, more than 20 ft. (6 m.) in diameter. This type has only been observed in open situations and its significance is doubtful. Superficially it resembles var. *pyramidalis* (Elwes and Henry) (see p. 238). It is uncommon in the native woods and is of minor importance.

III.   HABIT TYPES WITH FASTIGIATE BRANCHES

The Scots pine with the branches growing upwards at a very acute angle occur in most of the larger native pinewoods, and because of their peculiar habit are easily recognised. There are two principal variants in this category, trees with a definite main stem, and trees without a definite stem, or, in the latter case, if there is a stem, it consists of a compound axis composed of adpressed or fused branches.

Habit type No. 5. Fastigiate Scots pine with a definite stem

Crown form	Broadly columnar, with a diameter of 15 to 25 ft. (4·5 to 7·5 m.), and resembling that of a Lombardy poplar; irregular, no definite leader.
Stem	Forked to moderately persistent.
Angle of branching	Very acute.
Branch diameter	Variable. Generally coarse to very coarse.
Branch persistence	Persistent both in isolated trees and in close stands at all ages.
Foliage density	Moderately dense.
General appearance	A tall, forked tree with very numerous branches reaching down the stem almost to ground level. The crown is broadly columnar or "lobe" shaped and irregular in outline.

This native Scottish type (PL. XIII.c) closely resembles f. *fastigiata* Carrière, although the latter is generally described as having a more narrowly columnar crown than the Scottish variant. This type has been found both under fully lighted conditions at wood margins and in stands with up to three quarters canopy; it may be a genotype. Silviculturally the variant is undesirable.

Habit type No. 6. Fastigiate Scots pine with a compound stem

Crown form	Very bushy and irregular, mop-shaped, pyriform or globular; diameter 15 to 30 ft. (4·5 to 9·0 m.), never a definite leader, even when young.
Stem	Generally, but not always, deeply convoluted, and consisting of a number of fused stem-like units; in old trees the fusion is so complete as to resemble a true main axis.
Angle of branching	Strictly fastigiate.
Branch diameter	Coarse and very coarse.
Branch persistence	Very persistent.
Foliage density	Moderately dense to dense.
General appearance	Totally divorced from the common coniferous habit, resembling that of a much branched oak or beech. The compound stem, fastigiate habit and bushy crown are outstanding characteristics.

This variant (PL. XIII.d) is undoubtedly f. *condensata* Fries (Arnborg) (see p. 238). It is to be found in most native Scottish pine forests in groups of three to five trees. Where ten to twenty-year-old regeneration occurs nearby it includes bushy crowned fastigiate trees. There is the possibility that such a habit type might arise from browsing or damage of the crown when young, but it was observed that the young native Scots pine readily forms a new leader if it is allowed to grow unhindered after a long period of severe browsing. Browsed bushes rapidly assume a conic or sub-conic crown form when protected, as for example in the forest of Glentanar. It is unlikely, therefore, that this fastigiate habit type is the result of grazing. Examples of f. *condensata* Fries grow side by side with f. *horizontalis* Don and f. *ascensa* (*loc. cit.*) trees of comparable age and in identical conditions, and the form appears to be genetically controlled.

IV. HABIT TYPES WITH PENDULOUS BRANCHES

Trees with pendulous branches are not uncommon in the native woods but this habit can often be due to external factors. In some instances, heavy masses of foliage develop on long side branches and the latter are weighed down. In others, the leader of a tree may break off and the lateral branches extend to unusual length and droop downwards.

There are, however, two types with pendulous branches which seem to owe their habit more to genetic constitution than to purely mechanical factors. One has a comparatively narrow cylindrical crown and the other a wide dome shaped crown.

Habit type No. 7. Scots pine with pendulous branches and a cylindric crown

Crown form	Irregularly cylindric.
Stem	Moderately persistent, straightness variable.
Angle of branching	Pendulous in the lower two thirds of the crown, horizontal or ascending at the top.
Branch diameter	Variable; generally 3 to 6 in. (7·6 to 15·2 cm.).
Branch persistence	Persistent in isolated trees.
Foliage density	Moderately dense to sparse.
General appearance	An irregular tree of low vigour with pendulous branches.

Habit type No. 8. Scots pine with pendulous branches and a dome-shaped crown (PL. XIV.*a*).

Crown form	Wide and dome-shaped.
Stem	Forked to moderately persistent.
Angle of branching	Markedly pendulous in all parts of the crown except the top 20 per cent. where it is variable.
Branch diameter	Variable, generally 3 to 6 in. (7·6 to 15·2 cm.).
Branch persistence	Persistent.
Foliage density	Sparse to moderately dense.
General appearance	A broad, dome-shaped crown with long sweeping, pendulous branches and rather sparse foliage.

Both these types have been seen at wood margins and as isolated trees on sheltered, well drained sires. They stand side by side with other habit variants such as var. *horizontalis* Don and f. *ascensa* (*loc. cit.*) of comparable age. The pendulous branching is not wholly due to the weight of the foliage masses, as in both these variants the foliage is never more than moderately dense. In most instances the trees are of low vigour, and this, together with their undesirable habit, renders them unsuitable for silvicultural purposes. They are both very similar to *Pinus silvestris* L. var. *pendula* Caspary (see p. 238), and will be referred to by this term.

V. MISCELLANEOUS HABIT TYPES AND THEIR SIGNIFICANCE

The majority of the Scots pine in the native woodlands are of less definite or intermediate forms. Amongst these, there are characteristic habit variants which do not fall into any of the categories previously described but are nevertheless so distinct and common that their significance must be considered.

Habit type No. 9. The umbrella crown or "eagle's eyrie" (PL. XIV.*b*)

This characteristic type is known to all students of Scots pine and is regarded as a desirable type by many practical foresters. Its general habit is a straight, clean stem with thin bark, and a flat, umbrella-shaped, or sometimes slightly bushy crown, extending only a very short way down the stem. It frequently has a high proportion (more than 65 per cent.) of red heartwood. No examples in trees under 120 years old were seen.

It may be that the tree had a cylindric or cylindric-conic crown in earlier life, and, as it grew older, the leader was lost, the apical branches ramified, and the lower branches died. It assumed a dome-shaped and then a more or less globular crown. Finally the top branches extended and ramified, most of the lower branches died, and the tree formed its umbrella crown.

These trees grow in isolated positions, often free from competition, and yet have clean stems. It seems, therefore, that although the "umbrella" crown *per se* is due more to age rather than to a genetic factor, this type may well have inherent good self cleaning properties. The genetics of this type are worthy of further study.

Habit type No. 10. Irregular bushy crowns

In the larger native woodlands, there are Scots pine with irregular branches and bushy crowns, ranging from very large old trees with girths of 10 ft. (3·0 m.) or more to stunted plants. In many instances, the bushy crowns are obviously due to adverse environmental factors or to damage by insects, game, snow or wind. There are, however, many old (150 to 300 years) and apparently undamaged trees with bushy crowns and no particular branch angle that are growing on favourable, sheltered, and well drained sites. In such instances, it seems possible that a genetic factor may be partly responsible for the bushy habit. It has, however, been found that at Glentanar, Ballochbuie, Glen Feshie, and the Black Wood of Rannoch, old bushy crowned mother trees are surrounded by 40 to 120-year-old progeny, practically all of which have straight stems and conical or cylindric crowns when growing in close canopy (PL. XIV.c). It is unlikely, therefore, that the bushy habit is due solely to genetic factors, and if such factors are present they are recessive. It can only be conjectured that these trees owe their form partly to some unknown external factor. These bushy crowned trees with no definite branch angle should not be confused with Habit types Nos. 5 and 6.

Dwarfed Scots pine occur in most native woods, and are confined to marginal sites at the tree limit or where the drainage is poor. On these sites, trees of bushy and even prostrate form and less than 6 ft. (1·8 m.) high may be 40 to 50 years old. Such dwarfs are never seen on well drained, sheltered sites, and it seems that they owe their habit to limiting environmental factors.

Habit type No. 11. "Layered" foliage

In pine 50 to 120 years old the foliage may be in "layers", giving the crown a pagoda-like appearance. This "layering" is due to the side branches ramifying in a lateral plane to a much greater extent than in the vertical plane. It is independent of branch angle, and is found both in Habit types Nos. 1 and 3. The "layering" is more marked in trees with cylindric and cylindric-conic crowns, and is not generally well defined in old bushy crowned trees. It is most common in the younger stands of Scots pine in Glen Affric, Glen Cannich, and Glen Strathfarrar, and in the woods on the shore of Loch Maree. It has been observed on all types of site except extremely exposed and wet locations, and does not appear to be due to the environment. Its significance is doubtful.

THE DISTRIBUTION OF THE PRINCIPAL HABIT TYPES IN SCOTLAND

Owing to the influence of the environment in modifying the crown of Scots pine, only a few trees in comparatively few woodlands can be assigned with any confidence to any particular genotypic habit type. It is, therefore, impossible to assess accurately on a quantitative basis the proportions of the habit variants in the native pinewoods. One can, however, record the presence, absence and approximate frequency of the habit types in the larger native woods.

Only the clearly defined habit types have been considered in this assessment, and both their intrinsic characteristics and the conditions of competition and site under which they are growing have been taken into account:

Habit type No. 1, v. *horizontalis* Don	Horizontal branches retained in well stocked woods.
Habit type No. 3, f. *ascensa* (*loc. cit.*)	Ascending branches maintained in isolated trees.
Habit type No. 4, probably v. *pyramidalis* (Elwes and Henry)	Ascending branches and wide pyramidal crown retained in isolated trees.
Habit type No. 5, f. *fastigiata* Carrière	Fastigiate branches and definite main stem maintained in isolated trees or trees fully lighted at least on one side.
Habit type No. 6, f. *condensata* Fries	Fastigiate branches and composite stem retained in isolated trees.
Habit types Nos. 7 and 8, v. *pendula* Caspary	Pendulous branches retained on undamaged trees with moderately sparse foliage in open stands.

The distribution of these habit variants is given in Table III. The data show that Habit types Nos. 1 and 3 are frequent to abundant in all the larger native pinewoods. No. 6 is not uncommon, and is locally frequent in Rothiemurchus and the Black Wood of Rannoch. Nos. 4, 7, and 8 are thinly scattered in more than half of the woods. Habit type No. 5 is very rare. It is clear, therefore, that Scots pine in the native woods is heterogeneous in habit type.

As Don (1814) thought, v. *horizontalis* is abundant and the forms f. *fastigiata*, f. *condensata*, and v. *pendula* that are to be found in Scandinavia are also present in the Scottish woods, but the very narrow crown form found in Sweden is very rare in Scotland.

TABLE III OVERLEAF

TABLE III

THE DISTRIBUTION OF THE PRINCIPAL HABIT TYPES OF SCOTS PINE IN THE NATIVE PINEWOODS OF SCOTLAND

A = abundant   F = frequent   O = occasional
R = rare   L = local   — = absent

Habit type No.

	1 v. *horizontalis*	3 f. *ascensa*	4 v. *pyramidalis*	5 f. *fastigiata*	6 f. *condensata*	7 and 8 v. *pendula*
Deeside Group						
Ballochbuie	A	A	R	—	O	R
Glentanar	A	F	R	—	O	R
Mar	A	F	—	—	O	R
Speyside Group						
Abernethy	A	A	R	R	O	R
Rothiemurchus	A	A	O	R	LF	R
Glenmore	A	A	O	R	LF	R
Rannoch Group						
Black Wood of Rannoch	A	A	O	R	LF	R
Old Wood of Meggernie	F	F	—	—	O	R
Great Glen Group						
Glen Moriston	A	F	—	—	R	R
Glengarry	A	F	—	—	R	R
Loch Arkaig and Glen Mallie	F	A	—	—	R	R
Ardgour	A	F	R	—	O	R
Strath Glass Group						
Glen Affric	A	F	O	—	O	R
Glen Cannich	A	F	O	—	O	R
Glen Strathfarrar	A	F	R	—	R	R
Wester Ross Group						
Achnashellach	F	F	—	—	R	R
Coulin	F	F	—	—	R	—
Loch Maree	A	F	—	—	R	R
Shieldaig	F	F	—	—	R	R
Northern Group						
Rhidorroch	F	F	—	—	—	R
Amat	A	A	R	—	O	R
Southern Group						
Black Mount	F	F	R	—	O	R
Glen Orchy	LF	F	—	—	R	—
Tyndrum	F	F	O	—	R	R

CHAPTER 14

THE BARK OF SCOTS PINE

PREVIOUS WORK

THE VARIATIONS in the bark of Scots pine have been studied by research workers in Europe from four different points of view: the bark colour; the bark roughness and thickness; the height to which the rougher basal bark persists up the stem; and the bark units.

The colour of the bark. Many observers (Beissner, 1891; François, 1947; Hess, 1942; Vilmorin, 1862) have recorded differences in the colour of the bark of Scots pine. Beissner (1891) and Elwes and Henry (1908) describe the bark of var. *engadinensis* Heer as reddish, but it is not clear whether this is the basal bark or no, because Rubner (1934) describes it as yellowish. In some instances, however, the statements are more specific. François (1947) states that the bark of the so-called "noble race" of Scots pine in the Vosges is brownish to violet at the base of the stem and a lighter salmon colour higher up. In contrast, the bark of the pine in the nearby plains is blackish to dark bluish grey at the base of the tree and yellow to bright red at the top. Hess (1942) noted the presence of grey and red Scots pine bark variants in the Canton Valais, by the Rhône, probably referring to the basal bark, and he states that the grey-barked pine occurs on the dry slopes up to an elevation of 3330 ft. (1000 m.); the trees are seldom more than 50 ft. (15 m.) high, have flat crowns and strong branches, and are only suitable for firewood. The red-barked pine, on the other hand, is a superior type of tree, occurring at elevations of 3330 to 6670 ft. (1000 to 2000 m.), has pointed crowns and clean stems, and grows to a height of 83 ft. (25 m.). Vilmorin (Brown, 1878; Vilmorin, 1862) noted differences in the degrees of redness and greyness of the upper bark of Scots pine grown under uniform conditions in the provenance trials at Les Barres in France. There is, therefore, evidence that the colour of the bark varies in different types of Scots pine, but none of these investigations appear to take into account the variations in the colour of the bark at different stages in the development of the tree.

The roughness and thickness of the bark. Rough-barked and smooth-barked

Scots pine have been recorded in different parts of Europe, including Scotland (anon., 1941a; François, 1947; Wagenknecht, 1939). Wagenknecht (1939) found in a provenance trial that the pine of northern Latvia, Belgium, and East Prussia had a greater percentage of smooth-barked trees than those of the Brandenburg and Palatinate districts in Germany, the Haute Loire in France, and Inverness-shire in Scotland. He found that in all but a few instances the rough-barked trees had a greater increment during the previous 50 years than the smooth-barked trees. There is evidence (anon., 1941a; François, 1947) that the Scots pine in the Vosges, with relatively narrow crowns and straight stems, have a thinner bark at the base of the tree than the inferior type of Scots pine with broad crowns and crooked stems growing in the nearby plains. In Sweden, the bark of the North Swedish Scots pine, var. (spp.) *lapponica* Fries, is reported to be thinner than that of the pine from southerly pine districts in that country (Holmerz, 1888; Langlet, 1938; Rubner, 1934). Hejtmánek (1953a) found that Scots pine in Slovakia had thicker bark on deep moist rich soils than on poor soils, but he found no clear correlation between diameter increment and bark thickness. Vilmorin (1862) noted differences in the degree of fissuring of the basal bark of Scots pine grown in uniform conditions in the provenance trials at Les Barres, indicating that such differences are not solely due to the environment. These studies, therefore, suggest that geographical races of Scots pine may differ in the thickness and roughness of their bark.

The height to which the rougher basal bark persists up the stem. Sylven (1916) found that the pine in the South and Middle Scots pine regions of Sweden had the thick bark persisting higher up the stem than in north Sweden; this confirmed earlier work by Holmerz and Ortenblad (1886). Lindquist (1935–8), studying the correlations between the height to which the thick bark develops in the broad and narrow crowned types of Scots pine, found certain similarities and differences as follows:

	Percentage of stem with thick bark
Narrow crowned N. Swedish Scots pine	c. 20–30
Broad crowned N. Swedish Scots pine	c. 20–30
Narrow crowned S. Swedish Scots pine	c. 25–50
Broad crowned S. Swedish Scots pine	c. 50–60

He considered these differences to be genetically controlled. Wretlind (1936), however, regarded this opinion as invalid because Lindquist did not state the diameter of the stems investigated, and he suggested that the percentage of thick basal bark on the stems of the pine of north and south Sweden was probably dependent upon the age and development of the tree. Similar bark differences have been recorded for the Scots pine of the Vosges (anon., 1941*a*). The narrow crowned type of pine at the higher elevations has a smaller proportion of rough basal bark than the broader crowned Scots pine of the nearby plains. Wagen-knecht (1939) found that a high percentage of smooth bark on Scots pine was cor-related with a less branchy habit. He noted, however, that the height to which the rough bark reached up the stems increased with the diameter of the tree in all the races of Scots pine examined. Although these investigations did not take into account all the factors involved, they provide some evidence that the percentage of rough basal bark varies in different geographical regions, and perhaps with other characteristics of the pine.

The form of the bark units. The form of the bark units in the lower part of the stem is one of the most variable characters of Scots pine. The classification and significance of these bark variants has long been the subject of lively controversy, particularly in Germany. Seitz (1929-38, 1937) and Dengler (1938, 1944) studied the bark units in great detail. In his investigation of what he calls the "noble race" of Scots pine in Germany, Seitz differentiated three races, the form of the bark being the most distinct characteristic. He called the three races the Plattenkiefer (plate bark pine), Schuppenkiefer (scale bark pine) and Muschelkiefer (mussel bark pine). Seitz claimed that the other morphological characters were correlated with these three bark forms, and the following botanical terms were given to the varieties so formed:

> Plate bark – var. *seitzii* Schwerin (Seitz, 1926)
> Scale bark – var. *kienitzii* Seitz (1929-38)
> Mussel bark – var. *bonaparti* Seitz (1929-38)

Seitz (1929-38) described the varieties as follows:

Plate bark Scots pine (var. seitzii Schwerin)

Bark	Similar to the shell of a turtle. The units are separated vertically and hori-zontally, forming thin, smooth, rose-coloured plates.
Crown	When old, flattened like *Pinus pinea* L. (Umbrella pine). Generally open.
Stem	Tending to branch.
Branches	Yellow, like European larch. Laterally extensive.
Leaves	Scanty, yellow-green foliage.
Female cones	Apophysis not very prominent.
Wood	Uniform grain, low resin content, does not warp. The heartwood is very broad and a dark pink colour when dry. A "mild" wood used in joinery.

Scale bark Scots pine (var. kienitzii *Seitz)*

Bark	Divided vertically into coarse, relatively narrow, brown, partly overlapping scales. Very thick in the lower part of the stem. Similar to larch.
Crown	Conical and dense.
Stem	Bole persistent and not branching.
Branches	Brownish, like Japanese larch. Shorter and with a more upward tendency than in the plate type.
Leaves	Dark green. Leaves denser and more rigid than in the plate type.
Female cones	An elongated cone with a prominent apophysis.
Wood	A resinous wood of coarser grain than the plate type. A tendency to warp. Heartwood narrow and red-brown when dry. Used for rougher work.

Mussel bark Scots pine (var. bonaparti *Seitz)*

Bark	Consists of small, rounded brown scales. Much thinner than the scale type. Similar to spruce.
Crown	Extremely narrow and pointed. Very snow resistant.
Stem	Even straighter than in the scale type.
Branches	Similar to those of the scale type, but more flexible.
Leaves	Blue green.
Female cones	Almost the same as those of the plate type.
Wood	A wood with a long fine grain and very good cleavage. Used for furniture, instruments, etc.

Seitz found that the bark variants were independent of the age and increment of the trees and the environment in which they grew, suggesting that the three types were genetically distinct. He states also that the three types appear to "hybridise" freely, producing trees with intermediate morphological characteristics. He gives examples of trees with plate bark at the base and mussel bark higher up; trees with scale bark at the base and mussel bark higher up; and trees with scale bark below and plate bark higher up. He regards these as intermediate forms or hybrids. He also suggested that the plate type formed part of a "dry series" of Scots pine, producing most timber on dry sites, whilst the scale type and mussel type grow well on moister sites and form a "moist series." He considered it possible that the scale and mussel types form a snow resistant series. Dengler, however, opposed the view that the bark types distinguished by Seitz were genotypic (Dengler, 1938, 1944). He found that the older generation of trees in a two-storied Scots pine wood in Finland had plate bark while the younger generation in the same wood had scale bark. He suggested that plate bark was correlated with advanced age in Scots pine, and that the scale bark trees eventually adopted plate bark as they grew older, the period required for the transition appearing to depend upon soil fertility. He supported this hypothesis by showing that when the bark of a scale bark tree is filed down, plate-like bark is revealed beneath. In addition he found a similar correlation between bark type and age in *Pinus ponderosa*, *P. echinata*, *P. palustris*, and *P. taeda*. More recently it has been shown that young trees of *Pinus caribaea* have thick, grey furrowed bark whilst older trees have flat, squarish, reddish brown plated bark, which lends support to Dengler's view (Little, 1952). In opposition to Seitz's theory, Dengler stated that trees with plate bark had narrower rings than those with scale bark, indicating a bark type/increment correlation. Hejtmánek (1953a) studied the bark form of pine in Slovakia, and noted three types as Seitz had done. He concluded that the three bark types are primarily governed by the developmental stage of the tree, its rate of diameter growth, the site, and genetic factors. He found that the effect of the stage of development on the gradual change to the ultimate plate type is most marked in the younger ages, and this change is correlated with a decline in diameter increment. It is evident, therefore, that a more detailed study of the significance of the principal Scots pine bark variants is necessary before any general conclusions can be drawn.

Scots pine sometimes exhibits certain peculiar bark forms of unknown genetic significance. Fintelmann (1881) recorded a type of Scots pine with bark scales concentrated into rings in the lower part of the stem, the scales overlapping like shingles or slates on a roof. This type has since been recognised by other workers (Beissner, 1911, 1930; Caspary, 1882–3) and is generally called f. *annulata* Fintelmann or the shingle pine. It is not common, but has been recorded at Lake Constance on the German-Austrian-Swiss border. The "Knollenkiefer" is another unusual bark variant of Scots pine. It has numerous humps on the bark, and is generally referred to as f. *gibberosa* Kihlman (Beissner, 1891, 1909, 1911, 1930; Kihlman, 1906; Pardé, 1937). Stecki (1937) described a variant in which the bark had deep indentations arranged in regular parastichies (5/13) on the stem and young shoots. In cross section the annual rings undulate like those of the feather-wood pine ("Federholzkiefer") and goat wood ("Ziegenholz") of the sawmillers. There was no evidence that these indentations were due to pathogenic factors, and Stecki called the variant *sigillata pilsudskiana*.

DESCRIPTION OF THE BARK FORM VARIANTS IN SCOTLAND

A survey of the native pinewoods in Scotland showed that there were many bark form variants. These were classified as follows:

Plate bark types	plate	(P)
	thick plate	(TP)
	long plate	(LP)
	loose, shaggy or senescent plate	(SP)
	small unit plate	(SUP)
Ridge bark types	ridge	(R)
	thin ridge	(ThR)
Flake bark		(F)
Intermediate bark types	plate/ridge	(P/R)
	ridge/plate	(R/P)
	plate/flake	(P/F)
	flake/plate	(F/P)
	ridge/flake	(R/F)
	flake/ridge	(F/R)
Indefinite bark types		(Ind)
Abnormal bark types		—

This classification is purely artificial, being merely a convenient method of description of the variants irrespective of whether or no they are genotypic.

Plate bark (PL. XV.*a*)

This type is synonymous with Seitz's plate bark. In its true form it consists of thin, 5 to 20 mm., smooth, bark units in the basal 25 per cent. of the stem, light greyish to cinnamon-brown in colour, sometimes with a reddish component. The units are more or less isodiametric, generally less than twice as long as wide, but tending to elongate at the extreme base of the tree. They vary considerably in size, but are generally 10 to 20 cm. long. The units are separated by narrow, 5 to 10 mm., shallow fissures. The appearance is of a light-coloured, tight skin around the tree, with a reticulate pattern similar to the shell of a turtle. Higher up the stem the units become smaller and thinner before merging into orange red or yellow, thin papery bark at the top of the tree.
In addition to the true plate bark type there are a number of plate-like variants:

Thick plate: Units either short, 10 to 20 cm., or elongated, 20 to 40 cm.; surfaces smooth and pale grey-brown; 20 to 40 mm. thick.

Long plate: Units thin, 5 to 20 mm.; surface smooth, pale grey-brown to cinnamon-brown; length more than twice the width.

Loose, shaggy or senescent plate: Units thick, 15 to 30 mm.; surface smooth grey-brown to pale grey-brown or cinnamon-brown; frequently much elongated and hanging away from the stem at the base of the tree. In very old trees the bark has a dull, matt surface.

Small unit plate: Units small, 4 to 8 cm. and more or less isodiametric; thin 5 to 20 mm.; pale grey-brown or light cinnamon-brown; sometimes tending to slight concavity.

Ridge bark (PL. XV.*b*)

This type is synonymous with Seitz's scale bark. The true form consists of thick,

20 to 60 mm., rough bark units in the basal 25 per cent. of the stem, dark grey-brown in colour, sometimes appearing almost black. The units are always more than twice as long as wide and are separated by wide, deep, dark brown fissures. They vary in size, but are generally 15 to 30 cm. long, and tend to form an interlocking "plaited" pattern. Higher up the tree the units remain elongated but become smaller, thinner, and smoother before merging into the orange-red or yellow papery bark at the top. The general appearance of the bark is very rough, dark and sombre.

There is one minor variant:

Thin ridge: Units elongated and interlocking; colour dark grey-brown to brown; surfaces matt or slightly roughened; only 5 to 15 mm. thick at breast height.

Flake bark (PL. xv.c)

Synonymous with Seitz's mussel bark. The true form consists of small, 6 cm., more or less isodiametric bark units in the basal 25 per cent. of the stem. The length of the units is never more than twice the width. They are very thin, 2 to 15 mm., smooth, more or less concave, free at their edges, variable in colour but generally a dark grey-brown. At the extreme base of the stem, the bark is commonly dark-coloured and ridge-like. Higher up the tree the bark units generally retain their form becoming smaller and thinner, but sometimes the units tend to elongate slightly higher up the stem before merging into the orange-red or yellow papery bark. Trees with well developed flake bark generally merge into the upper papery bark at or below the middle of the stem. The lower half of the tree gives an impression of a rather dark-coloured, finely reticulated surface.

Intermediate bark types

Plate-ridge intermediates

Plate/Ridge: The bark units in the basal third of the stem have light-coloured, more or less smooth surfaces, and definite plant bark tendencies. They are, however, slightly like ridge bark in that they are thick, 20 to 60 mm., elongated and separated by deep fissures.

Ridge/Plate: Very like ridge bark in that the units in the basal 25 per cent, are dark-coloured, elongated, thick, 20 to 60 mm., and separated by deep fissures. The unit surfaces, however, have plate tendencies, as they are beginning to smooth over and patches of pale colour are apparent.

Plate-flake intermediates

Plate/Flake (PL. xv.d): In the basal third of the stem, the bark units consist of small concave plates, light grey-brown to cinnamon-brown in colour, and more or less free at the edges. The units are thin, 5 to 15 mm., and about 5 to 15 cm. long by 5 cm. wide. In general appearance the bark looks like a flake bark with unusually large, pale-coloured units. At the extreme base of the tree the units approximate to true plate bark. Higher up the stem the bark is almost flake, but lighter coloured. Trees with this bark type commonly have the upper orange-red or yellow upper papery bark persisting to or below the middle of the stem.

Flake/Plate: Almost identical with flake bark, but the surfaces tend to be smoother and a pale grey-brown or cinnamon-brown in colour. At the extreme base of the stem the plate tendency is most pronounced, whilst higher up the units are indistinguishable from flake bark. The upper papery bark generally reaches well down the stem.

Ridge-flake intermediates

Ridge/Flake: In the basal third of the stem the units are elongated and ridge-like, dark grey-brown in colour but rather thin, 10 to 20 mm. The units are free at the edges but not markedly concave. At the extreme base of the stem the units resemble ridge bark, and higher up may resemble true flake bark or be slightly elongate. This type is very like the thin ridge bark variant, but differs in that the margins of the units are free.

Flake/Ridge: In the basal third of the stem, the units are very like true flake bark but are more elongated. At the base of the stem, the bark is ridge-like. The bark colour is dark grey-brown, and the upper papery bark frequently persists below the middle of the stem.

These descriptions all refer to the basal bark. There are, however, a great many trees which have a definite bark type at the base of the stem, and a bark of an entirely different type in the zone between the basal bark and the upper papery bark. The following types were noted:

Base of the tree	Middle of the tree
Plate	Ridge or Thin Ridge
Plate	Ridge/Plate or Plate/Ridge
Plate	Plate/Flake
Small unit Plate	Plate/Flake, Flake/Plate or Flake
Ridge	Thin Ridge
Ridge	Ridge/Flake, Flake/Ridge or Flake
Flake	Flake only
Plate/Flake	Flake
Flake/Plate	Flake
Senescent Plate	Plate, Long Plate, Thick Plate, and Ridge

These intra-tree bark variants are similar to those described by Seitz and regarded by him as bark type hybrids.

Indefinite bark types

There are a great many bark forms in young, mature, and senescent Scots pine which cannot be accurately included in any of these classes. The commonest of these is when the units of the basal bark are elongated and thick like ridge bark, smooth surfaced, and light-coloured like plate bark, with free edges and a tendency to concavity like flake bark. This indefinite type may be a stage in the transition of one bark type to another or, if the view that Scots pine bark variants are genetically controlled is correct, it could be due to hybridisation between trees with plate, ridge, and flake bark over two or more generations.

PLATE XVI

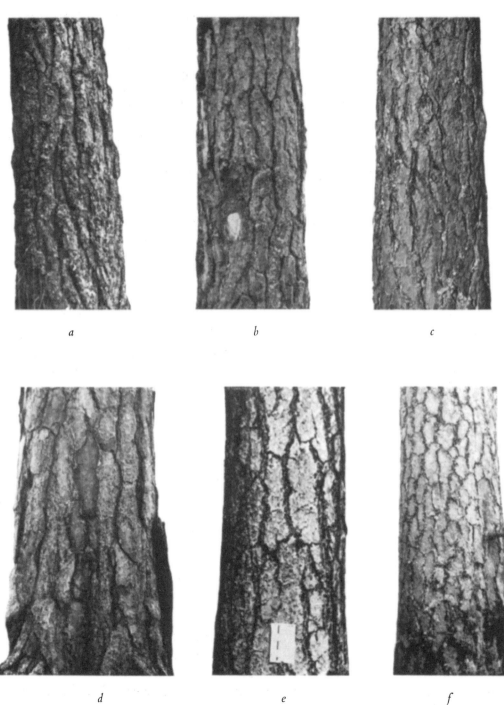

a   *b*   *c*

d   *e*   *f*

A SERIES, (*a*) TO (*f*), SHOWING THE SUCCESSIVE STAGES IN THE PROBABLE DEVELOPMENT
FROM RIDGE TO PLATE BARK (see pp. 259-60)

The peculiar bark form f. *annulata* Fintelmann was not found in Scotland.

Abnormal bark types

Stunting, fire, and deer cause the majority of abnormal bark forms. Stunted trees have bark forms ranging from thick distorted ridge/plate bark to very thin plate/flake bark, and if the branches reach low down the stems of such trees the bark distortion is even more marked. Trees which have been scorched by ground fires have the bark burned away irregularly to give many peculiar forms. Fire generally shortens ridge bark units and widens the fissures, roughens plate bark units, and burns away flake bark completely. Trees with the thicker ridge bark appear able to withstand ground fires which kill neighbouring trees with the thinner plate and flake barks. The effect of deer is limited. In spring the deer rub their antlers against Scots pine stems, wearing down the bark to the thin yellowish or orange-red under-bark, when the tree either forms distorted scar tissues or dies. In a particular region, a great many of the deer appear to favour one particular stem for this purpose, generally one with a smooth bark type such as plate. Such stems are rubbed almost bare.

THE SIGNIFICANCE OF THE BARK FORM VARIANTS IN SCOTLAND

The relationship between bark type and the age of the tree. The ages of a considerable number of trees showing typical plate, ridge, and flake barks were estimated by borings in five of the principal native woods. The reason why the flake bark sample was small is that the type is uncommon:

TABLE IV

Bark type	No. of Samples	Age of the trees in years		
		Mean	Standard Deviation	Range
Plate	73	188	20	150–232
Ridge	93	99	37	26–210
Flake	28	103	36	40–198

The data show: first, that the mean age of trees with plate bark is significantly higher than those with ridge or flake bark; secondly, that plate bark was not found on trees less than 150 years old in this sample, and the age of trees with plate bark varies less than those with ridge or flake bark; and lastly, that ridge and flake bark are to be found on trees with a wide range of age, including the very old, but not commonly over 150 years.

A similar investigation was carried out on trees with intermediate bark forms in the Black Wood of Rannoch:

S

TABLE V

Bark type	No. of Samples	Age of the trees in years		
		Mean	Standard Deviation	Range
Plate-Ridge	20	160	16	130–190
Plate-Flake	6	171	23	145–210
Ridge-Flake	10	52	15	38–85

The data suggest that intermediate bark types with plate bark tendencies (plate-ridge and plate-flake) are found on older trees than ridge-flake intermediates.

In the same wood the percentages of the principal bark types were estimated in a number of more or less even-aged groups of different ages. All the sample groups were 30 to 90 per cent. stocked, the older stands being more open than the younger stands. The approximate age class of each group was assessed by borings from ten trees per group including trees with the greatest and smallest girths in each stand:

TABLE VI

THE INCIDENCE OF THE BARK TYPES IN STANDS OF SCOTS PINE OF DIFFERENT AGES IN THE BLACK WOOD OF RANNOCH, PERTHSHIRE

Age of Stand (yrs)	Bark type						Samples
	Plate	Ridge	Flake	Plate/Ridge	Plate/Flake	Ridge/Flake	
	%	%	%	%	%	%	
40–60	—	70	4	—	—	26	100
40–60	—	80	6	—	—	15	100
40–60	—	85	6	—	—	9	50
60–80	—	80	4	—	—	16	50
60–80	—	84	5	1	—	10	50
80–110	—	76	2	4	—	18	50
80–110	—	80	6	6	—	8	50
110–140	—	60	4	20	—	16	40
140–160	20	30	—	40	10	—	40
160–200	48	4	—	44	4	—	25

These data show that whilst ridge bark and allied types predominate in stands less than 140 years old, plate bark and allied types predominate in older stands. In addition, plate bark was completely absent from stands of less than 140 years, although some trees in 60 to 80-year-old groups had plate tendencies. Flake bark was uncommon in all sample groups and at all ages, but was completely absent from stands of more than 140 years.

The form of the bark of Scots pine aged 190 to 300 years was recorded in various native pinewoods. The commonest type of abnormal bark associated with extreme age is one consisting of very large, rough, thick plate-like units, with their surfaces locally bleached. Sometimes the units hang away from the base of the tree to give the stem a shaggy appearance. Sometimes the bark units are so thick and roughened as to resemble a very coarse irregular ridge bark. It is only possible to assess the true bark type of such trees by examining the part of the stem above the zone of such abnormal development.

These investigations indicate that there is a relationship between the form of the bark and the age of the tree. The evidence supports Dengler's view that plate bark is associated with old age, but also indicates that all bark types do not necessarily become plate bark at maturity, some trees retaining ridge or flake bark to about 200 years. Seitz's opinion that the principal bark types occurred independently of the age of the tree is not correct so far as Scots pine in Scotland is concerned. Plate bark is most common in the 150 to 200 age class and has not been observed on trees younger than about 120 years. Seitz showed that ridge bark occurs on very old trees, but, while this has been confirmed, it is exceptional; and in most instances trees with ridge and flake bark are less than 140 years old.

If ridge bark and similar forms predominate in the younger stands (Table VI), and plate bark and allied types are restricted to older stands, most of the trees with ridge bark must develop into plate types as they mature. It is only possible to conjecture what bark forms the tree adopts in the process of transition from ridge to plate, but it is evident that there must be a thinning, smoothing, foreshortening, and adoption of a lighter colour by the units. It seems likely that at first the ridge units smooth over, becoming the plate/ridge intermediate forms. This is supported by the fact that the mean age of the trees with plate/ridge intermediate bark which were examined was 160 years, while the mean ages of plate and ridge bark trees were 188 and 99 years respectively, but some trees retain plate/ridge intermediate bark to at least 190 years. The next stage in the transition is less clear. Both ridge and plate/ridge bark are comparatively thick in comparison with plate bark, and there is no evidence of any sudden shedding of the bark in healthy Scots pine, hence the bark must become thinner very gradually over a long period. Before the final isodiametric plate units are formed, it seems likely that the bark passes through a phase of long plate units. There is definite evidence that this type gradually forms transverse fissures across its long, thin units to form shorter units approaching the isodiametric type (PL. XVI).

The flake bark does not enter into this transition at all and apparently forms part of another bark series. It does not commonly occur on old trees, and it is necessary to consider what form it adopts at maturity. It seems likely that the majority of trees with flake bark assume plate/flake bark at maturity, either as a final stage or as a transitional form. The plate/flake type is associated with advanced age and the units are similar to flake bark in their form, thinness, and concavity, being only larger, smoother and lighter coloured (PL. XVII). Furthermore both types are comparatively uncommon in their true forms. It may be that even plate/flake bark is not a final form because there is often small unit plate bark at the extreme base of trees of this type, with very small isodiametric units with little or no concavity, and it is possible that the latter is the final stage in this series.

There are, therefore, two probable series:

Ridge   —   Ridge/Plate   —   Long Plate   —   Plate
Flake   —   Plate/Flake   —   (Small Unit Plate)

The relationship between bark type and diameter increment. The rate of increase in diameter of a tree must have some influence on the form of the bark units, because the mechanical stresses set up may rupture the periderm or stimulate the cork cambium. The question arises, therefore, whether or no the principal bark types, plate, ridge and flake, are due directly to differences in the rate of diameter growth over long periods.

Increment borings were made on a number of trees in different native pinewoods that had typical plate, ridge, and flake bark types, were of similar height and girth, and were growing together under comparable conditions of site and competition. The borings gave the diameter increment over periods of 50 to 100 years. It was not practicable to get a sufficient number of such comparable sets of trees to give reliable statistical analysis. The data showed, however, that there is no consistent pattern of correlation between bark type and diameter increment, but there are certain trends. Plate bark is usually found on trees growing more slowly than ridge, but there are exceptions. Flake bark is generally found on trees growing faster than ridge, but there were instances of the reverse tendency. It may be concluded, therefore, that while diameter increment is probably a factor influencing bark type, it is not the principal cause. This conclusion is at variance with Seitz's view (1937) that bark type is independent of increment, but does not go so far as Dengler's (1944) that there is a correlation.

The effect of the environment upon the bark. Severe exposure causes a stunting and distortion of Scots pine together with the formation of abnormal bark units. The units may be twisted, and are generally smoothed and bleached by weathering,

PLATE XVII

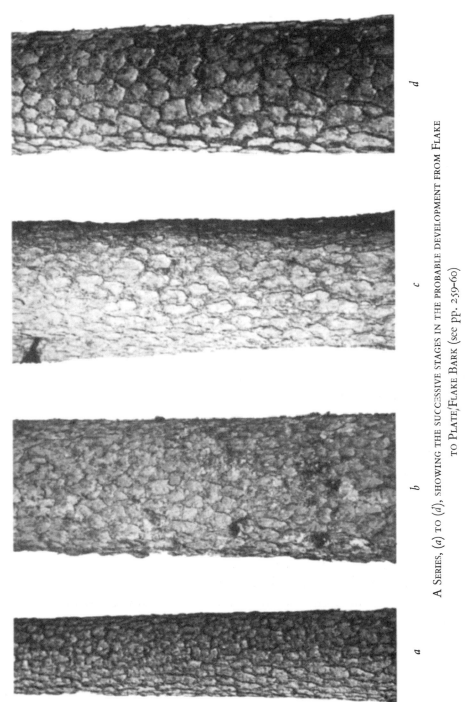

a   *b*   *c*   *d*

A SERIES, (*a*) TO (*d*), SHOWING THE SUCCESSIVE STAGES IN THE PROBABLE DEVELOPMENT FROM FLAKE
TO PLATE-FLAKE BARK (see pp. 259–60)

so that trees with ridge bark at exposed forest margins often adopt a bark form similar to plate/ridge or thick plate. These latter types are not, however, due solely to weathering as they occur on sheltered as well as exposed sites. While there is no doubt that the weathering causes a smoothing of the bark units, the normal smooth bark types such as plate, thin ridge, flake bark, and allied types are not ascribable to this cause, because they are found also on sheltered sites.

The principal bark types are to be found under all conditions of soil and natural drainage in the native pinewoods. In some, however, the plate bark type is often to be found on trees on poorly drained sites. The explanation is probably that such trees are very old, and have escaped felling in the past because they were stunted. It has been stated already that plate bark does not normally develop until an age of about 140 years is reached, but there is evidence that the age of transition is lower on more fertile soils.

The relationship between bark type and heartwood formation. This relationship was investigated by estimating the percentage of red heartwood at the stump in a number of trees of the principal bark types, growing under comparable conditions in seven native pinewoods. The trees ranged in age from 130 to 190 years. The number of estimates did not permit of reliable statistical analysis, but plate bark trees tended to have the highest percentage of heartwood, confirming Seitz's earlier statement (1929-38), but such trees were also older, and this and not bark type may be the more important factor. Trees with flake bark had the lowest percentage, but they were younger on the average. In trees of about the same age, the percentage of heartwood in the ridge bark type was only a little less than that in the plate type. From the practical point of view, plate bark trees in Scottish native pinewoods may be assumed to have a high percentage of red heartwood, irrespective of size. But practically all the trees over about 100 years in the native pinewoods have some red heartwood.

The genetics of the bark types. It has been shown that the factors controlling bark type are not so clearly defined as either Seitz or Dengler thought, the former regarding the plate, ridge, and flake barks as genetically determined, and the latter placing emphasis on the effects of age and increment on the trees. Age of tree may be important in two ways. First, it has been shown that plate bark is only found on old trees. Secondly, there may be a change in bark type with age, for example ridge to plate, and flake to plate/flake. While diameter increment may have some influence on the bark type, it is not the controlling factor. Further, trees with the different bark types are to be found growing side by side under the same site conditions. While the evidence is inconclusive, it is possible that the bark types are genetically controlled, and this can only be determined by long term progeny trials under controlled conditions. If there are bark genotypes, the available evidence suggests that they are as follows:

(a) Trees with plate bark or allied forms when over 120 years old, and ridge bark when younger.
(b) Trees which retain ridge bark throughout their life.
(c) Trees with plate-flake or small unit plate when mature and flake bark when younger.
(d) Trees which retain flake bark throughout their life.

If the existence of genotypic bark differences is accepted, the possibility of hybridisation has to be considered. Seitz (1929-38) recognised this possibility and described as hybrid trees these with one bark type in the lower part of the stem and another in the upper. It is, however, necessary to take into account the factor of bark development with age. In an older tree there is thin papery bark above, and thick bark at the basal part of the stem, with a different zone between, the three bark zones representing three stages in bark ripeness. It would seem, therefore, that a stem observed by Seitz with, for example, ridge bark higher up and plate bark lower down was merely a tree which had changed from ridge to plate below and remained ridge above. Most bark variations within trees can be attributed to such changes. Trees with flake bark above and ridge bark below do not, however, conform with this theory as it is unlikely that flake bark will develop into ridge. All flake bark stems, however, have a zone of thick ridge-like bark at their bases, and such trees may be flake bark stems with more basal ridge-like bark than usual. This may or may not be due to a flake × ridge cross. On these grounds the suggestion that trees with two bark types per stem are hybrids seems improbable. It seems more likely that the many indefinite and intermediate bark types in the basal third of the stem are the true bark hybrids.

The Distribution of the Scots Pine bark Variants in Scotland

The percentages of the bark types were assessed by sampling in all the major native pinewoods in each geographical group. All abnormal bark types were classified as "indefinite" and long plate, shaggy plate, and small unit plate were included as plate. The data are shown in Table VII.

TABLE VII

THE PERCENTAGE OF BARK TYPES IN THE MAJOR GEOGRAPHICAL GROUPS OF NATIVE SCOTS PINE WOODLANDS

Bark type	Deeside	Speyside	Rannoch	Great Glen	Strath Glass	Wester Ross	Northern	Southern	All Scotland
								Geographical Group	
P	34·8	18·0	24·1	41·5	30·2	29·8	21·2	54·5	33·7
TP	3·9	2·7	1·9	3·4	1·4	6·0	2·7	2·8	2·9
R	28·5	42·1	36·1	23·2	34·7	29·0	33·9	6·5	28·0
ThR	1·5	5·2	9·8	0·2	0·4	0·3	4·0	4·5	3·5
F	2·2	2·0	1·7	1·3	1·8	5·1	3·0	1·7	2·0
P/R	9·3	5·7	5·9	10·1	6·6	7·8	8·0	7·7	7·6
R/P	10·8	9·3	5·5	10·0	15·3	10·3	18·3	5·9	9·6
P/F	2·8	1·7	2·0	4·2	4·3	4·1	3·6	5·3	3·5
F/P	2·5	0·8	0·7	1·0	1·6	3·2	1·0	2·4	1·6
R/F	2·2	5·6	5·1	3·4	3·2	0·9	2·4	1·4	3·2
F/R	0·9	4·8	2·9	1·0	0·3	1·0	1·4	1·5	1·9
Ind	0·8	2·1	5·1	0·7	0·2	2·5	0·7	6·1	2·6
No. of Samples	2400	2300	2350	2091	1930	800	600	2195	15166

P=plate; TP=thick plate; R=ridge; ThR=thin ridge; F=flake; P/R=plate/ridge; R/P=ridge/plate; P/F=plate/flake; F/P=flake/plate; R/F=ridge/flake; F/R=flake/ridge; and Ind=indefinite

CHAPTER 15

THE BUDS, SHOOTS, AND LEAVES OF SCOTS PINE

BUDS

Previous work. The buds of Scots pine are generally oblong-ovate in form, 6·4 to 12·7 mm. long, with lance-shaped fringed scales. These scales are greyish red in colour with a coat of exuded resin (Beissner, 1930; Borthwick, 1906; Dallimore, 1954).

Variations in the bud colour and resin deposit have been recorded for a number of dwarf varieties of Scots pine, including variants such as light brown, brownish red, light red brown, dark crimson brown, red, and crimson, and buds which are either non-resinous or very resinous (Hornibrook, 1923, 1938). Nothing is known however, about how the bud colour and resin deposit characters vary within individual trees, or under different conditions of environment.

Variation in Scotland. Three bud characters were investigated: form, resin deposit, and colour. The first two varied considerably within individual trees, and hence could not be used to differentiate between trees. The colour, however, was found to be constant within each tree, and any slight variation was due to differences in the stage of ripening.

A study of the bud colour in 1000 pine distributed in different native woods showed that in over 90 per cent. the colour was red-grey-brown. In the remainder it was bright red, not unlike that in Douglas fir (*Pseudotsuga taxifolia*). There are, therefore, two bud colours variant in the native Scots pine in Scotland.

SHOOTS

SHOOT COLOUR

Previous work. The young shoots of Scots pine are usually stated to be green or greenish brown, smooth, and shiny, becoming greyish brown in the second year (Clapham, 1952; Dallimore, 1954). Those from trees of Scottish origin have been described as being reddish (Candolle, 1878), citron-grey-green, russet grey (Murray, 1920), and a reddish ash colour (Sowerby, 1868). Apart from this, very little is known about the variations in the colour of the shoot of Scots pine. The possibility of the existence of marked variations is indicated by the wide range of shoot colours which are found on the various dwarf and semi-dwarf horticultural varieties of Scots pine (Hornibrook, 1923, 1938).

Variation in Scotland. A study of the shoot colour in individual Scots pine showed that there is a sequence of colour change with age of shoot. The newly formed spring shoots are pale yellowish green, turning to green or green-brown in the first summer, and to pale brown during the following autumn and winter. In the second year they remain brown, and in the third become greyish brown. Older shoots show a reddish-orange colour flecked with grey brown. The time of change varies within individual trees, the rate being faster in the more vigorous shoots. In studying the variations in shoot colour between trees, it is necessary, therefore, to consider the overall transition as well as the age of the shoot.

An investigation of shoot colour in 500 mature trees in different native pine-woods showed that it did not vary appreciably except in the sequence already described.

MALE AND FEMALE SHOOTS

Previous work. Although Scots pine is essentially a monoecious species, some shoots, branches, and even whole trees are predominantly of one sex. There is evidence that the vegetative morphology of the shoots exhibits variations which depend upon whether or no the shoot has produced an abundance of male or female cones in successive years. For example according to Galpern (1949), the male branches are usually to be found at the base of the crown, and the shoots bearing male inflorescences are thin and flexible with sparsely distributed leaf fascicles, while those bearing female cones occur mainly on the south side near the top of the crown, and are much coarser, thicker, more rigid, and bear denser foliage. The purely vegetative shoots bearing neither male nor female cones over a period closely resemble the female shoots in their rigidity and foliage density. Sylven (1916) noted similar differences in Scots pine in Sweden, the foliage on the male shoots having a curious verticillate or whorl-like arrangement. Trees which bear a high proportion of male shoots, therefore, have a very different appearance to the trees with mainly female shoots. One type in Switzerland, north Germany, and the Tyrol exhibits this male character to such an extent that it is regarded by some workers as a distinct variety *monticola* Schröter. It produces a profusion of male inflorescences for eight or more years in succession, and retains its needles for as long as eight years (Beissner, 1930; Burbridge, 1939; Kirchner, 1908; Pohl, 1939; Schröter, 1895). The illustration provided by Kirchner *et al.* (1908) clearly shows the "whorling" leaf arrangement resembling that of the Japanese umbrella pine (*Sciadopitys verticillata*). It is not known to what extent the production of these masses of male inflorescences is due to genetic or environmental factors, but it has to be taken into account in studying the morphological variations in the leaves.

Variation in Scotland. A study of individual Scots pine in native pinewoods showed that the differences described by Galpern (1949) were to be found in Scotland. In addition, there are significantly more resin canals per leaf in leaves from female and vegetative shoots than from male shoots. These variations were allowed for in the study of leaf dimensions and anatomy, by confining the samples to predominantly female or vegetative shoots.

Scots pine which are predominantly male in character and resemble var. *monticola* Schröter in their vegetative morphology are to be found in all major native pinewoods, but only constitute about two per cent. of the total. These trees bear male inflorescences for more than four years in succession on shoots in all parts of the crown except the very top where the shoots are either vegetative or female; if female cones are produced at all they are confined to this part of the crown. Entirely male trees were found, and the vegetative shoots were restricted to the top of the crown. Such trees have a singular appearance, their widely separated "whorls" of leaves giving the impression of low foliar vigour. This character was found to remain constant up to four years, but what happens beyond that period is not known. Completely female and vegetative trees were not found in the native pinewoods, all trees bearing at least one branch of predominantly male character, generally at the base of the crown. In many trees both male and female flowers are produced on the same branch in the same season.

LEAVES

THE LEAF DIMENSIONS

Previous work. The length of the leaf of the Scots pine has been described as 2·5 to 10·2 cm. (Dallimore, 1954) and 3·0 to 8·0 (sometimes 10) cm. (Clapham, 1952). It has been found to vary in different Scots pine varieties and in different regions, and in some instances the leaves are so short that distinct short-leaved varieties have been differentiated:

v. *brevifolia* Heer	A tree with a narrow pointed crown and very short leaves found in Switzerland and Silesia (Christ, 1863).
v. *parvifolia* Heer	A small tree with bluish leaves less than 25 mm. long occurring in Lombardy and Sweden (Beissner, 1930; Engler, 1913b; Heer, 1862; Pardé, 1937; Rehder, 1940; Rosenbohm, 1882).

v. *microphylla* Schwerin	A tree with slender branches bearing thin, acute leaves only 10 to 15 mm. long. Probably synonymous with v. *parvifolia* Heer (Beissner, 1891, 1909, 1930; Dallimore, 1954; Elwes, 1908; Schwerin, 1906; Sylven, 1910).
v. *brachyphylla* Wittrock	Leaves 5 to 12 mm. long. Generally regarded as synonymous with v. *parvifolia* (Beissner, 1906; Sylven, 1910; Wittrock, 1906).

Beissner (1891) states that v. *microphylla* breeds true and does not revert, hence, in some instances, the short leaf character appears to be genetically controlled.

In addition to these extreme types a great many varieties and forms of Scots pine have been described as having short leaves, the majority of which are either dwarf types or from mountain or northerly regions:

v. *altaica* Ledebour (Gordon, 1858, 1880) (synonymous with v. *uralensis* Fitschen)
v. *compressa* Carrière (1867)
v. *engadinensis* Heer (Beissner, 1891, 1909; Heer, 1862)
v. *globosa* hort. (Bean, 1951)
v. *hercynica* Münch (1924)
v. *intermedia* Loudon (1883)
v. *lapponica* Fries (Schott, 1907)
v. *nana* Carrière (Carrière, 1867; Hornibrook, 1923, 1938)
v. *nevadensis* Christ (Christ, 1863; Elwes, 1908; Veitch, 1881, 1900)
v. *pygmaea* Beissner (Beissner, 1891, 1909, 1930; Hornibrook, 1923, 1938)
v. *scotica* Schott (Dallimore, 1954)
v. *tortuosa* Don (Don, 1814; Loudon, 1838)
v. *turfosa* Woerlein (Beissner, 1930; Woerlein, 1893)
v. *vindelica* Schott (Schott, 1907)

Scots pine with unusually long leaves have been described under the names of v. *latifolia* Gordon (syn. v. *persica* hort.) and v. *divaricata* Beissner (1930), the latter being unexpectedly a Scots pine of high elevations.

There is evidence that Scots pine growing in northern latitudes and at high elevations usually have shorter leaves than pine in more southerly and low lying situations. Sylven (1916) showed that the mean length of Scots pine in north Sweden is less than that in the south.

The mean length of the needles in mm.

	21–25	26–30	31–35	36–40	41–45	46–50	51–55
			per cent.				
N. Sweden	2·9	39·8	45·6	11·2	0·4	—	—
S. Sweden	—	—	13·9	33·3	29·2	22·2	1·4
Intermediate zone	—	6·25	12·5	50·0	25·0	6·25	—

In Germany, the mountain variety v. *hercynica* Münch has shorter and stiffer leaves than the pine of the adjacent lowlands, v. *supperrhenana* Schott and v. *borussica* Schott (Münch, 1924). Similarly the needles of the narrow crowned Scots pine in the Vosges Mountains of France are short (35 to 45 mm.), in comparison with both the pine of the adjacent plains (65 mm. or more), and the pine of the intermediate zone between mountains and lowlands (40 to 50 mm.) (anon., 1941*a*).

The leaf length varies considerably within individual Scots pine and even on individual shoots (Rinvall, 1914). The leaves of the leader and main branches are longer than those on the smaller twigs (Borthwick, 1906), and shaded leaves are smaller than those in well lighted positions (Liese, 1929). In the day length conditions of England (Wareing, 1949, 1950) and southern Russia (Tolsky, 1913), the Scots pine leaf ceases to increase in length in the August-September period of the first years. Wareing (1950) found that if Scots pine are exposed to a short photoperiod (10 hours) the leaves cease to elongate earlier and are shorter than those grown in normal day length conditions in England. This suggests that differences in the length of the leaves of Scots pine from different latitudes may be due to differences in the day length.

There is very little information available concerning the variations in the width of the Scots pine leaf. It is generally from 1 to 2 mm. wide (Clapham, 1952), and one variety from Asia Minor (v. *latifolia* Gordon) is described as having unusually wide leaves (Gordon, 1858, 1880).

The length : width ratio of the leaf was studied in Sweden by Sylven (1916), and he found that this value was significantly less in north than in south Sweden.

Variation in Scotland. A study of leaf length in individual native Scots pine showed that it is relatively constant in different parts of the crown except on the leader where the leaves are longer, and on very short shoots which have shorter leaves, and should not be used in sampling.

The effect of altitude and degree of natural drainage on leaf length was investigated in Glentanar Forest. It was found that at 900 ft. (270 m.) the mean length was 40 mm., and at 1400 ft. (420 m.) 32 mm., the differences being highly significant statistically. At a given elevation, the needle length was longer, 42 mm., where the natural drainage was good than where it was poor, 38 mm. The difference in this instance was just significant.

Leaf length was also investigated in thirty-one of the principal native pinewoods. It varied from woodland to woodland and group to group, but there were no definite topoclines either north to south or east to west.

The mean length of the native Scots pine leaf is 44, S.D. 6 mm., and is similar to that in south Sweden, where there is a range of 31 to 55 mm. (Sylven, 1916).

PLATE XVIII

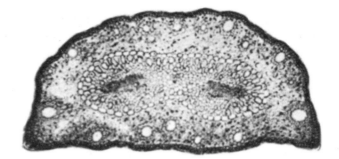

a

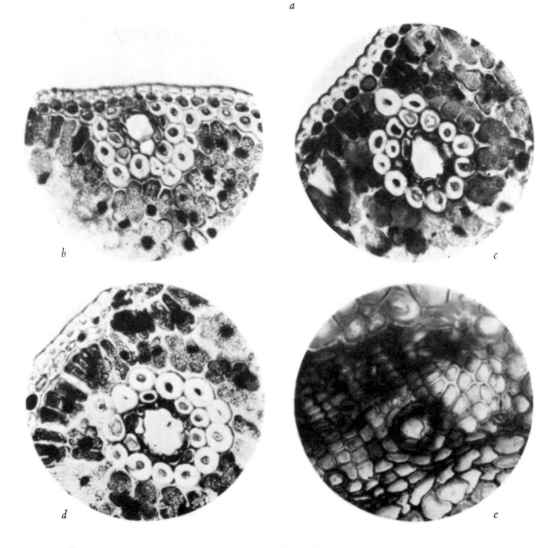

TRANSVERSE SECTIONS FROM THE MIDDLE OF SCOTS PINE LEAVES TO ILLUSTRATE POSITION
OF RESIN CANALS (see CHAPTER 15)

(*a*) Marginal, median, and stelar positions; (*b*) marginal canal with hypodermis forming
part of the sheath; (*c*) canal in an intermediate position linked to the hypodermis by
one thick-walled aclerosed cell; (*d*) medial canal separated from hypodermis by paren-
chyma of the mesophyll; (*e*) stelar canal in xylem of the leaf vascular bundle.

Site and not genetic factors appear to be more important in determining leaf length in Scotland and none of the short leaf varieties were found.

LEAF COLOUR

Previous work. The leaves of Scots pine are usually described as grey-green or blue-green in colour (Clapham, 1952; Dallimore, 1954; Poskin, 1949). A number of leaf colour variants have been recorded ranging from white or silvery to yellow-green or golden and even variegated, and some are so distinct that they have been called varieties.

The whiteness or silvery sheen is due to deposits of wax and varies in intensity; the most extreme type is var. *argentea* Steven, from the Caucasus, with both silvery leaves and cones, the former remaining white even when dry (Bean, 1951; Beissner, 1891, 1909; Carrière, 1867; Dallimore, 1954; Elwes, 1908; Gordon, 1858, 1880; Hornibrook, 1923, 1938; Loudon, 1883; Mouillefert, 1892-8; Rehder, 1940; Schwerin, 1906; Steven, 1838; Veitch, 1881, 1900). Other Scots pine varieties with a definite but less well marked glaucous sheen on the leaves are: v. *horizontalis* Don (1814); v. *nevadensis* Christ (1863); v. *latifolia* Gordon (1858, 1880); v. *genevensis* Beissner (Hornibrook, 1923, 1938); v. *parvifolia* Heer (1862); v. (ssp.) *scotica* Schott (Dallimore, 1954); v. *nana* Carrière (Hornibrook, 1923, 1938); and Auvergne (France) Scots pine (Büsgen, 1929; Schott, 1907). It is not known to what extent the environment influences the glaucous colour of Scots pine leaves. It has been shown, however, that the wax deposit on shaded leaves of *Abies* species is less than on well lighted leaves (Büsgen, 1929; Taubert, 1926), but this is probably less definite in the genus *Pinus*.

There are two named varieties of Scots pine which bear golden foliage: v. *aurea* Beissner, leaves of which are golden yellow in autumn and winter, becoming green in the following summer (Bean, 1951; Beissner, 1891, 1909; Dallimore, 1954; Elwes, 1908; Fraser, 1875; Rehder, 1940; Veitch, 1881, 1900); and v. *beissneriana* Schwerin which is very similar to v. *aurea*, but the leaves are green at first becoming golden yellow later (Beissner, 1909, 1930; Schwerin, 1906). Yellow, pale green and creamy leaves may be due to a low chlorophyll content (Langlet, 1942) induced by soil factors. Two Scots pine leaf colour variants with chlorophyll deficiencies have been described as *nivea* Schwerin (1906), and *variegata* Caspary (Bean, 1951; Beissner, 1891, 1909; Carrière, 1867; Dallimore, 1954; Degelius, 1943; Gordon, 1858, 1880; Langlet, 1937; Mouillefert, 1892-8). The former has leaves which are milk white at first, becoming greenish in the summer, and finally a dirty white. The plant grows well initially, but is very sensitive to transplanting. The latter has variegated leaves, green speckled white or creamy white. Degelius (1943) found v. *variegata* growing alongside Scots pine with normally coloured foliage, indicating that it is unlikely that the variegation is directly due to the environment. Eiche (1955) has studied spontaneous chlorophyll mutations in pine in Sweden.

A Scots pine leaf colour variant with grass-green leaves, v. *viridis compacta* Beissner (1930), has been recorded, but is only of horticultural interest.

It has been found that Scots pine from northern localities and other regions with severe winter climates have a striking yellow-brown or violet leaf colour in winter, contrasting with the dark green colour in southerly regions and under mild maritime climates. The yellow-brown winter leaf colour has been associated with frost hardiness (Büsgen, 1929; Engler, 1913*b*; Kienitz, 1922).

Dengler (1939) investigated the inheritance of the leaf colour in Scots pine. He found that a blue-needled female parent from France crossed with a yellow-needled male parent from Russia gave blue-needled progeny. The reverse cross gave a yellow-needled progeny. Leaf colour, however, is not always determined by the female parent, because a glaucous female parent from Scotland crossed with a yellow-needled male parent from Russia produced progeny with yellow needles. This evidence shows that, while the leaf colour is undoubtedly influenced by soil factors in many instances, it may be an inherent character.

Variation in Scotland. Before variations between trees can be studied, it is necessary to know how constant is the leaf colour within individual trees. It was found that there were seasonal variations, the leaf colour in summer being more glaucous than in winter. Within a tree, leaf colour is relatively constant throughout the crown, but shoots that have borne male flowers over a period of years have less glaucous foliage than female and vegetative shoots.

There are four summer leaf colour variants in the native pinewoods:

Glaucous or silvery	Leaves covered with a thick deposit of white wax giving a silvery sheen which fades somewhat in the first winter and the following seasons. The silvery appearance is most marked in July to August, but is never as glaucous as var. *argentea*, and does not extend to the cones.
Grey green	The leaves are green to dark green with a well developed waxy deposit which tends to fade in the first winter and the following seasons. It is never as silvery as the glaucous variant.
Bright green or deep green	Green leaves with little wax deposit at any time of the year.
Golden green or yellow green	Very pale yellowish-green leaves with a faint waxy bloom which rapidly fades and almost completely disappears. They are not as golden as the leaves of arboretum specimens of var. *aurea*.

Trees with glaucous and grey-green leaves predominate in the native woods, and are of all ages from three years upwards, of all degrees of vigour, and are found on all manner of sites. Moreover, leaves produced in successive seasons retain their distinctive colour. The other two leaf colour types are found on trees of low vigour, the colour being probably due to adverse site factors.

Only about ten per cent. of the trees growing on favourable sites develop a yellowish colour in the winter, which confirms the views of previous workers that the leaves of Scots pine in maritime climates generally remain green.

LEAF PERSISTENCE

Previous work. The average life of a Scots pine leaf is usually stated to be two to three years, but this is variable. The rate of growth of the shoot appears to be important, slow growing shoots retaining their leaves longer (Büsgen, 1929), and when these bear male flowers for several years in succession, the leaves may persist up to nine years (Borthwick, 1906; Sylven, 1916). Shade leaves persist longer than sun (Schrieber, 1924).

Latitude appears to have an influence; the leaves persist for four to nine years in north Sweden but only three to six in the south (Holmerz, 1888; Sylven, 1916). This may be due to climatic or inherent factors, but it has been found that, when Scots pine are transplanted from northern and mountain habitats to different climatic conditions, they retain their leaves for the same period as in their original habitat (Zedebauer, 1916). This suggests that leaf persistence is at least partly genetic.

The incidence of leaf diseases, such as *Lophodermium pinastri*, may cause premature leaf fall (Hartig, 1894; Hubert, 1931; Tubeuf, 1897) and certain strains of Scots pine, for example the Scottish, are more resistant to this disease (Ruzicka, 1929; Wiedemann, 1930).

Variation in Scotland. A study of leaf persistence in individual native trees showed that although it varied, the mean life was the same in all parts of the crown. It was also confirmed that leaves on male shoots persisted for periods up to eight years compared with less than five on other shoots.

The mean leaf persistence was determined in the principal native pinewoods of each geographical group. The results are shown in Table VIII.

There are differences between the groups, and some are statistically significant. For example, the leaves live longer in the Speyside and Rannoch groups than in the Southern, and in Deeside compared with Wester Ross. The mean persistence of the leaves of Scots pine in Scotland is between three and four years, the range being two to five. This is similar to that in south Sweden (Sylven, 1916).

TABLE VIII

LEAF PERSISTENCE IN SCOTS PINE

Geographical group	No. of sample trees	Mean leaf persistence in years			
		2	3	4	5
		per cent.			
Deeside	300	—	31·7	56·7	11·7
Speyside	250	0·4	21·2	70·0	8·4
Rannoch	100	—	32·0	46·0	22·0
Great Glen	290	2·1	46·9	49·7	1·4
Strath Glass	375	9·3	58·4	30·4	1·9
Wester Ross	250	2·8	61·1	34·8	0·8
Northern	190	2·1	60·5	37·4	—
Southern	350	13·4	76·9	9·7	—

OTHER EXTERNAL LEAF CHARACTERS

The leaf sheath. The leaf sheath of Scots pine consists of about ten scale leaves (Borthwick, 1906), and is approximately 0·8 cm. long, whitish at first, becoming grey later (Dallimore, 1954).

There is little variation in the colour of the sheath, except that there is a seasonal change from pale greyish brown in the first summer to dark brown in subsequent years.

Leaf twist. The leaves of Scots pine generally show some twisting which may sometimes be so marked as to be called a variety, for example v. *tortuosa* Don (1814), and v. *crispata* Schwerin (Beissner, 1930). Carrière (1867) found, however, that the leaf twist character is not constant.

Trees showing different degrees of twisting were seen in the native pinewoods in Scotland. Studies on young plants showed that marked twisting continued season after season in some, but not in others. Only one example of the persistence of twisting on an old tree was seen.

GENERAL LEAF ANATOMY

PL. XVIII.*a* illustrates a transverse section of a Scots pine leaf. It exhibits xerophilous characters; the epidermal cells are thick-walled with a small lumen and are covered by a layer of cutin on the outer walls, thus serving both as a waterproof covering and an exoskeleton. The hypodermis is well developed and consists of collenchyma with moderately thick walls and colourless cell contents. There are stomata on both sides of the leaf in pits filled with white wax and arranged in parallel rows. The leaf mesophyll consists of plate-shaped parenchymatous cells with markedly convoluted walls and large intercellular spaces, and contains two large resin canals, and up to fourteen smaller. It is stated in the literature that these canals are marginal. Each of these consists of a sheath of one or two layers of thick walled cells with an inner lining of 12 to 16 resin secreting, epithelial cells surrounding a central intercellular cavity. The central stele is surrounded by an endodermis with regular elliptic cells and contains two vascular bundles separated by a mass of thick walled cells with transfusion cells associated with the xylem masses (Borthwick, 1906; Haberlandt, 1914; Strasburger, 1930; Sutherland, 1934).

Preliminary studies showed that only two of these tissues are of use in studies of genotypic anatomical differences: The resin canals; and the development of the thick-walled cells separating the vascular bundles.

THE NUMBER OF RESIN CANALS PER LEAF

Previous work. The number of resin canals in the Scots pine leaf varies between two and fifteen (Wittrock, 1889). The short-leaved varieties, such as *microphylla*, have fewer canals than those with leaves of normal length (Sylven, 1910). It has also been found that the number is greater in pine in north Sweden than in south (Holmerz, 1888). Fieschi (1932) has found in *Pinus pinaster* that it is possible to separate the Atlantic and Mediterranean types by number of resin canals at the base of the leaf.

Variation in Scotland. Before investigating the difference in resin canal number per leaf between trees in the native pinewoods, it was necessary to elucidate the pattern of variation within individual trees, using sufficient numbers to permit of statistical analysis. It was found that the number of resin canals, as determined by transverse sections, varied from the base to the tip of the leaf and was highest near the middle. Shorter leaves, including those on shoots bearing male flowers in successive years, had a significantly smaller number than longer leaves. Although there was considerable variation from leaf to leaf, the mean number of canals per leaf was similar at different levels and aspects of the crown.

A study of trees of different ages showed that trees under about 20 years old had fewer resin canals than older trees. In mature trees with approximately the same mean leaf length and growing under similar conditions, there was a highly significant difference in the mean resin canal number between trees, which suggests that this may be genetically controlled.

Using this pattern of variation in devising sampling methods, the mean number of resin canals per leaf was determined in the principal native pinewoods.

T

It was found that it varied from forest to forest and group to group. For example, in the Deeside Group the number was significantly smaller in Glentanar than in the other woodlands, and also less in Rannoch and the Great Glen Groups than in the Speyside and Strath Glass Groups. The mean number for the native Scots pine in Scotland as a whole is 8·6, S.D. 1·6.

THE POSITION OF THE RESIN CANALS IN THE LEAF

Previous work. The position of the resin canal in the leaf is one diagnostic character used to distinguish different species in the genus *Pinus*. The usual terms for the description of the position are: marginal or peripheral, that is, touching the hypodermis; internal or central, against the endodermis; medial or parenchymatous, in the mesophyll; and septal, touching both endodermis and hypodermis. Some species of pine have resin canals in more than one position: *P. armandi*, two marginal, two medial; *P. coulteri*, medial, sometimes marginal; *P. halepensis* marginal with medial tendencies; and *P. tabulaeformis*, both marginal and medial (Dallimore, 1954; Engelmann, 1880; Huet, 1933).

Most authors state that the resin canals are marginal in Scots pine (Borthwick, 1906; Clapham, 1952; Dallimore, 1954; Huet, 1933). Others (Holmerz, 1888; Liese, 1929), however, have illustrated them in a medial position, while Moiseeva (1941) has stated that it is not uncommon to find canals in the stele. The position, therefore, is more variable than is generally recognised.

Variation in Scotland. A study of a number of trees showed that in some of them the resin canals were marginal throughout the length of the leaf, while in others some, but not all, of the canals followed an undulating course, ranging from marginal to medial. For this reason certain modifications in the terms used to describe the position of the resin canals were adopted:

Marginal	Closely connected to the hypodermis by two or more thick-walled cells or with the hypodermis forming part of the resin canal sheath (PL. XVIII.*b*).
Intermediate	Connected to the hypodermis by only one thick-walled cell (PL. XVIII.*c*).
Medial	Completely separate from the hypodermis, embedded in the mesophyll and surrounded by parenchyma (PL. XVIII.*d*).
Stelar	In the stele closely associated with the vascular bundles (PL. XVIII.*e*).

The positions of the resin canals were then studied in all the principal pine-woods, taking into account, in sampling, the pattern of variation discussed in the previous section. It was found that in a sample of 502 trees 35·5 per cent. had resin canals in marginal or intermediate positions only, 64·4 per cent. in marginal, intermediate, and medial positions, and 0·2 per cent. in marginal, intermediate, medial, and stelar positions. The native Scots pine in Scotland would, therefore, be more accurately described as having canals generally marginal or intermediate, often medial, and rarely stelar.

LEAF SCLERENCHYMA

Previous work. In the leaves of species of *Pinus*, there may be thick walled, sclerosed cells forming a protective sheath round the resin canals and also above and below the vascular bundles within the stele. Not all species of pine have sclerenchyma in both these positions, and early investigations indicated that in Scots pine such tissue was largely restricted to the resin canal region (Engelmann, 1880). Later work, however, showed that this was not so, and Huet (1933) described thick-walled cells within the stele, forming two arches over the phloem, and connected by thick-walled tissue four to five cells deep. He also noted that this tissue was not fully developed until the leaf was over a month old. There are no records of intra-specific variations in these characters in Scots pine.

Variation in Scotland. The protective layer round the resin canals was investigated, and in particular whether there were one or two layers of thick-walled cells. It was found that some trees had significantly more double layer sheaths than others.

Turning to the stelar mechanical tissue, it was found that there was a range of patterns from a single bar of cells to an H-shaped mass, and the type remained more or less constant within an individual tree. The patterns were classified as follows:

Well developed	A continuous mass of thick-walled sclerosed cells lying between and on both the adaxial and abaxial sides of the vascular bundles (Fig. 38a).
Moderately well developed	A continuous mass of thick-walled cells lying between and on the abaxial (but *not* the adaxial) side of the vascular bundles. The mass of thick-walled cells between the bundles is well developed and extends as far as the adaxial limits of the xylem (Fig. 38b).
Poorly developed	As "moderately well developed," but the sclerosed mass between the bundles is poorly developed. (Fig. 38c).

The distribution of these three classes of stelar tissue was investigated in the principal native pinewoods. It was found that there were significant differences in the percentages of the three classes both between individual trees and groups of woods. For example, Rannoch has a high percentage (35·0) of trees with poorly developed stelar mechanical tissue compared with Speyside (9·2), and

Strath Glass (7·9). Taking all the native woods, trees with well developed stelar mechanical tissue predominate (55·5).

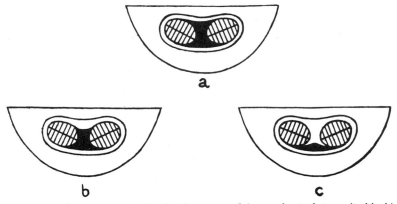

FIG. 38. The variations in the development of the mechanical tissue (in black) in the stele of the Scots pine leaf: (*a*) well developed; (*b*) moderately well developed; and (*c*) poorly developed (see p. 275).

THE HYPODERMIS

Previous work. The hypodermis of the Scots pine leaf is well developed, consisting of a row of slightly thickened cells, square or more often oblong in shape, with the long axis parallel to the leaf surface, and a large lumen with colourless contents. At the leaf corners, there are often two, and sometimes three, superimposed layers of hypodermal cells (Borthwick, 1906; Holmerz, 1888; Huet, 1933). Huet (1933) found, however, that in some species of the genus *Pinus* there were more layers of thinner-walled hypodermal cells at the base of the leaf than higher up. Sutherland (1934) noted in Scots pine in New Zealand that the leaf hypodermis consisted of two layers, a layer of sclerosed cells and a layer of flattened, thin walled cells which she refers to as a "water layer." This is at variance with the general descriptions provided by other authors.

Variation in Scotland. A study of the hypodermis in the principal native pine-woods showed that it consisted of one row of collenchyma on the abaxial and adaxial leaf surfaces, but a double layer of cells sometimes occurred in the immediate vicinity of resin canals. At the leaf corners, however, there were one to three layers of collenchyma, and analysis of the data showed that, although there was variation in individual trees within these limits, some trees had a significantly higher percentage of leaves with double and treble hypodermal layers than others. These differences within Scots pine may be genetically controlled. No evidence of the "water layer" described by Sutherland (1934) was seen.

THE COTYLEDONS

Previous work. The cotyledons of the Scots pine are usually five to six in number, 20 to 25 mm. long, curved, and triangular in cross section (Borthwick, 1906; Hickel, 1911). The range in number recorded by various authors is from three to ten (Borthwick, 1906; Boureau, 1939; Butts, 1940; Dangeard, 1892; Gordon, 1858; Groom, 1919; Hickel, 1911; Hofman, 1918; Lubbock, 1892; Tubeuf, 1892). It has been found that the number and length of the cotyledons of Scots pine were less in north than in south Sweden (Holmerz, 1888):

North Sweden   Cotyledon numbers 3-6, mean 4-5.
South Sweden   Cotyledon numbers 4-7, mean 5-6.
North Sweden   Length of cotyledons 6-17, mean 10 mm.
South Sweden   Length of cotyledons up to 26 mm.

Number and length in Scotland. A study was made of 700 seedlings raised from seed collected from 27 trees in different native woods. The mean cotyledon number was 5·1, S.D. 0·4, and the mean length was 19·2, S.D. 2·0 mm. Although the sample was too small to be representative, the results are similar to those in south Sweden.

CHAPTER 16

THE CONE, SEED, AND MALE INFLORESCENCE OF SCOTS PINE

THE CONE

COLOUR OF THE FEMALE CONE

Previous work. The female inflorescences develop in early summer at the end of shoots of the current year. Pollination takes place at this time, but fertilisation does not take place until the following spring, and the cone is not ripe until the end of that year (Büsgen, 1929). Prior to pollination, the female cone is about 0·6 cm. long and spherical. Its colour may be bright red, reddish brown, or greyish brown. It consists of thin, circular bract scales, and slightly shorter but more fleshy seminiferous scales, with dark red, pointed ends. After pollination, it increases in size and is carried downwards as the peduncle curves and elongates. The seminiferous scales become thicker and more woody, and in the autumn of the first year the cone is green and about 0·8 cm. long, 0·6 cm. wide, with a stalk 1·2 cm. long. It remains in this condition until the following spring when, under the stimulus of fertilisation, the cone becomes longer and more woody (Borthwick, 1906). It is then green, but becomes a shining light brown as it ripens, and finally greyish brown (Dallimore, 1954; Gilbert-Carter, 1936).

There is evidence of colour differences in mature cones in geographical races; v. *septentrionalis* (Schott), grey green-brown (Sylven, 1916); v. (ssp.) *lapponica* Fries, yellow and yellow-brown (Holmerz, 1888; Rehder, 1940; Rubner, 1934; Sylven, 1916); v. *engadinensis* Heer, pale yellow; and v. *nevadensis* Christ, red-grey (Beissner, 1891, 1909). Sylven (1916) found colour differences in Sweden. In the south the colour was generally grey-green-brown, in the north straw yellow, with or without a touch of brown-violet, and there were intermediates in both regions. There is some evidence also that Scots pine cones at the higher elevations are more yellow in colour (Holmerz, 1888).

Variation in Scotland. A study in the native pinewoods confirmed that there is a sequence of colour changes as the cone develops, hence it is necessary to define the stage when describing the colour. When the scales are becoming fleshy in the

278

first season, it is bright purplish or violet red, and there is no appreciable variation within individual trees or between trees.

A general survey of the native pinewoods showed that mature cones in the winter of the second year fall into four colour classes: grey-brown, grey-greenish brown, cinnamon brown, and yellowish. The green component in the second class never completely disappears and is not due to delay in ripening. There is often a temporary reddish tinge, but no definite red variety. The percentages of the different colour classes in the native pinewoods as a whole are 30·0, 60·9, 2·6, and 6·5 respectively. There is no evidence of any correlation between cone colour and site factors, and the predominance of the grey-greenish brown colour is similar to what has been found in south Sweden.

THE LENGTH OF THE MATURE CONE

Previous work. The cones of Scots pine are stated to vary from 2·5 to 7·6 cm. in length (Dallimore, 1954; Elwes, 1908; Sylven, 1916). As is to be expected, dwarf varieties have smaller cones, those of v. *nana* Carrière being only 1·8 cm. long (Bean, 1951), but in contrast v. *macrocarpa* Schröder has abnormally large cones (Beissner, 1930). Sylven (1916) found in Sweden as a whole that the cones were of moderate size, 3·1 to 3·9 cm. long, but longer cones, over 4·0 cm., and shorter, under 3·0, might predominate locally, the former being more common in the south and the latter in the north. There is little information about the effect of altitude on cone length, but it appears to decrease with increasing elevation (Holmerz, 1888). Forshell (1953) in recent work in Sweden has shown that cone length is characteristic for each mother tree, but varies in different years, and cones on "minus" trees are longer than on "plus." But she found no correlation with latitude.

Variation in Scotland. A study showed that the length of the cone varies within individual trees and is significantly smaller at the extreme top of the tree. This has to be taken into account in sampling. The cone length on a given shoot varies significantly from season to season, but the mean for the whole tree shows little seasonal change.

The influence of altitude on cone length was investigated in Glentanar Forest at 700 ft. (210 m.), 900 ft. (270 m.), 1000 ft. (300 m.), and 1300 ft. (390 m.). The mean cone length at 700 ft. (210 m.) was significantly greater than at 1300 ft. (390 m.).

The mean length of the cones was determined in the principal native pinewoods. It varied significantly from wood to wood, but when expressed per group there was little difference. The mean cone length for all the woods was found to be 3·8 cm., range 2·0 to 6·5. The mean value is the same as that previously recorded for v. *scotica* Schott (Dallimore, 1954; Elwes, 1908) and is similar to that for south Sweden (Sylven, 1916), but is smaller than that for v. *genuina* Heer 4 to 6 cm. (Czoppelt, 1938) and v. *engadinensis* Heer, 5·08 cm. (Elwes, 1908).

THE FORM AND APOPHYSIS OF THE CONE

Previous work. The cone scales of Scots pine at maturity are about 20 to 25 mm. long by 9 mm. broad, slightly tapered at the apex, and purplish brown in colour. The apophysis, or exposed part of the scale, is rhomboidal with well marked transverse and lateral ridges, and bears a central umbo or protuberance with a small reflexed mucro or prickle (Gilbert-Carter, 1936). The structure of the apophysis of Scots pine is variable, and has been studied by many workers. Three forms have been defined:

f. *plana* Christ (PL. XIX.*a*)

A cone type with a rather irregular, not very prominent apophysis, more than twice as wide as high, with a sharp lateral ridge. It includes a number of cone forms, from long and narrow to short and wide, all with the same apophysis characteristics. Cones with apophysis intermediate between *plana* and *gibba* or *plana* and *reflexa* types also occur (Beissner, 1891, 1909, 1930; Caspary, 1882–3; Christ, 1864, 1865; Sylven, 1916). F. *plana* has a wide distribution occurring in Germany, France, Britain, Switzerland (Caspary, 1882–3; Engler, 1913*b*), Sweden (Sylven, 1916), west Hungary and north-west Russia (Schott, 1907). Caspary regards var. *genuina* f. *plana* Christ as the common Scots pine of the first four of these localities.

f. *gibba* Christ (PL. XIX.*b*)

A cone type with an apophysis whose width is less than twice its height, with a broad, obtuse lateral ridge. The apophysis is broad and humped with more or less concave sides. This variant includes a wide range of cone forms from long and narrow to short and wide. Intermediate types with *gibba-reflexa* and *gibba-plana* tendencies are common (Beissner, 1891, 1909; Caspary, 1882–3; Christ, 1864, 1865; Sylven, 1916). It has a wide distribution, occurring in England, France and Germany (Caspary, 1882–3), Rumania (Czoppelt, 1938), west Hungary (Schott, 1907), Scandinavia and north-west Russia (Schott, 1907; Sylven, 1916), and the upper Alps and south-western Europe (Engler, 1913*b*).

f. (v.) *reflexa* Heer (PL. XIX.*c*). Synonymous with v. *volkmanni* Caspary (1882–3)

A cone type with a prominent cone scale apophysis whose height may exceed its width, curved in the form of a hook up to 5 mm. long. These hooks are generally recurved towards the base of the cone, but are sometimes directed towards the cone apex (Beissner, 1891, 1909; Caspary, 1882–3; Elwes, 1908; Heer, 1862; Murray, 1920). It is found in East Prussia (Caspary, 1882–3), in the marshy valleys of the Swiss Alps, in the lowlands of Germany (Veitch, 1881, 1900) and in Sweden (Sylven, 1916).

PLATE XIX

a   *b*   *c*

d

FOUR PREVIOUSLY DESCRIBED CONE VARIANTS IN NATIVE SCOTS PINE (see CHAPTER 16)
(*a*) F. *plana* Christ; (*b*) f. *gibba* Christ; (*c*) f. (v.) *reflexa* Heer; (*d*) f. *conis
aggregatis* Syreitschikow, dense clusters of cones in successive seasons.

PLATE XX

Nine cone types, (A) to (I), defined in Table IX, p. 282

The nomenclature of Scots pine with hooked apophysis is confused, some authors correlating this with other morphological features. For example, Beissner (1891, 1909) states that trees of the f. *reflexa* type have limited height growth, irregular crowns, leaves 6 cm. long, and long narrow cones borne on a long cone stalk. In this instance the term *reflexa* refers to a particular type of Scots pine rather than to a cone variant, but Murray (1920) found no correlation of stem and crown characters with the hooked apophysis. Scots pine with cones having prominent hooks have been given other names, the most important of which are v. *hamata* Steven and v. *uncinata* Don. The former has been elevated to specific rank in Russia as *P. hamata* Steven (Galpern, 1949).

Sylven (1916) found in Sweden that f. *plana* was the commonest and f. *reflexa* was least common and he recognised a number of intermediate types. In some areas the cones were all of one type, and in others they were mixed together.

Variation in Scotland. When the cone was studied, it was found that the different forms already described did not permit of clear differentiation, and that it was better to divide cones, first into three major classes based on the extent to which the apophysis was raised, and secondly to sub-divide each into three on the form of the cone as determined by the length/diameter ratio, thus making nine classes in all. These will be described later. In order, however, to compare types of apophysis in Scotland with those of other countries, the percentages of f. *plana*, f. *gibba*, and f. *reflexa* as already defined were estimated in the principal native pinewoods. It was found that there were highly significant differences between both individual woods and groups, but no clear correlation with geographical region or climate. All three are found in all the groups, but *plana* and *gibba* are more numerous except in Strath Glass. Taking all groups together, the percentages of *plana*, *gibba* and *reflexa* are 42·4, 39·9, and 17·7 respectively in a sample of 2650 trees. These differ from those found either in north or south Sweden by Sylven (1916).

Before devising the new classification referred to above, it was necessary to determine whether the degree to which the apophysis was raised and the shape of the cone as expressed by the length/diameter ratio were sufficiently constant within individual trees to enable these characters to be used with confidence. An investigation showed that this was so. The classification is given in Table IX, and the cone types illustrated in PL. XX.

TABLE IX OVERLEAF

TABLE IX

THE CONE FORM AND APOPHYSIS VARIANTS IN SCOTLAND

Apophysis development on the upper surface in the basal third of the cone	Form of the cone (length (l): diameter (d))		Cone Type
Perfectly flat or concave, apart from occasional protusion of umbo and prickle	Elongated	(l:d = >2·1)	A
	Conic	(l:d = 1·8-2·1)	B
	Broad	(l:d = <1·8)	C
Raised; height equal to or less than half the width; pyramidal, or rounded, or hooked or irregular	Elongated	(l:d = >2·1)	D
	Conic	(l:d = 1·8-2·1)	E
	Broad	(l:d = <1·8)	F
Prominent; height more than half the width; pyramidal or hooked	Elongated	(l:d = >2·1)	G
	Conic	(l:d = 1·8-2·1)	H
	Broad	(l:d = <1·8)	I

This classification was applied in the native pinewoods and the results are given in Table X.

TABLE X

THE MEAN PERCENTAGES OF SCOTS PINE CONE TYPES IN THE MAJOR GEOGRAPHICAL GROUPS OF NATIVE PINEWOODS IN SCOTLAND

Geographical group	No. of sample trees	Cone types								
		A	B	C	D	E	F	G	H	I
Deeside	500	1·4	10.2	2·4	3·0	40·4	6·0	2·4	26·8	7·4
Speyside	550	2·5	10·7	5·8	5·8	42·5	11·6	1·3	14·5	5·1
Rannoch	300	3·3	10·3	3·0	9·3	40·0	8·7	4·3	18·7	2·3
Great Glen	470	3·4	11·9	1·1	9·6	38·7	5·7	7·0	20·2	2·3
Strath Glass	425	2·8	9·4	2·6	6·6	30·1	4·7	9·4	28·0	6·4
Wester Ross	350	1·4	16·9	5·6	2·9	45·9	10·9	1·4	10·6	4·6
Northern	200	2·5	7·5	2·0	11·5	39·0	3·5	8·0	24·0	2·0
Southern	640	0·8	10·2	2·3	5·6	39·1	12·2	2·3	19·7	7·8
All Scotland	3435	2·2	10·9	3·1	6·3	39·4	8·4	4·1	20·2	5·2

Thus trees with flat or concave apophyses are least numerous, and the conic form predominates within each apophysis class. While the percentages of the different types vary from group to group, the pattern of variation in each is not dissimilar, and no evidence was found of any correlation between cone type and site factors. Further, no relationship was found between the cone type and the habit or other characteristics of the tree, which is at variance with the views of some other workers (Beissner, 1891, 1909; Galpern, 1949).

ABNORMAL CONES

Previous work. Scots pine sometimes produces unusually large clusters of 5 to 145 cones, usually on the leader and more seldom on the side branches (PL. XIX.*d*) (anon., 1941*b*; anon., 1942; Beissner, 1930; Carrière, 1867; Kirchner, 1908; Pardé, 1937; Sorauer, 1909). These pine have been called either f. *conis aggregatis* Syreitschikow (Beissner, 1891, 1909, 1930; Pardé, 1937; Syreitschikow, 1906) or f. *conglomerata* Carrière (1867), the former being the more common name. Apart from these peculiar cone clusters, such trees appear to be normally developed, although sometimes a little smaller than adjacent trees with normal cone production. The cones in the clusters may be of normal size or abnormally small, and generally have rather long peduncles. They bear normal but small seeds (anon., 1941*b*; anon., 1942).

An unusual type was observed by Kurdiani (1926-7) in Scots pine growing in the Georgian Caucasus. In the stands he examined, one third of the trees produced either more than the normal two to three cones per fruiting branch or bore cones in the middle of the season's growth instead of at the end. He suggested that these were mutations.

Abnormal cones in Scotland. A typical example of f. *conis aggregatis* was found in Badan Dubh Wood, Glen Feshie (PL. XIX.*d*). Large clusters of cones were borne on each of three successive seasons' growth of the leader, and the cones were distributed along more than half of each season's growth, each arising in the axil of a scale leaf and replacing the normal two-leaf bundle. The cones which had ripened in the season 1951 were of a normal f. *gibba* type (type E) with a mean length of 4·4 cm. The cones in the clusters produced in 1952 and 1953 were in many cases abnormally small (2·0 to 4·0 cm. long) or partially aborted. The tree was otherwise normal.

A common cone abnormality in Scotland is where the cone axis and apical scales fail to develop normally. On some trees more than half the cones have this defect, and the abortion is much more common in some woodlands than in others. There is no obvious pathological cause. Such cones generally have prominent apophyses.

In a few instances, trees were seen in which up to 70 per cent. of the cones showed a marked twist at the apex. It did not appear to have been caused by a pathogen.

THE SEED

THE SEED DIMENSIONS

Previous work. The seed of Scots pine varies in length from 3·5 to 5·5 mm. (Borthwick, 1906; Clapham, 1952; Dallimore, 1954; Gilbert-Carter, 1936), and there are records that some geographical varieties have larger seeds than others, for example v. *superrhenana* Schott in the Upper Rhine has large seeds, whilst v. (ssp.) *lapponica* Fries has small seeds (Schott, 1907).

Voychal (1946) found that the linear dimensions of the seed varied less than the seed weight, but was unable to correlate the linear dimensions of the seed with any other character. Righter (1945) regards the seed-size as being due more to the environment than to any genetic factor. Simák (1953 *a* and *b*) carried out detailed investigations on the form and size of the seed of Scots pine. He found that within a single cone the seeds from the basal and apical scales were smaller than those from the middle. The absolute seed size was found to be dependent upon external factors, such as seasonal weather; it increased with cone size; there was some indication that it was influenced by the position of the cone in the crown; and it increased with increasing cone weight.

These studies indicate that whilst trees may differ significantly in the mean size of their seeds, their linear dimensions are influenced to such an extent by external factors that there is great difficulty in assessing the genetical significance of such variations.

Variation in Scotland. It was found on investigation that both seed length and the length/width ratio varied within the tree in a random fashion and without correlation with the position in the crown. During a period of three years, there were seasonal differences in length, which almost approached the level of significance, but the length/width ratio did not vary.

Although seed length is influenced, therefore, by external factors, it was estimated in the principal native woods on comparable sites. The mean obtained was 4·2, S.D. 0·5 mm.

SEED WEIGHT

Previous work. The weight of Scots pine seed has been found to vary in different parts of Europe. Rafn (1915) and Hickel (1911) state that the heaviest seed comes from Scotland, rarely less than 6 gm. per 1000 seeds, and the smallest from Finland, sometimes weighing less than 4 gm. In Sweden, seed from the south is heavier, 4 to 5 gm., compared with that from the north, 2·5 to 4·5 gm., and there were differences in nearby localities (Sylven, 1916). Strohmeyer (1938) was unable to find any correlation between seed weight and site, but he found that seed weight was influenced by the age of the tree, old trees usually bearing lighter seed than younger. Forshell (1953) states that the seed weight is, on average, higher in "minus" trees than in "plus" trees, and that seed weight increases with cone size. There appears to be a correlation between the weight of the seed and the cone characters, Trost (1926) finding that the seed from cones with slightly raised and prominent cone scale apophyses is heavier than the seed from cones with flat apophyses.

Variation in Scotland. Seed weight within individual trees was investigated using standard sampling procedure, and it was found that it did not vary, provided the seed was taken from cones of average length for the tree.

The seed weight was determined in twelve of the native woods in the Deeside, Strath Glass, Northern, and Southern groups, and the weight per 1000 seeds was found to be 4·96, S.D. 1·06 gm. This is a lower value than that given for Scotland by Hickel (1911) and Rafn (1915); their samples may not have come from old trees in native woodlands.

SEED COLOUR

Previous work. The seed of Scots pine varies from dark grey or blackish (Dallimore, 1954; Gilbert-Carter, 1936) to light brown (Borthwick, 1906), and brown (Groom, 1919), while Hickel (1911) has pointed out that there are light and dark coloured seed, the former being often empty, and the colour may be affected by attrition during cleaning.

There is some evidence that Scots pine in different geographical regions differ in their seed colour, ranging from brown to black (Gilchrist, 1871; Schott, 1907). In Sweden, Sylven (1916) differentiated three colour classes: black to dark brown, brown to yellow, and bright yellow to white; while he also obtained mottled types. All classes were found throughout the country, but the darker seed was commoner in the south, and the lighter in the north.

Little is known about the significance of these colour differences, but they depend on the degree of ripening, and it has been found that seed from grafted stock growing under favourable conditions is darker than that grown in the natural forest, irrespective of the basic seed colour of the genotype (Simák, 1954). This suggests that environment plays a part. Nevertheless, trees growing side by side may differ in their seed colour, and each produces seed of the same colour year by year (Busgen, 1929), which suggests genetic control.

Variation in Scotland. Preliminary studies showed that, when allowance was made for different degrees of ripening, the colour of the full seed during the winter was uniform from cones in all parts of the crown of a tree. It was also confirmed that seed colour remained constant in a given tree in successive years, at least up to three, but that the colour may differ from tree to tree. Four colour classes were differentiated in the native pinewoods:

Light coloured	Yellowish brown, pale grey-brown, and pale grey.
Brown	Brown, cinnamon, russet brown, and grey-brown.
Dark coloured	Dark grey-brown, dark brown, and almost black.
Mottled	A combination of any of the colours mentioned, the mottling showing on the exposed face of the seed.

The colour variants were found on all manner of sites, and adjacent trees often show different colours, which suggests that external factors are not the cause.

The percentages of the different colour classes were estimated in all the principal native woodlands, and were found to be 10·2 for the light coloured, 49·1 for the brown, 36·7 for the dark, and 4·0 for the mottled. There were no striking differences between the different groups of forests.

THE FORM OF THE SEED-WING

Previous work. The seed-wing of Scots pine is 15 to 20 mm. in length, and two to four times as long as the seed (Bentham, 1945; Clapham, 1952; Dallimore, 1954; Gilbert-Carter, 1936; Sowerby, 1868). It exhibits considerable variation in form (Büsgen, 1929), but the mean form is relatively constant within a tree (Büsgen, 1929; Sylven, 1916). Sylven (1916) described three seed-wing types in Sweden; the normal, the short broad, and long narrow types.

Variation in Scotland. The form of the seed-wing varies considerably within a single cone, those from the basal scales being short and broad, and those from the apical long and narrow. Samples for study were taken, therefore, from the middle of the cone. A study showed that the form of the wing, as expressed by the length/width ratio, while varying within an individual tree, was not correlated with the position of the cone in the crown. Different trees may have different limits in the variation of this ratio. It was also found that the mean length/width ratio in successive seasons varied little.

Three form types were defined for the native woods on the basis of the length/width ratio:

Long seed-wing	more than 3·8
Normal	3·1 to 3·8
Broad	less than 3·1

These are similar to those described by Sylven for Sweden.

Estimates made in the principal native pinewoods gave the following percentages: long, 4·2; normal, 83·6; and broad, 12·2.

THE COLOUR AND STRIPING OF THE SEED-WING

Previous work. The seed-wing of Scots pine is usually light buff in colour, but sometimes darker, and occasionally striped (Hickel, 1911). Numerous colour variants have been described, yellowish (Sylven, 1916), reddish (Gilchrist, 1871), red-brown (Rubner, 1934; Schott, 1907; Sylven, 1916), and greyish violet. Wings with stripes or alternating light and dark coloured bands have often been illustrated (Hickel, 1911; Seitz, 1927; Simák, 1954; Sylven, 1916), but little is known about this character except that it varies from tree to tree (Büsgen, 1929).

Sylven (1916) described three colour variants in Sweden: yellowish red-brown, red-brown, and violet-brown. The first predominates in the north and the last in the south. It has been found also that the colour is darker on grafted stock compared with that under natural forest conditions (Simák, 1954).

Variation in Scotland. Studies showed that the colour and degree of striping, when present, of the seed-wing were constant within an individual cone and on a tree. The colour depends on the degree of drying or ripening of the wing and the following classification is based on its winter appearance.

Four seed-wing colour types in the native woods were defined:

Pale brown to yellow-brown	A very pale wing, striped or unstriped.
Buff to brown	Often with a reddish or violet tip or margin.
Pink-brown, violet-brown or russet	Brown with a pink, violet or reddish tinge; tip and margin often dark violet or red; striped or unstriped.
Dark brown or dark red-brown	Usually unstriped, but occasionally striped.

The degree of striping depends on cell wall deposits of a substance which is slightly soluble in xylol, less so in alcohol, insoluble in water and stains with Sudan III. It may be resinous in character. Striping can be more closely defined as follows:

Well defined stripes	Dark bands more than 0·25 mm. wide.
Faint stripes	Dark bands present, but less than 0·25 mm. wide.
Unstriped	Dark or light bands absent.

The percentages of the different seed-wing colour types were estimated in the principal native pinewoods. It was found that while there were significant differences between a number of the groups, there was no consistent pattern or topocline. Taking them all together, the percentages are as follows: pale brown, 18·6; buff to brown, 27·3; pink-brown, 35·5; and dark brown, 18·6. In these classes as a whole, 21·2 per cent. were striped, 39·3 showed faint striping, and 39·5 were unstriped.

THE MALE INFLORESCENCE

COLOUR OF THE MALE INFLORESCENCE

Previous work. The colour is generally yellow (Borthwick, 1906; Groom, 1919; Poskin, 1949), but there are references to a range of colours from very pale to red. Both Lambert (1832) and Beissner (1891) refer to a whitish variant, but the red is more definite. It may be pale rose to deep carmine-brown, and this type is found in most parts of Europe (Bechstein, 1821; Beissner, 1891, 1909, 1930; Braun, 1871; Buchenau, 1885; Caspary, 1882-3; Elwes, 1908; Grozdov 1945; Kirchner, 1908; Sanio, 1871; Tubeuf, 1897; Vilmorin, 1862). It is generally referred to by one of two names f. (v.) *erythranthera* Sanio (1871) or f. (v.) *rubriflora* Buchenau (1885). This type must not be confused, of course, with the colour of immature inflorescences which are reddish because of the colour of the bud scales. F. *erythranthera* has been described by Beissner (1891, 1909) as a tree with brown-carmine male cones, red buds, red-brown bark, and short, grey leaves which is found singly in pinewoods in Prussia and Saxony, and is supposed to form whole stands in Scotland where it is stated to have tall, straight slender stems, and was formerly included in the same class as the "Ship-mast" pine in seed catalogues of the nineteenth century.

Variation in Scotland. It was found that the colour of the male inflorescence was constant within individual trees at the stage immediately prior to anthesis, and from season to season.

Three different colour variants were defined in the native woods: bright yellow, violet-yellow, and violet-red. These colours were not correlated with age of the trees or site, and the trees that bore each were sometimes growing side by side. The first two types are the commonest in all the native woods, while the violet-red is only found in about a quarter of them. No correlation was found with other morphological characteristics as was stated by Beissner (1891, 1909).

THE POLLEN

Previous work. The pollen grain of Scots pine like other pine species has a round or elliptical main body, with two large air-sacs or wings. Its exine has a reticulated pattern, and there is a small marginal ridge at the base of the sacs. The diameter of the central body is from 44·2μ to 52·0μ, but may be as small as 32μ (Wodehouse, 1935). Various authors have given the size of the whole fresh grain, including the air-sacs, as about 54-66-78μ, the middle value being the mean (Erdtman, 1943).

In a classification of pollen in species of pine, Scots pine comes into a class along with *P. leucodermis*, *P. mugo* and its varieties (Campo-Duplan, 1950). It is possible but difficult to differentiate the pollen of Scots from that of Mountain pine and *P. cembra* (Hörman, 1929). Marcet (1951) investigated the variation in the dimensions of pollen grains of Scots pine from different regions. While he found variation even within individual trees, there were significant differences between the length and breadth of the air-sacs in each of six different provenances studied. Lindquist (1935) investigated the pollen grains of broad and narrow crowned Scots pine in Sweden with the following results.

Type	Air-sac Length (μ)	
	Range	Mean
Broad crown in south Sweden	30·14-35·65	33·66
Narrow crown in south Sweden	35·79-40·09	37·84
Broad crown in north Sweden Narrow crown in north Sweden	35·95-37·55	37·13

Variation in Scotland. In studying the pollen grain, the measurements made, following Marcet (1951), were the length (L) and width (W) of the main body and the length of the air-sac (S) (see Fig. 39).

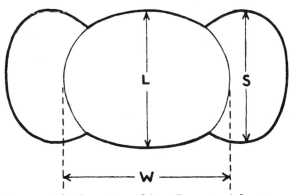

FIG. 39. The dimensions of the pollen grains (after Marcet, 1951) referred to in the text (see above); the length (L) and width (W) of the main body of the grain, and the length of the air-sac (S).

It was found that there were considerable variations within individual trees. A study of the dimensions between trees in different native woods showed that

U

there might be significant differences, particularly in the width of the body, but further investigation is required to confirm this. In a sample of ten trees, the mean width was found to be 43.5μ, and length 38.2μ. The air-sac length was determined in a number of forests, and, while there were also significant differences between trees, the means for the different pinewoods were similar. The average for the 29 trees studied was found to be 33.7, S.D. 3.1μ, which is similar to that found in the broad crowned Scots pine in south Sweden (Lindquist, 1935).

CHAPTER 17

SOME CONCLUSIONS ABOUT THE MORPHOLOGY OF SCOTS PINE IN SCOTLAND

THE DETAILED MORPHOLOGY

In CHAPTERS 12 to 16, the detailed morphology of the native Scots pine in Scotland has been described. The principal conclusions may now be stated.

Habit	Principally v. *horizontalis* Don and f. *ascensa* Carlisle. Other types present are f. *condensata* Fries, f. *fastigiata* Carrière, f. *pyramidalis* (Elwes and Henry), f. *pendula* Caspary, and many indefinite and intermediate forms.
Bark	Mainly plate and ridge bark with a few flake bark and many intermediate forms. Bark colour ranges from pale grey-brown or cinnamon-brown to dark grey-brown in the lower part of the stem, and from orange-red to orange-yellow at the top of the tree.
Shoots	Pale yellowish green at first, becoming green or green-brown in the first summer, and pale brown in the following autumn and winter; in subsequent years becomes greyish brown and finally reddish orange.
Buds	Usually red-grey-brown. Rarely bright red.
Leaf length	Mean = 44·0, Standard Deviation 6·0 mm. (565 sample trees).
Leaf breadth	Mean = 1·56, S.D. 0·15 mm. (565 sample trees).
Leaf colour	In the summer of the first year generally grey-green, but occasionally glaucous. Bright green and yellow-green colours also occur but are of doubtful significance. In the winter of the first year the colour is dark grey-green in most trees, but may occasionally be yellow.
Leaf persistence	Mean = three to four years, ranging from two to five.
Leaf sheath	Pale grey-brown in the first summer becoming dark brown in subsequent years. About 8 to 10 mm. long.
Leaf twist	Slightly twisted, rarely very twisted.
Number of resin canals per leaf	Mean = 8·6, S.D. 1·6 (574 sample trees).
Position of the resin canal in the leaf	Generally marginal and/or intermediate, frequently medial, and rarely stelar.

Resin canal sheath	One to two layers of thick-walled cells.
Stelar mechanical tissue	Well developed 55·5 per cent.; moderately well developed 29·9 per cent.; and poorly developed 14·6 per cent. (582 sample trees).
Hypodermis	One layer of collenchyma on the abaxial and adaxial leaf surfaces, with one to three layers at the leaf corners.
Cotyledons	Mean number of cotyledons = 5·1, S.D. 0·4. Mean length of cotyledons = 19·2, S.D. 2·0 mm. (700 sample seedlings from 27 sample trees).
Female cone colour	At two weeks a bright purplish red in all trees. When mature 30·0 per cent. grey-brown, 60·9 grey-green-brown, 2·6 cinnamon-brown, and 6·5 yellowish (1125 sample trees).
Cone length	Mean = 3·8, range 2·0 to 6·5 mm. (1099 sample trees).
Cone apophysis	42·4 per cent. f. *plana* Christ, 39·9 f. *gibba* Christ, and 17·7 f. *reflexa* Heer (2650 sample trees).
Cone form and apophysis	A = 2·2 per cent. E = 39·4 per cent. B = 10·9 per cent. F = 8·4 per cent. C = 3·1 per cent. G = 4·1 per cent. D = 6·3 per cent. H = 20·2 per cent. I = 5.2 per cent. (3435 sample trees).
Seed length	Mean = 4·2, S.D. 0·5 mm. (288 sample trees).
Seed weight	Mean = 4·96, S.D. 1·06 gm. per 1000 seeds (61 sample trees).
Seed colour	10·2 per cent. light-coloured, 49·1 brown, 36·7 dark-coloured, and 4·0 mottled (450 sample trees).
Seed-wing form	4·2 per cent. long, 83·6 normal, 12·2 broad (640 sample trees).
Seed-wing colour	18·6 per cent. pale brown to yellow-brown, 27·3 buff to brown, 35·5 pink-brown, violet-brown or russet, 18·6 dark brown or dark red-brown (425 sample trees).
Seed-wing stripe	21·2 per cent. striped, 39·3 faintly striped, and 39·5 unstriped (640 sample trees).
Male inflorescence colour	Generally yellow or pink-yellow; occasionally violet-red.
Pollen grain body dimensions	Mean length = 38·2 μ (10 sample trees). Mean width = 43·5 μ (10 sample trees).
Pollen grain air-sac length	Mean = 33·7, S.D. 3·1 μ (29 sample trees).

GENETICAL SIGNIFICANCE AND CORRELATION OF MORPHOLOGICAL VARIATIONS

During the discussion of the morphological variations in the preceding chapters, some evidence has been presented on the influence of genetical and environmental factors in causing the observed differences. Some of the characters that have been found to vary within Scots pine are those which differ from species to species not only in the genus *Pinus*, but in the *Coniferae* as a whole, such as cone and leaf structure, and are likely, therefore, to be genetically controlled. Moreover, further evidence of the respective roles of genetic structure and site factors will gradually become available as controlled provenance studies become older, and there is an extension of the use of both tree progeny trials and clonal material from individual trees under more uniform conditions of site than the natural forest provides.

The variations described can be classified from the practical silvicultural point of view into those that are useful to the forester and those that are not. For example, habit of growth is important. It is, however, definitely influenced by conditions of competition, and if one wishes to select a particular habit type, it would increase the certainty of doing so, if it was linked with some other character, such as cone apophyses, which is not so influenced. The data were analysed to determine whether there was any evidence of such linkages.

CORRELATION BETWEEN HABIT TYPE AND CONE AND SEED CHARACTERS

Trees of four typical habit types, v. *horizontalis*, f. *ascensa*, f. *condensata*, f. *pendula* were selected where environment was unlikely to obscure the type, and the cones were sampled using the methods previously elaborated. The size of the sample varied from 10 to 25 trees. An analysis of the data of the nine cone types already defined from each of the four habit types showed that there was no correlation between these two variables. When cone type was defined as f. *plana*, f. *gibba*, and f. *reflexa*, there was also no correlation with the habit types.

CORRELATION BETWEEN HABIT TYPE AND STELE MECHANICAL TISSUE

The sampling was as before. It was found that the percentages of the three classes of mechanical tissue in the stele were similar in the four habit types, although the former character is one that may vary between species of pine (Huet, 1933).

CORRELATION BETWEEN BARK AND CONE AND SEED CHARACTERS

Samples of cones were taken from trees over 160 years old, growing under typical conditions in different native woods which had the four bark types, which as stated in Chapter 14 appeared to be genetically controlled: Plate, Ridge, Flake, and Plate/Flake. No correlation was found between bark type and cone type, seed-wing form, and seed-wing colour.

CORRELATION BETWEEN BARK AND HABIT TYPES

No quantitative data were obtained, but after a field study the following conclusions were reached:

(*a*) Trees over 150 years old with Plate bark exhibited a wide range of habit types.

(*b*) Trees, 150 to 180 years old with Ridge bark, varied considerably in their habit type.

(*c*) Trees that retain Flake bark to over 150 years have an inferior habit, as regards crookedness and branchiness compared with those with Plate/Flake intermediate type.

(*d*) Plate bark was never seen on f. *condensata* and f. *fastigiata*, the bark being always an intermediate or indefinite type.

CONCLUSION

These data show that no help can be got from the characters that are not influenced by conditions of environment when selecting trees of particular habit types.

A COMPARISON OF THE NATIVE SCOTS PINE OF SCOTLAND AND SWEDEN

The only part of the general habitat of Scots pine where morphological variations have been studied hitherto in the necessary detail is Sweden (Holmerz, 1888; Lindquist, 1935, 1937; Sylven, 1916). It is only possible, therefore, to compare the results obtained in Scotland with those of that country. In Sweden two geographical varieties have been defined, *lapponica* in the north, and *septentrionalis* in the south. In previous chapters the pattern of morphological variation in north and south Sweden has been outlined and the following comparisons with Scotland can be made.

1. The narrow crown type of Scots pine is uncommon in native Scottish pinewoods. This is also characteristic in south compared with north Sweden.

2. The Scots pine in Scotland also resembles that of south rather than north Sweden in the following characters: Mean leaf dimensions per tree; mean persistence of the leaf; mean number and length of the cotyledons per seedling; percentage of cone colour variants; and mean length of the pollen grain air-sac.

3. The mean cone length per tree is similar in Scotland and Sweden as a whole.

4. The percentages of the Scots pine seed colour variants in Scotland is intermediate between those in north and south Sweden.

5. The percentages of the f. *plana*, f. *gibba*, and f. *reflexa* cone types (PL. X.*a, b, c*) in Scotland are different from those in both north and south Sweden.

6. The unusual habit type, f. *condensata*, recorded in east-middle Sweden is found in the Scottish pinewoods (PL. IV.*d*).

The morphological variations in the native pine in Scotland are similar, there-fore, to those in Sweden, and particularly in south Sweden. The species reached both countries in early post-glacial times. If the variants are genetically controlled and were already present in early post-glacial times, these similarities would suggest that the Scots pine in both countries derive from the same population of survivors at lower latitudes during glacial times. On the other hand, the differ-ences that have been found between south and north Sweden suggest the possi-bility of mutations and/or the effect of natural selection since the species reached that country. On such a view, it would appear that the range of morphological variations in Scotland and south Sweden is similar to that in the populations of earlier post-glacial times.

SYSTEMATIC POSITION OF THE NATIVE SCOTS PINE IN SCOTLAND

The problem from the taxonomic point of view is whether to consider the native Scots pine as a sub-species, a variety or race, or part of a *Rassenkreis*, applying that term to the Scots pine in all parts of its habitat (Huxley, 1948; Lawrence, 1951; Richens, 1945). Unfortunately there are no generally agreed definitions of a sub-species and variety. Lawrence (1951) recently gave a number of alternative definitions, one of which for a sub-species is: "Major morphological variations of a species that have geographic distributions of their own, which are distinct from the area occupied by other sub-species of the same species." The term "race" is used in different senses by different authors; Richens' (1945) definition is: "A naturally occurring variety." None of these definitions describe what one wishes to convey in the present case which is that the native Scots pine in Scotland is a heterogeneous population from the point of view of its morphology and anatomy, and it exhibits no major or unique morphological character, although it has a distinctive geographical distribution. One could call it the Scottish part of a *Rassenkreis*, but in the circumstances it is not proposed to change the previous practice of calling it a geographical variety, *P. silvestris* L. v. *scotica* Schott. Its detailed morphology is given on pp. 291-2. It has close affinities with v. *septen-trionalis* Schott, in south Sweden.

PRACTICAL APPLICATIONS

From one point of view, the native pinewoods of Scotland are historical monu-ments. There are now no extensive areas of Scots pine in Europe where the trees range in age up to 300 years. Some of the limited areas of such trees in Scandin-avian countries have been formed into nature reserves for their preservation. The larger native pinewoods in Scotland, in spite of the vicissitudes through which they have passed, and the marks of destructive exploitation and fire that they bear, are still characteristic communities of our native vegetation, with their own distinctive ecological characteristics. These arguments alone would justify their preservation, but there are also practical reasons why this should be done. This study has shown that in spite of selective felling they still contain a wide range of morphological variations, and no doubt physiological qualities, for example hardiness to climatic factors, and resistance to diseases, reflected in the ability of the trees to persist to a great age. They are, therefore, a reservoir of the genes or genetical characters of this variety of Scots pine. Some of these are of use in forestry in this country today, and will be discussed now; others may be of value in the future.

The most important immediate use to which the trees in these woods can be put is as a source of seed, and also scion material for grafting for the later production of seed in orchards, where the stock is to be used either on upland sites where the conditions of climate and soil are adverse, or when it is desired to produce high quality slower growing timber.

The habit type, v. *horizontalis* (PL. XIII.*a*), has been shown in Chapter 13 to possess valuable qualities of straightness of stem, with short and light branches. No conclusive evidence was obtained on its relative rate of growth, but there is some evidence that it is not the fastest growing type. Nevertheless, it is considered to be the most desirable type to grow under the conditions already mentioned, and a faster growing strain may be found within it by testing the progeny from individual trees of this variety. F. *ascensa* (PL. XIII.*b*) is a less desirable habit type, because it is more branchy, but there is some evidence that it is faster growing than v. *horizontalis*, and it would be worth while to cross the two types, using grafted material to accelerate seed production, to determine whether the intra-specific hybrid has the good qualities of its parents. F. *condensata* (PL. XIII.*d*) and f. *fastigiata* (PL. XIII.*c*) are undesirable types from the silvicultural point of view, but the latter has been found to be of horticultural value in North America.

One of the current silvicultural problems in this country is to select a suitable strain of Scots pine for sites in the high rainfall areas in the west for which there are no suitable alternative species. This investigation has shown that there are no distinctive morphological variations as between the lower and higher rainfall regions, but whether or no there are physiological differences is not known. Leaf persistence is one factor of importance, because planted Scots pine in the west may retain their needles for only one or two years. No data are known on the relative rate of photosynthesis with increasing age of needles, but it is likely to decrease. Nevertheless, it is desirable to use a strain which retains its needles as long as possible. In Chapter 15, it has been shown that leaf persistence in the native pine is longer in the eastern than in the western groups, but even in the latter it is usually three or more years, which contrasts with one or two years for trees in plantations of unknown origin. It would, therefore, be safer to use pine of native origin, and preferably from the western woods, for use in these high rainfall regions.

It might be thought that the trees in the native pinewoods are too old for the selection of special strains. In one respect their age has one great advantage in that the full potentialities of the trees have had ample time to be revealed, and they have shown that they are capable of growing under the climatic and other site conditions of their habitat to an age beyond that normally necessary under controlled silviculture and management. Their only disadvantage is that cone production is less than in younger woods, but the seed has been shown to be of good quality. Moreover, although current shoot growth is small, it has been found that the shoots are suitable scion material for grafting.

CHAPTER 18

THE FUTURE OF THE NATIVE PINEWOODS OF SCOTLAND

IN THE preceding chapters, reasons have been given why the native pinewoods should have a future. First, they are the authentic home of the distinctive strains of Scots pine at the western extremity of its natural distribution. Some of these strains are already important in the forestry of Britain and other countries, and others may be in the future, hence from a practical point of view this source should be maintained. Secondly, the native pinewoods are one of the most interesting survivals of our native vegetation, with a distinctive flora and fauna. There is now general recognition in all civilised countries that such survivals should be preserved on an adequate scale, and it would be a national loss if these pinewoods were allowed to disappear. Finally, they can be considered to be not the least important of the historical monuments of Scotland. They need never disappear if appropriate steps are taken.

The present condition of the native pinewoods has been described in some detail in Chapters 3 to 11. From the point of view of their future, the first and most important consideration is their present age structure. Most of the pine are old, the principal age class being from 140 to 190 years. There are relatively few trees under 100 years old, and current natural regeneration is both exceptional and on a small scale. While there is evidence that the absolute physical age of the native pine is about 400 years, most do not survive beyond 250 years. This sets a limit to their future under present conditions. Apart from the missing younger generations, the present pattern of the age structure is semi-irregular, with groups or larger stands of trees of about the same age, but hoary old mother trees may stand amongst their younger progeny. The second important characteristic of the native pinewoods is that, except for limited areas, the stocking is low and the production of timber is, therefore, less than it could be. And even more important consequence of this low stocking is that it leads to a rank growth of the field layer communities, which is one reason for the paucity of natural regeneration. The understocking may also be leading to progressive, if slow, deterioration of the soil, particularly where there is continuous removal of herbage by grazing. Malcolm

(1957) in Studies at Rannoch and Black Mount woodlands found that when forest cover was removed there was a deterioration in the physical condition of the soil. Thirdly, while the pine are remarkably healthy, there is a steady loss of old trees by death, even in the absence of felling or destruction by fire or other accidental causes.

If no positive action is taken for the preservation and perpetuation of the native pinewoods, it is not difficult to foresee their future, because their past history provides the answer. The smaller remnants will gradually disappear, and the larger woodlands shrink in area as heather burning on adjacent grazings bites into their margins. The stocking within them will gradually become more open as the older trees die, and all the evidence suggests that the conditions of vegetation, humus, and soil will become less favourable for natural regeneration. These changes, however, will be slow, and this is perhaps the greatest danger, because the not too discerning eye may not see the corrosive action of time on the pinewoods before it is too late to ensure their perpetuation. The long life-span of the pine is, however, also a source of hope. There is as yet time to ensure that many of the native pinewoods will continue in perpetuity.

Positive action to protect and regenerate these woodlands has been taken in the past, and it is of value to recapitulate how far such action was effective, why it may have failed, and in what ways it was misdirected. The efforts that were made in the second half of the eighteenth century by the Commissioners for the Forfeited Estates in some forests, for example at Rannoch and Arkaig, to protect natural regeneration from grazing, to supplement it by sowing pine seed and by planting seedlings, and to deal with competing vegetation, have been described in earlier chapters. The methods used at Rothiemurchus at the beginning of the last century whereby felling was concentrated in blocks, and natural regeneration then protected from grazing animals, have also been mentioned. There is evidence that these efforts were rewarded, at least with partial success. The failure, as is so often the case in forestry, was to continue these practices for a sufficiently long period, and to improve them in the light of experience. In more recent times, the Forestry Commission has acquired the whole or part of the native pinewoods at Glenmore, Rannoch, Glen Moriston, Glengarry, Achnashellach, Glen Affric, Glen Cannich, Glen Loy, and Guisachan. In some of these forests, experiments have been carried out on methods to secure natural regeneration and on the sowing of seed of Scots pine and other conifers. The results, mentioned in Chapter 3, have on the whole been disappointing, but they have at least helped to elucidate some of the problems. The Nature Conservancy is also concerned with problems of natural regeneration in one or two of the native pinewoods. Apart from these research efforts, the Forestry Commission have tended to manage the native pinewoods in their ownership in the same way as other woodlands. Much of normal forestry practice is, of course, appropriate to all woodlands, for example adequate protection. The Forestry Commission and some other owners have been rightly concerned to improve the stocking in the woodlands. Unfortunately in the past, for example at Glenmore, non-native strains of Scots pine have been introduced, which will mean that in the future there will be the risk of cross-pollination between the native and the introduced strains. Coniferous species other than Scots pine have also been planted in some of the native woodlands. It is true that our only indigeneous tree conifer is not the most suitable and productive species for some of the site conditions in the native pinewoods, hence the reason for the use of other species. This, of course, will not endanger the future maintenance of the distinctive strains of Scots pine, but it will change the ecological conditions in these woodlands. Where they are extensive, and there are large areas with only scattered native pine, it is only reasonable that at least part of such land should be used for normal productive forestry, but the most distinctive parts of the native pinewoods should be maintained in their natural condition.

The first thing needed to ensure the future of the native pinewoods is the appreciation by as many of their owners as possible that they are a unique national heritage. It is hoped that this book will help to lead to such an appreciation, and that it will encourage owners to do everything possible to ensure their perpetuation, as far as their resources permit. The aim should be the preservation of native pinewoods in all the different climatic and site conditions under which they are now growing. The smallest remnants which are no longer distinctive pinewood communities are less important than the others, but they should be preserved as long as possible for their historical interest. In the largest woodlands, particularly where there are extensive areas with only scattered pine, it may not be practicable to preserve the whole area as distinctive and specially treated natural pinewoods, but as much as possible should be so preserved. The central problem is, of course, to increase the amount of regeneration, thereby providing in the course of time the younger age classes now missing in the woodlands, and at the same time gradually to improve their stocking. While regeneration by natural and artificial means – by sowing and planting – have each their respective place in general forestry practice, natural regeneration is clearly to be preferred in the native pinewoods for a number of reasons, but particularly because it will best ensure that the range of morphological variants or strains of Scots pine is perpetuated, the importance of which has been stressed already. Previous work and the present study have not provided the answer as to how best to ensure natural regeneration in these woodlands. It is clear that the problem is one of great difficulty and calls for further investigation. Some of this work, however, does not require specialists, and an interested and informed owner and his forester could help to increase knowledge, as has been done, for example, at Glentanar. The problem has been discussed in some detail in Chapter 3, and various suggestions made in the light of all the present evidence. It is unlikely, however, that natural regeneration will be sufficiently successful in all the woodlands to ensure their perpetuation. It is almost certain that some sowing or planting with be necessary, and in the light of past experience the latter is more likely to be successful. It is, of course, essential that the plants be raised from seed collected in the native pinewood to ensure succession of the same strains. In the future as in the past, it will be necessary to exclude grazing animals, wild and domestic, where regeneration is proceeding, and in most instances it will probably be more economic to exclude them from the whole woodland than from selected portions of it. Any heather burning either within the woodlands or on their margins should be strictly controlled. A long and sustained effort will be required if the future of the native pinewoods is to be ensured. The aim should be, say over about a century, to build up gradually a reasonable balance of age classes, old and young, so that there will always be a succession of trees of different ages. The age structure should be semi-irregular as it is today in some of the larger and better preserved woodlands, a mosaic of groups and stands of varying extent up to a few acres, each consisting of trees of about the same age and together providing a range in age from the youngest to the oldest, but not necessarily a continuous range of age or any exact mathematical balance in age or size classes, which is unusual in natural pinewoods as a whole. The other native tree species would, of course, continue to play their role in the woodlands, and regeneration by birches and rowan may later lead to the reoccupation of the ground by pine, as in the past. It is believed that such a forest would also preserve its associated natural non-tree flora and fauna, and come closer to what the natural pinewoods were like some two to three centuries ago before heavy exploitation began.

It would probably help to further this enterprise if the different owners, public and private, together with foresters and other biologists specially interested in the native pinewoods, were linked together informally, so that there could be a periodic exchange of information about them, and also some co-operative planning of investigations. This should not be difficult to organise, and perhaps the two government departments interested, the Forestry Commission and the Nature Conservancy, might take the lead.

THE FIELD LAYER COMMUNITIES IN THE NATIVE PINEWOODS OF SCOTLAND

I. COMMUNITIES WHERE SCOTS PINE IS DOMINANT AND BIRCHES ARE NOT MORE THAN LOCALLY FREQUENT

1. WELL STOCKED STANDS

Community No. 1. **A dry moss community.**

Canopy	Complete or almost complete.
Soil	Dry, podsolised over drift.
Remarks	Dominated completely by mosses; the vegetation cover of the soil is generally less than 50 per cent. The needle litter may be as thick as 2 in. (5·1 cm.). Common in the east of Scotland.

Species usually present

Dicranella spp.	O[1]
Dicranum scoparium	O–L F
Hylocomium splendens	O–L F
Hypnum cupressiforme	O–L F
Pleurozium (Hypnum) schreberi	O
Rhytidiadelphus triquetrus (Hylocomium triquetrum)	L F

Species sometimes present

Calluna vulgaris	O
Deschampsia flexuosa	O
Oxalis acetosella	O
Vaccinium vitis-idaea	O
Isothecium (Eurhynchium) myosuroides	L F
Leucobryum glaucum	O
Plagiothecium undulatum	L F
Cladonia spp.	O

Community No. 2. **A moist moss community.**

Canopy	Complete or almost complete.

[1] For definitions of abbreviations see Table II, page 70.

Soil   Well drained but moist, podsolised with 1 to 3 in. (2·5 to 7·6 cm.)
            raw humus.
Remarks   A moister site than Community No. 1 with a much richer flora. The
            mosses form a mat up to 6 in. (15·2 cm.) thick and frequently form
            moss cushions. Rare in the east of Scotland, common in the west.

Species usually present

Deschampsia flexuosa	O–L F
Melampyrum sylvaticum	O
Vaccinium myrtillus	O
V. vitis-idaea	O–L F
Hylocomium splendens	A–L D
Hypnum cupressiforme	L A
Plagiothecium undulatum	L F
Pleurozium (Hypnum) schreberi	A–L D
Ptilium (Hypnum) crista-castrensis	O–L F
Polytrichum commune	L F
Rhytidiadelphus loreus (Hylocomium loreum)	F
R. triquetrus	L F
Scapania gracilis	F
Sphagnum spp.	F–L A
Cladonia spp.	O

Species sometimes present

Blechnum spicant	O
Calluna vulgaris (4 in.) (10·2 cm.)	L F
Empetrum nigrum	L F
Erica tetralix	L F
E. cinerea	O
Galium hercynicum	O
Molinia caerulea	L F
Potentilla erecta	O
Mnium hornum	L F
M. punctatum	R
M. undulatum	L F

Community No. 3. A *Vaccinium/Deschampsia/Hypnaceous* moss community.
   Canopy   Almost complete.
   Soil   Dry, podsolised with raw humus.
   Remarks   Widespread in all parts of Scotland under a close pine canopy.

Species usually present

Calluna vulgaris (6-12 in.) (15·2-30·5 cm.)	F–L A
Deschampsia flexuosa	F
Luzula pilosa	O
Vaccinium myrtillus	CD–D
V. vitis idaea	A–CD–D
Dicranella spp.	O
Dicranum majus	O
D. scoparium	O–L F
Hylocomium splendens	A–L CD
Hypnum cupressiforme	L F
Pleurozium schreberi	A–L CD
Rhytidiadelphus loreus	F–L A
R. triquetrus	L A

Species sometimes present

Blechnum spicant	O
Empetrum nigrum	L F
Erica cinerea	L F
Goodyera repens	O
Oxalis acetosella	O
Pyrola media	O
Ramischia secunda	R
Trientalis europaea	O
Isothecium myosuroides	L F

Community No. 4. A *Deschampsia flexuosa/Hypnaceous* moss community.

Canopy	About three-quarters complete.
Soil	Dry, podsolised over glacial drift.
Remarks	General in eastern and central Scotland. Not widespread in the west. It is frequently invaded by *Calluna* and other species.

Species usually present

Calluna vulgaris (to 12 in.) (30·5 cm.)	F
Deschampsia flexuosa	D
Galium hercynicum	O
Luzula pilosa	O
Vaccinium myrtillus	O–L F
V. vitis-idaea	O–L F
Hylocomium splendens	F
Pleurozium schreberi	F
Rhytidiadelphus loreus	O–L F
R. triquetrus	L F

X

Species sometimes present

Anthoxanthum odoratum	L F
Oxalis acetosella	O
Pteridium aquilinum	L F
Pyrola media	O
Trientalis europaea	O–L F

Community No. 5. A dry *Calluna/Vaccinium/Deschampsia/*moss community.

Canopy	About three-quarters complete.
Soil	Dry, podsolised over glacial drift.
Remarks	A variable community depending upon soils, moisture, and lighting. Occurs frequently in the eastern pinewoods, but is less common in the west.

Species usually present

Calluna vulgaris (6–12 in.) (15·2–30·5 cm.)	A–CD–D
Deschampsia flexuosa	O–L F–L A
Luzula pilosa	O
Melampyrum sylvaticum	O–L F
Potentilla erecta	O
Vaccinium myrtillus	A–CD–L D
V. vitis-idaea	A–CD–L D
Dicranella spp.	O
Dicranum majus	O
D. scoparium	O–L F
Hylocomium splendens	F–L A–L CD
Hypnum cupressiforme	F–L A–L CD
Pleurozium schreberi	O–L F
Rhytidiadelphus loreus	O–L F
R. triquetrus	O–L F

Species sometimes present

Empetrum nigrum	L F
Erica cinerea	O–L F
E. tetralix	L F
Goodyera repens	O
Pteridium aquilinum	L F
Pyrola media	O
Sorbus aucuparia	O
Trientalis europaea	O
Isothecium myosuroides	L F
Plagiothecium undulatum	O
Cladonia spp.	O

Community No. 6. A moist *Calluna/Vaccinium/Deschampsia/*moss community.

Canopy   About three-quarters complete or less.

Soil   Moist, podsolised with 1 to 2 in. (2·5 to 5·1 cm.) of raw humus or peat.

Remarks   A common community in both the east and west of Scotland. Typically it consists of rank heather with a well developed moss mat beneath.

Species usually present

Blechnum spicant	O
Calluna vulgaris (12-36 in.) (30·5-91·4 cm.)	D
Deschampsia flexuosa	O–L F
Erica cinerea	O
E. tetralix	O
Potentilla erecta	O
Vaccinium myrtillus	F–L A
V. vitis-idaea	F–L A
Dicranum majus	O
D. scoparium	O–L F
Hylocomium splendens	A–L CD
Hypnum cupressiforme	L F
Pleurozium schreberi	A–L CD
Polytrichium commune	L F
Ptilium crista-castrensis	O
Rhytidiadelphus loreus	O–L F
R. triquetrus	L F
Scapania gracilis	L F
Sphagnum spp.	F–L A

Species sometimes present

Carex echinata	O
C. flava	O
Equisetum sylvaticum	L F
Galium hercynicum	L F
Listera cordata	R–O
Luzula pilosa	O
Melampyrum sylvaticum	O
Molinia caerulea	L F
Pinguicula vulgaris	O
Polygala vulgaris	R
Pteridium aquilinum	L A
Pyrola media	O
Succisa pratensis (Scabiosa succisa)	O
Trichophorum caespitosum	O
Trientalis europaea	O

Mnium hornum	L F
M. undulatum	L F
M. punctatum	R
Plagiothecium undulatum	L F
Cladonia spp.	F

2. OPEN STANDS

Community No. 7. A grass pinewood community.

Canopy   About one half or more.

Soil   Dry, podsolised, over glacial drift or on old river terraces.

Remarks   This community is only very local on sites where pine dominates. It is more common where birch is locally frequent. It occurs both in eastern and western Scotland.

Species usually present

Agrostis spp. (*A. tenuis* etc.)	A
Anthoxanthum odoratum	A–L CD
Blechnum spicant	O
Deschampsia flexuosa	A–CD
Dryopteris filix-mas	O
Euphrasia spp.	L F
Festuca spp. (*F. ovina, F. vivipara,* etc.)	A–L CD
Galium hercynicum	O–L F
Holcus spp. (*H. lanatus, H. mollis*)	L F
Luzula campestris	O
L. pilosa	O
Lysimachia nemorum	O
Molinia caerulea	O–L F
Oxalis acetosella	O
Potentilla erecta	O
Ranunculus ficaria	O
Sorbus aucuparia (to 12 in.) (30·5 cm.)	O
Dicranella spp.	O
Dicranum scoparium	O–L F
Hylocomium splendens	O–L F
Hypnum cupressiforme	L F
Plagiothecium undulatum	O
Pleurozium schreberi	L F
Polytrichum commune	L F
Pseudoscleropodium (*Brachythecium*) *purum*	O–L F
Rhytidiadelphus loreus	O
R. squarrosus	O–R
R. triquetrus	L F

Species sometimes present

Calluna vulgaris (to 6 in.) (15·2 cm.)	F
Digitalis purpurea	R
Empetrum nigrum	R
Erica cinerea	O
Listera cordata	R
Pteridium aquilinum	L A
Trientalis europaea	O
Dicranum majus	O
Scapania gracilis	L F
Sphagum spp.	O–L F

Community No. 8. A moist *Calluna/Vaccinium/Eriophorum/Sphagnum* community.

Canopy   Variable up to about one half.

Soil   Poorly drained, podsolised with 2 to 3 in. (5·1 to 7·6 cm.) of raw humus or 2 to 6 in. (5·1 to 15·2 cm.) of peat.

Remarks   A common community throughout Scotland. It is a variant of Nos. 5 and 6 in which the drainage has deteriorated, followed by an invasion by *Eriophorum*, *Trichophorum* and *Sphagnum*.

Species usually present

Calluna vulgaris (12-24 in.) (30·5-61·0 cm.)	D
Carex spp. (*C. echinata*, *C. panicea*, *C. flava*, etc.)	F
Deschampsia flexuosa	F
Empetrum nigrum	L F
Erica tetralix	F
Eriophorum angustifolium	A–L CD
E. vaginatum	A–L CD
Molinia caerulea	O–L F–L A
Succisa pratensis	O
Trichophorum caespitosum	F–L A
Breutelia chrysocoma (*arcuata*)	O
Polytrichum commune	L F
Sphagnum spp.	F–L A

Species sometimes present

Myrica gale	O–L F
Narthecium ossifragum	O
Orchis maculata	O

Community No. 9. A *Calluna/Molinia* community.

Canopy   Variable up to about one half.

Soil   Moist podsols, and moist peat, over glacial drift.
Remarks   A very common community in the west of Scotland, but less common
in the east. It occurs under a wide range of conditions of soil and
canopy density.

Species usually present

Blechnum spicant	O
Calluna vulgaris (8–24 in.) (20·3–61 cm.)	CD–L D
Carex spp. (*C. echinata, C. panicea,* etc.)	F
Deschampsia flexuosa	O–L F
Erica cinerea	O
E. tetralix	F
Eriophorum vaginatum	L F
E. angustifolium	L F
Juncus squarrosus	O
Molinia caerulea	A–L CD
Narthecium ossifragum	O
Succisa pratensis	O
Trichophorum caespitosium	O–L F
Vaccinium myrtillus	O
V. vitis-idaea	O–L F
Hylocomium splendens	O–L F
Pleurozium schreberi	O–L F
Rhytidiadelphus loreus	O
Sphagnum spp.	L F

Species sometimes present

Arctostaphylos uva-ursi	R
Empetrum nigrum	L F
E. hermaphroditum	L F
Galium hercynicum	O
Juncus conglomeratus	L F
J. effusus	L F
Myrica gale	L F
Orchis maculata	O–L F
Potentilla erecta	O
Aulacomnium palustre	L F
Breutelia chrysocoma	O
Hypnum cupressiforme	L F
Rhacomitrium languinosum	O–L F
Pleurozia purpurea	R
Pellia epiphylla	R

3. COMMUNITIES UNDER SCATTERED PINE.

Community No. 10. A *Callunetum.*

Canopy	Scattered pine.
Soil	Variable. This community occurs both on podsolised soil with a thin (1-2 in.) (2·5-5·1 cm.) layer of raw humus and on comparatively well drained peat less than 12 in. (30·5 cm.) thick. The common factor is good drainage.
Remarks	This community arises when either No. 5 or No. 6 is dominated by *Calluna* in this open situation. In its true form it is not common, but intermediate stages between this community and Nos. 5 and 6 are widespread. It is more common in eastern Scotland than in the west.

Species usually present

Calluna vulgaris (6-30 in.) (15·2-76·2 cm.)	D
Erica cinerea	O–L F
E. tetralix	O–L F
Potentilla erecta	O
Trichophorum caespitosum	O
Vaccinium vitis-idaea	O–L F
Hylocomium splendens	F
Pleurozium schreberi	F
Cladonia sylvatica	O–L F
C. coccifera	O

Species sometimes present

Arctostaphylos uva-ursi	L F
Sarothamnus (*Cytisus*) *scoparius*	L F
Lycopodium selago	O
L. clavatum	O
L. alpinum	R
Pteridium aquilinum	L F
Hedwigia ciliata (on rocks)	R
Hypnum cupressiforme	L F
Polytrichum juniperinum (on rocks)	L F
Rhacomitrium lanuginosum	O–L F

Community No. 11. A *Calluna/Trichophorum* community.

Canopy	Scattered pine.
Soil	Variable. The community occurs on moist sites with moderately good drainage and either a thin layer (2 in.) (5·1 cm.) of raw humus on the surface or up to 10 in. (25·4 cm.) of comparatively well drained peat. Generally over glacial drift.

Remarks   A widespread community in both east and west Scotland, but more common in the west than in the east. It is particularly characteristic of the marginal pine forest where the trees begin to thin out.

Species usually present

Calluna vulgaris (6-18 in.) (15·2-45·7 cm.)	CD–D
Deschampsia flexuosa	O
Empetrum nigrum	O–L F
Erica tetralix	O–L F
Eriophorum angustifolium	O–L F
E. vaginatum	O–L F
Festuca ovina	O
Trichophorum caespitosum	F–L CD
Vaccinium myrtillus	O
V. vitis-idaea	O–L F
Hylocomium splendens	O
Pleurozium schreberi	O
Polytrichum juniperinum (on rocks)	L F
Rhacomitrium lanuginosum	L F
Sphagnum spp.	L F
Cladonia sylvatica	O–L F

Species sometimes present

Antennaria dioica	R
Arctostaphylos uva-ursi	L F
Arctous alpina	R
Carex spp.	O–L F
Empetrum hermaphroditum	L F
Juncus squarrosus	O
Lycopodium selago	O
Myrica gale	L F
Nardus stricta	L F
Pteridium aquilinum	L F
Succisa pratensis	O
Breutelia chrysocoma	O
Sphagnum spp.	L F

Community No. 12. A *Molinia/Trichophorum* community.

Canopy   Scattered pine.
Soil   Moist peat, 12 in. (30·5 cm.) or more deep over glacial drift.
Remarks   Widespread in the west of Scotland, very local in the east. Common at the margins and along the fringes of clearings.

Species usually present

Calluna vulgaris	O–L F
Carex spp.	F
Deschampsia flexuosa	L F
Erica tetralix	F
Eriophorum angustifolium	A–L CD
E. vaginatum	A–L CD
Juncus squarrosus	L F
Lycopodium selago	O
Molinia caerulea	CD–L D
Narthecium ossifragum	O–L F
Succisa pratensis	O
Trichophorum caespitosum	CD–L D
Hylocomium splendens	O–L F
Pleurozium schreberi	O–L F
Rhacomitrium lanuginosum	L F
Sphagnum spp.	F–L A
Cladonia sylvatica	O–F

Species sometimes present

Empetrum nigrum	O–L F
Festuca ovina	O
Juncus articulatus	L F
J. conglomeratus	L F
J. effusus	L F
Myrica gale	L F
Potentilla erecta	O
Aulacomnium palustre	L F

II. COMMUNITIES UNDER STANDS IN WHICH THE BIRCHES ARE ABUNDANT OR CO-DOMINANT WITH THE SCOTS PINE

Community No. 13. A *Calluna*/grass/*Vaccinium*/moss community.

Canopy	Variable, from one quarter to three-quarters complete.
Soil	Dry or moist, podsolised, with very little raw humus and no peat.
Remarks	This community is intermediate between those of typical well drained pinewood for example Nos. 5 or 6, and those of well drained birchwood. General throughout Scotland, but more common in the west than in the east.

Species usually present

Agrostis spp. (*A. tenuis* etc.)	L F
Anthoxanthum odoratum	F

Blechnum spicant	O
Calluna vulgaris (6–12 in.) (15·2–30·5 cm.)	CD–D
Deschampsia flexuosa	F–L A
Festuca spp. (*F. ovina*, *F. vivipara*)	F
Luzula pilosa	O
Oxalis acetosella	O–L F
Ranunculus ficaria	O
Vaccinium myrtillus	F–L CD
V. vitis idaea	F–L A
Dicranella spp.	O–L F
Dicranum majus	O
D. scoparium	O–L F
Hylocomium splendens	A
Hypnum cupressiforme	L F
Plagiothecium undulatum	O
Pleurozium schreberi	A
Polytrichum commune	L F
Pseudoscleropodium purum	L F
Rhytidiadelphus loreus	O–L F
R. squarrosus	L F
R. triquetrus	L F
Scapania gracilis	O–L F

Species sometimes present

Digitalis purpurea	R
Galium hercynicum	O
Luzula campestris	O
L. sylvatica	L F
Melampyrum sylvaticum	O
Molinia caerulea	L F
Pedicularis sylvatica	O
Potentilla erecta	O
Pteridium aquilinum	L F
Ptilium crista-castrensis	O
Sphagnum spp.	L F

Community No. 14. A grass/moss community.

Canopy	Variable, from one quarter to three-quarters complete.
Soil	Dry to moist, slightly podsolised or a brown forest soil with little or no surface raw humus or peat.
Remarks	A community more common in the west of Scotland than in the east, and generally associated with a high percentage of birch (CD–L D) in the tree layer.

Species usually present

Agrostis spp. (*A. tenuis* etc.)	F–L A
Anthoxanthum odoratum	A–L CD
Blechnum spicant	O
Brachypodium sylvaticum	L F
Calluna vulgaris (3–8 in.) (8–20 cm.)	F
Deschampsia flexuosa	CD–L D
Dryopteris filix-mas	O–R
Festuca spp. (*F. viviparum, F. ovina*, etc.)	F–L A
Galium hercynicum	O
Holcus spp.	L F
Luzula pilosa	O
Lysimachia nemorum	O
Molinia caerulea	O–L F
Oxalis acetosella	O–L F
Poa spp.	L F
Potentilla erecta	O
Ranunculus ficaria	O
Vaccinium myrtillus	F
V. vitis-idaea	L F
Viola riviniana	O–L F
Hylocomium splendens	A
Hypnum cupressiforme	O–L F
Plagiothecium undulatum	O
Pleurozium schreberi	L F
Polytrichum commune	L F
Pseudoscleropodium purum	F
Ptilium crista-castrensis	L F
Rhytidiadelphus loreus	F
R. squarrosus	F
R. triquetrus	F
Scapania gracilis	L F
Sphagnum spp.	L F

Species sometimes present

Digitalis purpurea	R
Empetrum nigrum	O
Erica cinerea	O–L F
E. tetralix	O
Luzula campestris	O
L. sylvatica	L F
Nardus stricta	O

Pteridium aquilinum   L F
Trientalis europaea   O–L F

III. FLUSH AND BOG COMMUNITIES OF PINEWOOD

Community No. 15. An *Eriophorum*/*Trichophorum*/*Sphagnum* flush or bog community.

Canopy   Scattered pine or none.

Soil   Wet, poorly drained peat ranging in depth from 6 to 50 in. (15·2 to
           127 cm.) or more.

Remarks   A widespread community throughout Scotland, but more common
           in the west than the east.

Species usually present

Calluna vulgaris (2-4 in.) (5·1-10·2 cm.)   F
Carex echinata   F
C. microglochin   L F
C. flava   L F
C. pulicaris   L F
Drosera rotundifolia   O
Erica cinerea   O
E. tetralix   F
Eriophorum angustifolium   CD
E. vaginatum   CD
Narthecium ossifragum   F
Succisa pratensis   O
Trichophorum caespitosum   A–CD

Aulacomnium palustre   L F
Pleurozia purpurea   O
Polytrichum commune   L F
Rhacomitrium lanuginosum   L F
Sphagnum spp.   A

Cladonia spp.   F

Species sometimes present

Drosera intermedia   L F
Empetrum hermaphroditum   L F
E. nigrum   L F
Juncus squarrosus   O
Lycopodium selago   O
Molinia caerulea   L A
Myrica gale   L F

Campylopus spp.   O
Pohlia nutans   L F

Community No. 16. A *Molinia* flush community.

Canopy	Variable, less than one half complete.
Soil	Moist to wet, poorly drained, podsolised, generally with more than 5 in. (12·7 cm.) of surface peat.
Remarks	A very common flush type in localities with impeded drainage and peat. In the pinewoods of the east of Scotland, it is confined to very wet bogs, but it is common throughout western Scotland in hollows and flat ground which are not necessarily boggy.

Species usually present

Carex spp. (*C. panicea, C. echinata,* etc.)	F
Erica tetralix	O–L F
Eriophorum angustifolium	L F
E. vaginatum	L F
Molinia caerulea	D
Potentilla erecta	O
Succisa pratensis	O
Trichophorum caespitosum	L F
Polytrichum commune	F–L A
Sphagnum spp.	A

Species sometimes present

Deschampsia flexuosa	O–L F
Galium uliginosum	O
Juncus articulatus	L F
J. conglomeratus	L F
J. effusus	L F
J. squarrosus	O
Myrica gale	O–L F
Narthecium ossifragum	O–L F
Orchis maculata	L F
Breutelia chrysocoma	O
Aulacomnium palustre	L F

Community No. 17. A *Juncus communis* flush or bog community.

Canopy	Scattered pine or none.
Soil	Wet, podsolised alluvium or thin peat. Drainage very poor.
Remarks	A common community in pinewoods in all parts of Scotland but especially in the west. It seldom covers large areas except on alluvial pastures which are subject to periodic flooding.

Species usually present

Eriophorum angustifolium	O–L F
E. vaginatum	O–L F
Galium uliginosum	O–R
Juncus conglomeratus	CD–D
J. effusus	CD–D
Potentilla erecta	O
Polytrichum commune	F–L A
Sphagnum spp.	A

Species sometimes present

Erica tetralix	O–L F
Molinia caerulea	L F
Myrica gale	O
Aulacomnium palustre	L F

Community No. *18.* A *Juncus articulatus* flush or bog community.

Canopy	Scattered pine or none.
Soil	Wet, peaty hollows and wet alluvial pastures. Drainage very poor.
Remarks	Found locally in the west, but rare in the east.

Species usually present

Eriophorum angustifolium	L F
E. vaginatum	L F
Juncus articulatus	D
Sphagnum spp.	A

Species sometimes present

Galium palustre	O
Juncus conglomeratus	L F
J. effusus	L F
Polytrichum commune	L F

Community No. *19.* A *Sphagnum* spp. bog community.

Canopy	None.
Soil	Wet peat with standing water and local peat hags.
Remarks	These bogs are common in the western pinewoods, but less so in the east. The peat is completely waterlogged. Never more than local.

Species usually present

Carex spp.	F
Drosera rotundifolia	O
Eriophorum angustifolium	F
E. vaginatum	F
Narthecium ossifragum	F
Aulacomnium palustre	L F
Polytrichum commune	L F
Sphagnum spp.	D
Cladonia spp.	L F

Species sometimes present

Drosera intermedia	O
Menyanthes trifoliata	O
Molinia caerulea	L F
Myrica gale	L F
Succisa pratensis	O
Trichophorum caespitosum	O

PLANT LIST

THE following is a list of plants found within the boundaries of the native pinewoods of Scotland, including the birch and oak communities closely associated with them. It is not claimed that the list is complete as, for example, *Corallorhiza trifida* was not found, and Tansley (1949) states that this species is characteristic and even confined to the old pine forests. Introduced species of trees such as *Picea* spp., *Larix* spp., *Pseudotsuga taxifolia*, *Pinus contorta*, etc. which have been planted in some of the woods such as Abernethy and Glenmore, and the pasture grasses of cultivated land within the forest boundaries have been omitted from the list intentionally. The frequencies of the more common species in the defined field layer communities are given in Appendix I.

Trees and large shrubs
    Alnus glutinosa
    Betula pubescens
    B. verrucosa
    Corylus avellana — Not common. Birchwoods, oakwoods and banks of streams.
    Crataegus monogyna — Not common. Near derelict crofts on open ground, e.g. Ardgour.
    Fraxinus excelsior — Not common. With birch, e.g. Ardgour.
    Ilex aquifolium — Most common west of the Great Glen.
    Juniperus communis
    Pinus silvestris
    Populus tremula — Not common. Usually in open places.
    Prunus padus — Not common. Usually by streams or in birchwoods, e.g. Glentanar and Barisdale.
    Quercus petraea
    Q. robur
    Salix atrocinerea
    S. aurita
    S. caprea
    S. herbacea — Rare. Wet scree. Loch Maree.
    S. pentandra — Not common. Glen Nevis.
    S. repens — Rare. Open, wet ground. Coulin.
    Sorbus aucuparia

Small shrubs, herbs, ferns and grasses

Achillea millefolium	Paths.
A. ptarmica	Rare. Sides of streams, e.g. Glentanar.
Agrostis canina	
A. stolonifera	Not common, e.g. Glentanar, Glen Strathfarrar.
A. tenuis	
Ajuga reptans	Birchwoods and oakwoods.
Alchemilla alpina	Edges of woods and open places.
A. vulgaris agg.	Grassy, open places. Mainly west of the Great Glen.
Anemone nemorosa	Most common in birchwoods but often under pine.
Antennaria dioica	Rocky crevices in open places.
Anthoxanthum odoratum	
Arctostaphylos uva-ursi	Dry, open places and sides of paths.
Arctous alpina	Very rare. Upper tree limit. Achnashellach, Glen Cannich, Loch Maree.
Asplenium viride	Very rare. Limestone outcrop. Rhidorroch.
Athrium filix-femina	Usually in birchwoods and oakwoods but sometimes under pine.
Bellis perennis	Paths.
Blechnum spicant	
Brachypodium sylvaticum	Birchwoods.
Calluna vulgaris	
Campanula rotundifolia	
Carduus heterophyllus	
C. palustre	
Carex acuta	
C. binervis	
C. distans	
C. echinata	
C. flava	
C. limosa	
C. nigra	
C. panicea	
C. pauciflora	
C. pulicaris	
Cerastium vulgatum	
Chamaenerion angustifolium	Not common. Burned sites near habitation.
Chamaepericlymenum suecicum	Very rare. Glenmore.
Chrysosplenium oppositifolium	Rare. Birchwoods of Northern Group.

Y

Conopodium majus	Edges of woods.
Cynosurus cristatus	Edges of birchwoods. Probably an escape from cultivated ground.
Deschampsia caespitosa	
D. flexuosa	
Digitalis purpurea	Not common but present on low ground in most woods.
Drosera anglica?	Very rare. Loch Maree.
D. intermedia	Local. Most common in Great Glen, Strath Glass, Wester Ross and Rannoch.
D. rotundifolia	Bogs.
Dryopteris filix-mas	
D. spinulosa	
Eleocharis palustris	
Empetrum hermaphroditum	Local. Upper tree limit. Less common in the west than east.
E. nigrum	
Endymion nonscriptus	Birchwoods.
Epilobium montanum	
Equisetum arvense	Bogs.
E. palustre	Bogs.
E. sylvaticum	
Erica cinerea	
E. tetralix	
Eriophorum angustifolium	
E. vaginatum	
Euphrasia nemorosa	Paths.
E. scotica	Upper tree limit. Usually near birchwoods.
Festuca ovina	
F. rubra	
F. vivipara	
Fragaria vesca	Birchwoods and oakwoods.
Galium boreale	Rocky sites at upper tree limit.
G. hercynicum	
G. palustre	Bogs.
G. verum	Birchwoods, oakwoods and grassy areas.
Genista anglica	
Gentianella amarella	Paths and open grassy places at upper tree limit.
Geranium robertianum	Paths and birchwoods.
G. sylvaticum	Birchwoods and oakwoods.
Geum rivale	Sides of streams.

Goodyera repens	Pinewoods. Most common in Deeside and Speyside.
Gymnadenia conopsea	
Hammarbya paludosa	Rare. Bogs. Glenmore and Rothiemurchus.
Hedera helix	Usually in birchwoods and oakwoods, but sometimes on pine in the west.
Helianthemum chamaecistus	Very rare. Basic pockets at edge of woods. Glentanar.
Holcus lanatus	
H. mollis	
Hypericum humifusum	
H. perforatum	Birchwoods, oakwoods and grassy sides of paths.
H. pulchrum	
Juncus alpinus	Very rare. Uper tree limit. Glentanar.
J. articulatus	Bogs.
J. bufonius	Paths, ditches.
J. bulbosus	Wet paths, ditches.
J. conglomeratus	
J. effusus	
J. kochii	Rare. Glentanar.
J. squarrosus	
J. trifidus	Rare. Upper tree limit. Glenmore and Rothiemurchus.
Lapsana communis	Paths and open places.
Lathyrus montanus	
Linnaea borealis	Very rare. Ballochbuie. Recorded for Glenmore.
Linum catharticum	
Listera cordata	Thinly scattered in all geographical groups of pinewoods.
Lobelia dortmanna	Locally frequent at edges of lochs, e.g. Glenmore, Glengarry.
Loiseleuria procumbens	Upper tree limit. Rothiemurchus.
Lonicera periclymenum	Usually in birchwoods but sometimes on pine in the west.
Lotus corniculatus	
Luzula campestris	Grassy places.
L. multiflora	
L. pilosa	
L. sylvatica	Usually in birch and oakwoods, but often under pine and by streams.
Lycopodium alpinum	

L. annotinum	Local. Usually in birchwoods but sometimes under pine. Deeside, Speyside and Strath Glass.
L. clavatum	Open places.
L. indundatum	Rare. Glenmore.
L. selago	Open places.
Lysimachia nemorum	Birchwoods, oakwoods and paths.
L. nummularia	Usually in birchwoods and oakwoods but sometimes under pine.
Melampyrum pratense	Birchwoods.
M. sylvaticum	
Melica nutans	Very rare. Glen Moriston.
M. uniflora	Birchwoods and oakwoods.
Menyanthes trifoliata	Peat bogs and stagnant pools west of the Great Glen.
Mercurialis perennis	Very rare. Birchwoods. Glen Strathfarrar.
Molinia caerulea	
Moneses uniflora	Very rare. Deeside and Speyside.
Myosotis arvensis	Open grassy places. Usually in birchwoods.
M. palustris	Bogs.
Myrica gale	
Nardus stricta	Paths and open places.
Narthecium ossifragum	Bogs and open peaty sites.
Orchis latifolia	Rare. Glen Moriston.
O. maculata	
Oxalis acetosella	
Oxycoccus microcarpus	Not common, but in most woods.
O. palustris	Rare. Most woods.
Parnassia palustris	Rare. Sides of streams and in bogs. Great Glen, Strath Glass and Southern.
Pedicularis sylvatica	
Phragmites communis	Lochs and rivers.
Pinguicula vulgaris	Wet, open places.
Plantago lanceolata	Paths.
Platanthera bifolia	Open, grassy places. Deeside, Great Glen, and Northern.
Poa alpina	Rare. On rocks. Upper tree limit.
P. annua	
P. nemoralis	
P. trivialis	
Polygala vulgaris	
Polygonum viviparum	Open, grassy places.

Polypodium vulgare	
Polystichum lobatum	
Potamogeton natans	Stagnant water.
P. polygonifolius	Stagnant water.
Potentilla anserina	Very rare. River shingle. Ballochbuie.
P. erecta	
Primula vulgaris	Birchwoods and oakwoods.
Prunella vulgaris	Paths.
Pteridium aquilinum	
Pyrola media	Pinewoods.
P. minor	Pinewoods.
Ramischia secunda	Rare. Deeside and Speyside.
Ranunculus acris	
R. bulbosus	Not common. Dry, grassy patches in birchwoods.
R. ficaria	Usually in birchwoods but sometimes under pine.
R. flammula	Stony loch margins.
R. repens	Open, grassy places.
Rhinanthus lochabrensis	In Glen Nevis
Rhododendron ponticum	An escape from policy gardens. Only in the west. Coulin.
Rosa canina	Edges of woods and sides of paths.
Rubus chamaemorus	Not common. Upper tree limit. Deeside, Speyside, and Wester Ross.
R. idaeus	Rare. Sides of paths in broadleaved woodlands.
Rumex acetosa	Paths.
R. acetosella	Paths and grassy places.
Sanicula europaea	Very rare. Basic pocket in Glen Moriston pinewoods.
Sarothamnus scoparius	
Saxifraga aizoides	Open places on wet gravels and by streams.
S. oppositifolia	Usually at upper tree limit, but sometimes under pine.
S. stellaris	Rare. Springs and moist rocky crevices in open places.
Sedum anglicum	Very rare. On rocks on islands of Loch Maree.
Senecio jacobaea	Usually near derelict crofts.
Sieglingia decumbens	Birchwoods.
Solidago virgaurea	Sides of paths and in grassy open places.
Stellaria alsine	

S. graminea
S. holostea
Succisa pratensis
Taraxacum paludosum
Teucrium scorodonia   Usually in birchwoods and oakwoods. Rarely associated with pine.

Thelypteris dryopteris
Thymus serpyllum   Paths and open places.
Tofieldia pusilla   Bogs and peaty places.
Trichophorum caespitosum
Trientalis europaea   Locally common in both birch and pine-woods.
Trifolium repens   Paths and open grassy places.
Ulex europaeus   Edges of woods and sides of paths.
U. minor
Urtica dioica   Near derelict crofts.
Utricularis vulgaris   Stagnant pools.
Vaccinium myrtillus
V. uliginosum   Rare. Glenmore.
V. vitis-idaea
Veronica chamaedrys   Birchwoods, oakwoods, and sides of paths.
V. officinalis
Viola canina   Birchwoods, oakwoods, and grassy sites.
V. riviniana

Mosses, liverworts and lichens

Antitrichia curtipendula   Not common. Tree bases. Strath Glass.
Atrichum undulatum   Usually in birchwoods, but sometimes under pine.
Aulacomnium palustre   Bogs.
Bartramia pomiformis   Rocks in open places.
Bazzania trilobata   Rare. Birch and oakwoods. Great Glen.
Blindia acuta
Brachythecium rivulare   Wet rocks in open places.
Breutelia chrysocoma   Moist peat in open places.
Bryum erythrocarpum   Rare. Sandy sites. Deeside and Speyside.
B. pseudotriquetrum   Bogs.
Calypogeia trichomanis
Campylopus atrovirens   Wet rock faces and edges of pools.
C. flexuosus   Wet peaty rock debris.
C. pyriformis
Cephalozia bicuspidata   Decayed tree stumps.
Cerania vermicularis   Very rare. On thin peat at Glen Quoich tree limit.

Cetraria glauca	Tree stumps.
Cladonia cenotea	Rare. Decayed tree stumps. Deeside, Rannoch.
C. coccifera	
C. cornuta	
C. digitata	Rare. Decayed tree stumps. Speyside.
C. fimbriata	
C. flabelliformis	
C. gracilis	Rocks in open places. Deeside and Speyside.
C. pyxidata	
C. rangiferina	Not common, but in all groups.
C. squamosa	Very rare. Decayed tree stumps. Deeside.
C. sylvatica	
C. uncinalis	Rare. Rocks. Wester Ross.
Climacium dendroides	Edges of lochs and rivers. Deeside.
Dicranella heteromalla	
D. squarrosa	Rocky sides of streams near upper tree limit.
Dicranum fuscescens	
D. majus	
D. scoparium	
Diplophyllum albicans	
Eurynchium praelongum	
Evernia prunastri	Tree trunks of pine.
Fontinalis antipyretica	Streams.
Grimmia sp.	Rocks in open places.
Hedwigia ciliata	Rare. On rocks.
Hookeria lucens	Rare. Moist, shaded crevices.
Hylocomium brevirostre	Usually at upper tree limit.
H. splendens	
Hyocomium flagellare	Wet rocks and shingle in open places.
Hypnum cupressiforme	
Isothecium myosuroides	
Leconora subfusca	Tree trunks. Deeside and Speyside.
Lepidozia reptans	
Leucobryum glaucum	
Lobaria pulmonaria	
Lophoclea bidentata	
Marchantia polymorpha	Rare. Burned ground under pine. Northern.
Mnium hornum	
M. punctatum	
M. undulatum	
Parmelia ambigua	Rare. Tree trunks. Deeside and Speyside.

P. physodes	Tree trunks.
Pellia epiphylla	
Peltigera canina	Rare. On rocks by streams.
Philonotis fontana	On wet rocks and in bogs.
Plagiothecium undulatum	
Pleurozea purpurea	Wet peat.
Pleurozium schreberi	
Pohlia nutans	Peat hags.
Polytrichum alpestre	Rare. Bogs.
P. commune	
P. formosum	Birch and oakwoods.
P. juniperinum	Thin peat on boulders in open places.
Pseudoscleropodium purum	Birchwoods, oakwoods, and grassy sites.
Ptilium crista-castrensis	
Rhacomitrium aciculare	River shingle.
R. fasciculare	Rocks.
R. lanuginosum	
Rhytidiadelphus loreus	
R. squarrosus	
R. triquetrus	
Scapania curta	
S. gracilis	
S. undulata	
Sphaerophorus globosus	
Sphagnum compactum	
S. cuspidatum	
S. girgensohnii?	Rare. Bogs. Deeside.
S. magellanicum	Not common. Wester Ross.
S. palustre	
S. papillosum	
S. plumulosum	
S. recurvum	Stagnant pools. Wester Ross.
S. rubellum	
S. squarrosum	Not Common. Deeside.
S. subsecundum	
S. tenellum	Not common. Wester Ross.
Stereocaulon coralloides	
S. denudatum	
S. tomentosum	
Tetraphis pellucida	Tree stumps.
Thuidium tamariscinum	
Usnea barbata	Tree trunks and branches.
U. florida	Tree trunks and branches.

BIBLIOGRAPHY

Anon.	1745-81	Forfeited Estates Papers: Lochiel. Register House, Edinburgh.
Anon.	1745-84	Forfeited Estates Papers: Barisdale. Register House, Edinburgh.
Anon.	1745-85	Forfeited Estates Papers: Strowan. Register House, Edinburgh.
Anon.	1814	*Rotuli Scotiae*, 1, 6.
Anon.	1814-72	*Acts of the Parliaments of Scotland*, **1-8**. London, Edinburgh.
Anon.	1837	*Liber Sancte Marie de Melros*, ed. C. Innes. Edinburgh.
Anon.	1845	*New Statistical Account of Scotland*, **1-15**. Edinburgh.
Anon.	1855	*The Black Book of Taymouth (with other papers from the Breadalbane charter room)*. Edinburgh.
Anon.	1868	*Facsimiles of National Manuscripts of Scotland*. Ordnance Survey, Southampton.
Anon.	1878-93	*Exchequer Rolls of Scotland*, **1** (1264-1359), **2** (1359-1379), **3** (1379-1406), **4** (1406-1436), **5** (1437-1454), **6** (1455-1460), **7** (1460-1469), **8** (1470-1479), **9** (1480-1487), **10** (1488-1496), **11** (1497-1501), **12** (1502-1507), **13** (1508-1513) and **14** (1513-1522).
Anon.	1886	*Ordnance Survey Gazetteer of Scotland, a survey of Scottish Topography*, **1-6**. Edinburgh.
Anon.	1887	*Excursions to the Royal forests at Balmoral by the Royal Scottish Arboricultural Society*. Edinburgh.
Anon.	1895	Geological Survey of Scotland. 1 in. to 1 mile map 75 (Tomintoul). Southampton.
Anon.	1897	Geological Survey of Scotland. 1 in. to 1 mile map 66 (Banchory). Southampton.
Anon.	1903	*Ordnance Survey Gazetteer of Scotland*, 1-3. London.
Anon.	1911	Geological Survey of Scotland, 1 in. to 1 mile map 65 (Balmoral). Southampton.
Anon.	1912	Geological Survey of Scotland, 1 in. to 1 mile map 93 (Alness). Southampton.
Anon.	1913 (*a*)	Geological Survey of Scotland, 1 in. to 1 mile map 64 (Kingussie). Southampton. Also the corresponding memoir by Barrow, G. *et al.* 1913, *The Geology of Upper Strathspey, Gaick and the Forest of Atholl*. Edinburgh.
Anon.	1913 (*b*)	Geological Survey of Scotland, 1 in. to 1 mile map 82 (Lochcarron). 3rd edition. Southampton. Also the corresponding memoir by Peach, B. N. *et al.* 1913, *The Geology of Central Ross-shire*. Edinburgh.

ANON.   1914   Geological Survey of Scotland, 1 in. to 1 mile map 74 (Grantown-
                                     on-Spey). 3rd edition. Southampton. Also the corresponding
                                     memoir by Hinxman, L. W. and Anderson, E. M. 1915, *The Geology
                                     of Mid-Strathspey and Strathdearn.* Edinburgh.

ANON.   1919   *The Book of Normals of the meteorological elements for the British Isles
                                     for periods ending 1915.* London.

ANON.   1923   Geological Survey of Scotland, 1 in. to 1 mile map 54 (Rannoch).
                                     Southampton. Also the corresponding memoir by Hinxman, L. W.
                                     et al. 1923, *The Geology of Corrour and the Moor of Rannoch.* Edin-
                                     burgh.

ANON.   1925   Geological Survey of Scotland, 1 in. to 1 mile map 102 (Lairg).
                                     Southampton.

ANON.   1928   *Growth and yield of conifers in Great Britain.* Forestry Commission
                                     Bulletin No. 10. London.

ANON.   1932   *Conifers in cultivation.* R. hort. Soc. London.

ANON.   1937   *Bolshoi Sovetskii Atlas Mira.* Moscow.

ANON.   1941 (*a*) Les fôrets de pin silvestre des Vosges. *Rev. Eaux For.,* 9th series,
                                     79, 799.

ANON.   1941 (*b*) Kottejuka pa tall. *Skogsägaren,* **17** (1), 19.

ANON.   1942   Kotterekord från Blekinge. *Skogsägaren,* **18** (2), 36.

ANON.   1948 (*a*) Geological Survey of Scotland, 1 in. to 1 mile map 53 (Ben Nevis).
                                     3rd edition. Southampton. Also the corresponding memoir by
                                     Bailey, E. B. *et al.* 1916. *The Geology of Ben Nevis, Glencoe and the
                                     surrounding country.* Edinburgh.

ANON.   1948 (*b*) Geological Survey "Ten Mile" map of Great Britain, No. 1.
                                     London.

ANON.   1949   The map of the average annual rainfall, 1881–1915. Ordnance
                                     Survey. London.

ANON.   1952 (*a*) *Check list of the Birds of Great Britain and Ireland.* British Ornitho-
                                     logists' Union. London. With corrections as recommended in *Ibis,*
                                     1956, **98,** 157.

ANON.   1952 (*b*) *Climatological Atlas of the British Isles.* London.

ANON.   1953–5   *British rainfall: report on the distribution of rain in space and time over
                                     Great Britain and Northern Ireland.* Meteorological Office. London.

ANON.   1954–5   Karta Lesov SSSR. 1:2,500,000. Sheets 1 to 30. *Glavnoe upravlenie
                                     geodezii i kartografii.* MVD SSSR. Moscow.

ANON.   1955   *Report of the Nature Conservancy for the year ended 30 September
                                     1955.*

ANON.   1956 (*a*) Map of Roman Britain. 3rd edition. Ordnance Survey.

ANON.   1956 (*b*) Glentanar Estate Records (unpublished).

ABLETT, W. H.   1880   *English trees and tree planting.* London.

*Acts of the Parliaments
of Scotland,* see Anon. 1814–72

AHLMANN, H. A.   1953   *Glacier Variations and Climate Fluctuations.* Bowman Memorial
                                     Lecture, American Geographical Society. New York.

ANDERSEN, K. F.   1954   Gales and gale damage to forests with special reference to the effects of the storm of 31st January 1953, in the north-east of Scotland. *Forestry*, **27** (2), 97.

ANDERSON, A. O.   1922   *Early sources of Scottish history A.D. 500-1286*, **1** and **2**. Edinburgh.
   (editor)

ANDERSON, J.   1895   Notice of a cave recently discovered at Oban. *Proc. Soc. Antiq. Scot.*, **29**, 211.

ANDERSON, J. G. C.   1922   C. Tacitus, *Agricola*. Oxford.
   (editor)

ANDERSON, J. G. C.   1949, 1956 Geology, in *Glenmore National Forest Park Guide*. London.

ANDERSON, M. L. and   1955   Division of Scotland into climatic sub-regions as an aid to silvi-
   FAIRBAIRN, W. A.   culture. *Bulletin of the Forestry Department, University of Edinburgh*, No. 1.

ANDERSON, W. L. *et al.* 1864   *The Scottish Nation; or the surnames, families, literature, honours and biographical history of the people of Scotland*. 1st edition, **1-3**. Edinburgh.

ANIC, M.   1954   Personal communication.

ARNBORG, T.   1941   Busktallen. En inventering. *Skogen*, **28**, 174.
                          1946 (*a*) *Pinus sylvestris* f. *condensata* – kvastallen. *Svenska SkogsvFören. Tidskr.*, **44** (4), 329.
                          1946 (*b*) Kvastallen – en marklig tallras. *Tidskr. Hushall. SkogsvStyr. Gavl.*, No. 3.

AVERY, J.   1725-30   A plan of the Murray Firth etc. Public Library, Inverness.

BALDWIN, H. I.   1942   *Forest Tree Seed of the North Temperate Regions*. Waltham, Mass.

BALFOUR, F. R. S.   1932   The history of conifers in Scotland and their discovery by Scotsmen. In *Conifers in Cultivation*, 177. R. hort. Soc., London (anon. 1932).

BARROW, G. W. S.   1956   *Feudal Britain*. London.

BAXTER, E. V. and   1953   *The Birds of Scotland, their history, distribution and migration*, **1-2**.
   RINTOUL, L. J.   Edinburgh.

BEAN, W. J.   1951   *Trees and Shrubs hardy in the British Isles*, **1-3**. 7th edn. London.

BECHSTEIN, —   1821   *Forstbotanik*. 4th edn. Erfurt.

BEISSNER, L.   1891, 1909 *Handbuch der Nadelholzkunde*. Berlin.
                          1898   Neue und Interessantes über Conifern. *Mitt. deutsch. dendrol. Ges.*, **7**, 365.
                          1906   Mitteilungen über Coniferen. *Mitt. deutsch. dendrol. Ges.*, **15**, 82.
                          1911   *Mitt. deutsch. dendrol. Ges.*, **20**, 349.

BEISSNER, L. and   1930   *Handbuch der Nadelholzkunde*. 3rd edn. Berlin.
   FITSCHEN, J.

BENTHAM, G. and   1945   *Handbook of the British flora*. 7th edn. Ashford.
   HOOKER, J. D.

BERNHARD, —   1931   Die Kiefern Kleinasiens. *Mitt. deutsch. dendrol. Ges.*, **43**, 29.

BILHAM, E. G.   1938   *The Climate of the British Isles*. London.

Black Book of Taymouth,
   see Anon.   1855

BLACKBURN, K. B.   1946   On a peat from the island of Barra, Outer Hebrides. Data for the study of post-glacial history, X. *New Phytol.*, **45**, 44.

BLAEU, J.   1654   *Atlas*: Lib. 12, Tom. 5: *Scotia quae est Europae.* Amsterdam.

BLYTT, A.   1876   *Essay on the immigration of Norwegian Flora.* Christiania.

BORTHWICK, A. W.   1906   The life history of *Pinus sylvestris. Trans. R. Eng. arbor. Soc.*, **6**, 205.

BOUREAU, E.   1939   *Ann. Sci. nat. (Bot.)*, **11** (1), 1.

BOUTCHER, W.   1775   *A Treatise on Forest-Trees.* Edinburgh.

BRADLEY, H.   1885   Ptolemy's Geography of the British Isles. *Archaeologia*, **48**, 379.

BRAUN, A.   1871   In Rehder, A. 1912, q.v.

BREMNER, A.   1934 (*a*)   The surface geology of the Aberdeen district. *Rep. Brit. Assoc. Adv. Sci.*, App., 16.

                        1934 (*b*)   The glaciation of Moray and ice movements in the North of Scotland. *Trans. Edin. geol. Soc.*, **13**, 17.

                        1936   Glacial and Post-glacial Geology. *Trans. Edin. geol. Soc.*, **13**, 260.

BREMNER, R. L.   1923   *The Norsemen in Alban.* Glasgow.

BRØGGER, A. W.   1929   *Ancient Emigrants.* Oxford.

BROOKS, F. T.   1953   *Plant Diseases.* 2nd edn. London, New York and Toronto.

BROWN, J. C.   1878   *Pine Plantations on the Sand Wastes of France.* Edinburgh.

BROWN, P. HUME   1891   *Early Travellers in Scotland.* Edinburgh.

BROWN, P. HUME   1892   *Tours in Scotland 1677 and 1681 by Thomas Kirk and Ralph Thoresby.*
(editor)   Edinburgh.

BROWN, P. HUME   1915   *The Register of the Privy Council of Scotland.* 3rd series, **8** (1683-1684).
(editor)   Glasgow.

BRUCE-MITFORD, R. L. S. 1956   *Recent Archaeological Excavations.* London.
(editor)

BUCHAN, A.   1880   The Tay Bridge storm of the 28th December 1879. *J. Scot. meteorol. Soc.* New Series, **5**, 355.

BUCHENAU, —   1885   *Flora von Bremen und Oldenburg.* Bremen.

BURBRIDGE, —   (1939)   In Pohl, F. 1939, q.v.

BUSGEN, M., MÜNCH, E.   1929   *The Structure and Life of Forest Trees.* London.
and THOMSON, T.

BUTTS, D. and   1940   Cotyledon numbers in conifers. *Trans. Ill. Acad. Sci.*, **33** (2), 58.
BUCHOLZ, J. T.

CALDER, S. T.   1952   Report on the excavation of a Neolithic temple at Stanydale in the parish of Standsting, Shetland. *Proc. Soc. Antiq. Scot.*, **84**, 185.

CALLENDAR, S. G. *et al.* 1927   Preliminary report on caves containing palaeolithic relics near Inchnadamph, Sutherland. *Proc. Soc. Antiq. Scot.*, **61**, 169.

CAMERON, SIR E.   1892   *Memoirs of Sir Ewan Cameron of Locheill, Chief of the Clan Cameron.* Abbotsford Club, Edinburgh.

CAMPBELL, D.   1886   *The Lairds of Glenlyon.* Perth.
                        1888   *The Book of Garth and Fortingall.* Inverness.

CAMPBELL, R. and   1934   Glacial and inter-glacial deposits at Benholm, Kincardineshire. *Rep. Brit. Assoc. Adv. Sci.*, 313.
ROBERTSON, I. M.

CAMPO-DUPLAN, M. VAN 1950   Récherches sur la phylogénie des Abietinées d'après leurs grains de pollen. *Trav. Lab. for. Toulouse*, **4**, 183.

CANDOLLE, DE   (1878)   In Brown, J. C. 1878, q.v.

CARLISLE, A.   1954   The morphological and silvicultural variations of the native Scots pine (*P. silvestris* L.) of Scotland. Unpublished thesis. University of Aberdeen.

CARLISLE, A. and CROOKE, M.   1951   *Scolytus ratzeburgi* in Inverness-shire. *Scot. For.*, **5** (4), 131.

CARRIÈRE, E. A.   1867   *Traité général des conifères.* New edn. Paris.

CASH, C. G.   1905 (*a*)   The Loch-an-Eilein ospreys. *Cairngorm Club Journal*, **4**, 125.
   1905 (*b*)   Timber floating at Rothiemurchus. *Cairngorm Club Journal*, **4**, 301.

CASPARY, R.   1866   *Schr. phys.-ökon. Ges. Königsb.*, **7**, 49.
   1882-3   *Schr. phys.-ökon. Ges. Königsb.*, **23**, 43 and 209.

CHADWICK, H. M.   1949   *Early Scotland.* Cambridge.

CHAMBERS, R.   1861   *Domestic Annals of Scotland from the Revolution to the Rebellion of 1745*, **1-3**, Edinburgh.

CHARLESWORTH, J. K.   1956   The late-glacial history of the Highlands and Islands of Scotland. *Trans. Roy. Soc. Edin.*, **62** (3), 769.
   1957   *The Quaternary Era with special reference to its Glaciation*, **1** and **2**. London.

CHILDE, V. G.   1946   *Scotland before the Scots.* London.
   1947   *Prehistoric communities of the British Isles.* 2nd edn. London.

CHILDE, V. G. and THORNEYCROFT, W.   1938   The experimental production of the phenomenon distinctive of vitrified forts. *Proc. Soc. Antiq. Scot.*, **72**, 44.

CHRIST, H.   1863   *Verh. naturf. Ges. Basel.*, **3** (4).
   1864   Beitrage zur Kenntnis europischer *Pinus* – Arten. *Flora, oder allegemeine botanische Zeitung*, **47**, 145.
   1865   Der Formenkreise der europäischen *Pinus* – Arten. In Caspary, 1882-3 (*b*), q.v.
   1907   *Flore de la Suisse.* Basel, Geneva and Lyon.

CLAPHAM, A. R., TUTIN, T. G. and WARBURG, E. F.   1952   *The Flora of the British Isles.* Cambridge.

CLARK, J. G. D.   1932   *The Mesolithic Age in Britain.* Cambridge.
   1945   Farmers and forests in Neolithic Europe. *Antiquity*, **19**, 57.
   1947   Sheep and swine in the husbandry of prehistoric Europe. *Antiquity*, **21**, 122.
   1952   *Prehistoric Europe: The economic basis.* London.
   1954   *Excavations at Star Carr; an early Mesolithic site at Seamer near Scarborough, Yorkshire.* Cambridge.
   1956   In *Recent archaeological excavations in Britain*. Ed. R. L. S. Bruce-Mitford. London.
   1958   Notes on the Obanian with special reference to antler and bone-work. *Proc. Soc. Antiq. Scot.*, **89**, 91.

CORDINER, C.   1780   *Antiquities and scenery of the north of Scotland. In a series of letters to Thomas Pennant, Esq.* London.

CRAWFORD, O. G. S. 1949 *Topography of Roman Scotland north of the Antonine Wall.* Cambridge.

CROMARTY, GEORGE, EARL OF 1710 An account of the mosses in Scotland. In a letter from the Right Honourable George, Earl of Cromertie etc. to Dr Hans Sloane. *Philosophical Transactions* (Royal Society, London), **27**, 296.

CROMBIE, J. M. 1861 *Braemar.* Aberdeen.

CZOPPELT, H. 1938 The natural distribution of Scots pine in the forest of Brosteni. *Rev. Pădurilor,* **50**, 765.

DALLIMORE, W. and JACKSON, A. B. 1954 *Handbook of the Coniferae.* London.

DANGEARD, P. A. 1892 *La Botaniste.* 3rd edn. Paris.

DARLING, F. F. 1947 *Natural History in the Highlands and Islands.* London.
  1955 *West Highland Survey.* Oxford.

DEGELIUS, G. 1943 Tall med försenad klorofyllbildning. *Skogen,* **30**, 79.

DENGLER, A. 1904 *Die Horizontalverbreitung der Kiefer (Pinus silvestris L.).* Neudamm.
  1938 Über Platten- und Schuppenborke bei der Kiefer. *Z. Forst-u. Jagdw.,* **70**, 1.
  1939 Über die Entwicklung künstlicher kiefernkreuzungen. *Z. Forst-u. Jagdw.,* **71**, 457.
  1944 *Waldbau.* 3rd edn. Berlin.

DICKIE, G. 1843 Forests and other trees in Aberdeenshire. *Quart. J. Agric.,* 393.

DIXON, H. N. 1954 *The Student's Handbook of British Mosses.* 3rd edn. Eastbourne.

DIXON, J. H. 1886 *Gairloch, its records, traditions* etc. Edinburgh.

DON, G. 1814 *Mem. Caledon. hort. Soc.,* **1**, 123.

DONALDSON, J. 1794 *General View of the Agriculture of the County of Elgin and Moray lying between the Spey and the Findhorn.* London.

DONISTHORPE, H. ST. J. K. 1927 *British Ants.* London. Also in Darling, F. F., 1947, q.v.

DONNER, J. J. 1957 The geology and vegetation of late-glacial retreat stages in Scotland. *Trans. Roy. Soc. Edin.,* **63**, 221.

DREVER, H. I. 1939 *Geological Magazine,* **76** (906), 501.
  1943 The geology of Ardgour, Argyllshire. *Trans. Roy. Soc. Edin.,* **60** (1), 141.

DURNO, S. E. 1956 Pollen analysis of peat deposits. *Scott. geog. Mag.,* **72** (3), 177.
  1957 Certain aspects of vegetational history in north-east Scotland. *Scott. geog. Mag.,* **73** (3), 176.

EASSON, D. E. (editor) 1947 *Charters of the Abbey of Couper-Angus.* **1** (A.D. 1166–1376) and **2** (A.D. 1389–1608). Edinburgh.

EDWARDS, M. V. and PINCHIN, R. D. 1953 Forestry Commission, *Rep. For. Res.,* 56.

EHRENBERG, C., GUS-TAFFSON, A., FORSHELL, C. P. and SIMÁK, M. 1955 Seed quality and the principles of forest genetics. *Hereditas,* **41**, 291.

EICHE, V. 1955 Spontaneous chlorophyll mutations in Scots pine (*Pinus silvestris* L.). *Medd. SkogsforsknInst., Stockh.,* **45** (13), 1.

ELISEU, H. 1942 *Nocoes de Silvicultura.* 2nd edn., **1**. Leiria.

ELWES, H. J. and   1908   *The Trees of Great Britain and Ireland*, **3**. Edinburgh.
  HENRY, A.

EMILIANI, C.   1956   Note on absolute chronology of human evolution. *Science*, **123**, 924.

ENGELMANN, G.   1880   Revision of the genus *Pinus*. *Trans. Acad. Sci. St. Louis*, **4** (1), 161.

ENGLER, A.   1913 (*a*) Der heutige Stand der forstlichen Samenprovenienzfrage. *Naturw. Z. Forst- u. Landw.*, **11**.

                         1913 (*b*) Einfluss der Provenienz des Samens auf die Eigenschaften der forstlichen Holzgewachse. *Mitt. schweiz. Centr. forstl. Versuch.*, **10** (3), 192.

ENQUIST, F.   1933   Trädgränsundersökningar. *Svenska SkogsvFören. Tidskr.*, 145.

ERDTMAN, G.   1924   Studies in the micropalaeontology of post-glacial deposits in Northern Scotland and the Scotch Isles. *J. Linn. Soc.* (Bot.), **46**, 449.

                         1928   Studies in the postarctic history of the forests of north-western Europe I. Investigations in the British Isles. *Geol. Fören. Stockh. Förh.*, **50**, 123.

                         1929   Some aspects of post-glacial history of British forests. *J. Ecology*, **17**, 1.

                         1943   *An Introduction to Pollen Analysis*. Waltham, Mass.

EVELYN, J.   1664   *Sylva, or a Discourse of Forest Trees*. London.

                         1776   *Sylva*, ed. A. Hunter. York

*Exchequer Rolls of
  Scotland*, see Anon.   1878-93

FAEGRI, K. and   1950   *A Textbook of modern Pollen Analysis*. Copenhagen.
  IVERSON, J.

FARQUHARSON, J.   1775   In Evelyn, J. 1776, *Sylva*, ed. A. Hunter. York.

FARRINGTON, A. and   1951   The End-moraine north of Flamborough Head. *Proc. geol. Assoc., Lond.*, **62**, 106.
  MITCHELL, G. F.

FIESCHI, V.   1932   Anatomie de la feuille chez les pins maritimes. *Trav. Lab. for. Toulouse*, Tome **1**, Article 18.

FINTELMANN, H.   1881   In Caspary, 1882-3, q.v.

FIRBAS, F.   1949, 1952 *Spät- und nacheiszeitliche Waldegschichte Mitteleuropas nordlich der Alpen*, **1** and **2**. Jena.

FLINT, R. F.   1947   *Glacial Geology and the Pleistocene Epoch*. New York and London.

FLINT, R. F.   1957   *Glacial and Pleistocene Geology*. New York and London.

FIRST *Statistical Account*,
  see Sinclair   1791-9

FORESTRY COMMISSION   1949, 1956 *Glenmore National Forest Park Guide*. London.

FORSHELL, C. P.   1953   Kottens och fröets utbildning efter själv och korsbefruktning hos tall (*P. silvestris*). *Medd. SkogsforsknInst.*, Stockh., **43** (10), 1.

FORSYTH, A.   1897   Notes on the York Building Company in Abernethy, 1728. *Trans. Inverness sci. Soc. fld. Club*, **5**, 186.

FORSYTH, W.   1900   *In the shadow of the Cairngorms*. Inverness.

FOX, C.   1938   *The Personality of Britain*. 3rd edn. Cardiff.

FRANÇOIS, L.   1947   Le pin silvestre de race noble de Saint-Die des Vosges. *Rev. Eaux For.*, **58** (5-9), 265.

FRASER, G. K.   1933   *Studies of Scottish moorlands in relation to tree growth.* Forestry Commission Bulletin No. 15. London.

     1943, 1948   *Peat Deposits of Scotland*, Parts I and II. Department of Scientific and Industrial Research, and Geological Survey of Great Britain: Scotland. Wartime Pamphlet No. 36.

FRASER, G. K. and GODWIN, H.   1955   Two Scottish pollen diagrams: Carnwath Moss, Lanarkshire, and Strichen Moss, Aberdeenshire. Data for the study of post-glacial history, XVII. *New Phytol.*, **54** (2), 216.

FRASER, G. M.   1921   *The Old Deeside Road, its course, history and associations.* Aberdeen.

FRASER, H.   1875   *A Book of Ornamental Conifers.* Edinburgh and London.

FRASER, J.   1949, 1956   Forests and Plantations, in *Glenmore National Forest Park Guide.* Forestry Commission, London.

FRASER, W.   1883   *The Chiefs of Grant*, **1-3**. Edinburgh.

FRIES, T. M.   1890   Strödda bidrag till kannedom om Skandinaviens barrträd. *Bot. Notiser.*

GALPERN, G. D.   1949   O lesnoy sosne v SSSR. *Priroda*, Moskva, **38** (5), 51.

GEIKIE, J.   1866   On the buried forests and peat mosses of Scotland and the changes of climate which they indicate. *Trans. Roy. Soc. Edin.*, **24**, 363.

     1874, 1894   *The Great Ice Age and its relation to the antiquity of man.* London.

     1879   Discovery of an ancient canoe in the old alluvium of the Tay at Perth. *Scottish Naturalist*, **5**, 1.

GILBERT-CARTER, H.   1936   *British Trees and Shrubs.* Oxford.

GILCHRIST, W.   1871   Report on Scots fir (*P. sylvestris*) its cultivation and varieties. *Trans. R. Scot. arb. Soc.*, **6**, 304.

GILPIN, W.   1834   See Lauder, Sir T. D. (editor). 1834.

GLENTANAR, LORD and YOUNG, R. D.   1948   Food production from hill pastures. *Scot. Agric.* (Summer number), 4.

GODWIN, H.   1934   Pollen analysis: an outline of the problems and potentialities of the method. *New Phytol.*, **33**, 278, 325.

     1940   Pollen analysis and forest history of England and Wales. *New Phytol.*, **39**, 370.

     1943   Coastal peat-beds of the British Isles and North Sea. *J. Ecology*, **31**, 199.

     1944 (*a*)   Neolithic forest clearance. *Nature*, **153**, 511.

     1944 (*b*)   Age and origin of the "Breckland" heaths in East Anglia. *Nature*, **154**, 6.

     1945   Coastal peat-beds of the North Sea Region as indices of sea-level changes. *New Phytol.*, **44**, 29.

     1951   Pollen analysis (Palynology). *Endeavour*, **10** (37), 5.

     1956   *The History of the British Flora.* Cambridge.

GORDON, G.   1858, 1880   The *Pinetum.* London.

GORDON, S.   1949, 1956   The wild life of Glenmore, in *Glenmore National Forest Park Guide.* Forestry Commission, London.

GRAEBNER, —   1899   Über die Moorkiefer. *Naturw. Wschr.*, **15** (46), 545.

GRAHAM, A.   1952   Spruce and pine in two Scottish prehistoric buildings. *Arch. News. Letter*, **4** (9), 133.

GRAHAM, A.   1953   Archaeological gleanings from dark-age records. *Proc. Soc. Antiq. Scot.*, **85**, 64.

GRANT, E.   1898   *Memoirs of a Highland Lady, 1797-1827*, ed. Lady Strachey. London.

GRIGOR, J.   1831   *The Gardeners' Magazine.* 1st series, **8**, 10.

1834   Report on the native pine forests of Scotland. *Prize Essays Trans. Highl. agric. Soc. Scot.* 2nd series, **6**, 122.

1868, 1881 *Arboriculture.* Edinburgh.

GROOM, P.   1919   *Trees and their Life Histories.* London.

GROSSE, H.   1932   Zur Frage der Kiefernrassen. *Mitt. deutsch. dendrol. Ges.*, **7**, 49.

GROSSHEIM, A. A.   1939   *Plants of the Caucasus.* 2nd edn. Baku.

GROZDOV, B. V.   1945   O Bryanskoy botanischeskoy 'anomalii'. *Bot. Z. (Bot. Zh. SSSR)*, **30**, 178.

GUILLEBAUD, W. H.   1933   Scots pine in Morayshire and Strathspey. *Forestry*, **7** (2), 137.

GULISASVILI, V. Z.   1951   Rasprostranenie lesoobrazujuščih hvoĭnyh porod v Zakavkazje i vzaimootnošenija mezdu nimi. *Bot. Z. (Bot. Zh. SSSR)*, **36** (3), 277. Also in *For. Abstr.*, **13** (5), 3670.

GUNN, W. F.   1885   The woods, forests and forestry of Ross-shire. *Trans. Highl. agric. Soc. Scot.* 4th series, **17**, 133.

HABERLANDT, G.   1914   *Physiological Plant Anatomy.* Trans. M. Drummond. London.

HADDINGTON, EARL OF   1765   *A Short Treatise on Forest Trees.* Edinburgh.

HAMILTON, J. R. C.   1956   *Excavations at Jarlshof, Shetland.* Ministry of Works Archaeological Reports, No. 1. Edinburgh.

HARDY, M.   1905   *Esquisse de la géographie et de la végétation des Highlands d'Écosse.* Paris.

HARTIG, R.   1894   *Text-book of the Diseases of Trees.* Trans. W. Somerville. London.

HEER, —   1862   Section der Botanik und Zoologie. I. Die Arten und Abarten. *Verh. schweiz. Naturf. Ges.*, Luzern, 177.

HEJTMÁNEK, J.   1953 (a)   Příspěvek k otázce proměnlivosti borky u borovice lesní. *Preslia*, **25** (1), 75.

1953 (b)   Reliktní borové porosty v západní části velké Fatry. *Práce vyzkum Ust. lesn. ČSR*, **3**, 279.

HESS, E.   1942   Die autochthonen Föhrenrassen des Wallis. *Schweiz. Z. Forstw.*, **93**, 1.

HICKEL, R.   1911   *Graines et plantules*, **1** and **2**. Paris.

1914   Les races de pin sylvestre. *Rev. Eaux For.*, **38**, 84.

HILL, J. B.   1905   Memoirs of the Geological Survey. *The Geology of mid-Argyll* (Explanation of 1 in. to 1 mile map 37). Glasgow.

HIPPEL, VON   1866   *Pinus silvestris* mit hangenden Zweigen. *Schr. phys.-ökon Ges. Königsb.*, **7**, 49.

HOFMAN, J. V.   1918   *Bull. Univ. Minn.*, U.S.A.

HOLLOM, P. A. D.   1952   *The Handbook of British Birds.* London.

z

HOLMERZ, C. G. and   1886   In Sylven, N. 1916, q.v.
   ORTENBLAD, T.

                            1888   Om den hognordiska tallformen *Pinus silvestris* L. *lapponica* Fries.
                                        K. svenska VetenskAkad. Handl., **13** (3), 11. Also in Sylven, N.
                                        1916, q.v.

HOOPES, J.   1868   *Book of Evergreens.* New York.

HÖRMAN, H.   1929   Die pollenanalytische Unterscheidung von *Pinus montana, P. sil-
                                        vestris* und *P. cembra. Öst. bot. Z.*, **78**, 215.

HORNELL, J.   1946   *Water transport: Origins and Evolution.* Cambridge.

HORNIEROOK, M.   1923, 1938 *Dwarf and slow growing Conifers.* London.

HUBERT, E. E.   1931   *Outline of Forest Pathology.* New York.

HUET, M.   1933   Détermination de différentes éspèces de pins par l'étude anatomique
                                        de l'aiguille. *Bull. Soc. for. Belg.*, **36**, 66.

HULTEN, E.   1927   *The flora of Kamchatka and the adjacent Islands.* Stockholm.

HUNTER, T.   1883   *Woods, Forests and Estates in Perthshire.* Perth.

HUNTLY, CHARLES 11th   1894   *Records of Aboyne.* Aberdeen.
   MARQUIS OF

HUXLEY, J.   1948   *Evolution, the Modern Synthesis.* London.

ILVESSALO, Y.   1949   The forests of present-day Finland. *Comm. Inst. for. Fenn.*, **35** (6), 1·

INNES-WILL, N.   1948   Old Scots pines in Wester Ross. *Scot. For.*, **2** (3-4), 10.

IRMAK, A.   1954   Personal communication.

IVERSON, J.   1941   In Godwin, H. 1944 (a). Neolithic forest clearance. *Nature*, **153**, 511.

JAMES VI, KING   1621   In *Report on the manuscripts of the Earl of Mar.* Historical Mss. Com-
                                        mission. 1904. Edinburgh.

JAMIESON, T. F.   1862   On the ice-worn rocks of Scotland. *J. geol. Soc. Lond.*, **18**, 164.

JESSEN, K.   1949   Studies in Late Quaternary deposits and flora-history of Ireland.
                                        Proc. Roy. Irish Acad., **52** (B, **6**), 85.

JOHNSON, I.   1956   Personal communication.

JONASSEN, H.   1950   *Recent pollen sedimentation and Jutland heath diagrams.* Copenhagen.

JONES, E. W.   1945   The structure and reproduction of the virgin forest of the north
                                        temperate zone. *New Phytol.*, **44**, 130.

                            1947   Scots pine regeneration in a New Forest inclosure. *Forestry*, **21** (2),
                                        151.

KAYACIK, H.   1954   Türkiye çamlari ve bunlarin çoğrafi yayiliṣlari üzerinde araṣtirmalar·
                                        Istanbul Univ. Orm. Fak. Derg. Series A, Tome 4, Fasc. 1, Et. 2, 44·

KIENITZ, M.   1911   Formen and Abarten der gemeinen Kiefer (*Pinus silvestris* L.). *Z.
                                        Forst- u. Jagdw.*, **43**, 4·

                            1922   In Büsgen, M., Münch, E. and Thomson, T., 1929, q.v.

KIHLMAN, —   (1906)   In Beissner, L., 1906, q.v.

KIMBLE, G. H. T. and   1955   *Geography of the Northlands.* American Geographical Society Publi-
   GOOD, D.   cation. New York and London.

KIRCHNER, O., LOEW, E.   1908   *Lebensgeschichte der Blutenpflanzen Mitteleuropas.* Stuttgart.
   and SCHRÖTER, C.

KIRK, T.   1677   In Brown, P. Hume (editor). 1892, q.v.

KLOET, G. S. and HINCKS, W. D. 1945 *A check list of British Insects.* Stockport.

KNOCH, K. and REICHEL, E. 1937 *Die Verteilung der Temperatur. Atlas der deutschen Lebensraum in Mitteleuropa,* Karte No. 5. Leipzig. Also in Firbas, F., 1949, q.v.

KNOX, E. M. 1954 Pollen analysis of a peat at Kingsteps quarry, Nairn. *Trans. bot. Soc. Edin.,* **36**, 3.

KOSSENAKIS, G. 1954 Personal communication.

KRUBERG, J. 1937 About the geographical distribution of *Pinus silvestris* in the Asiatic part of the U.S.S.R. *Sci. Mem. Herz. St. pedag. Leningrad Inst. St. Inst. Sci. Pedag.,* **4** (2), 241.

KURDIANI, S. 1926-7 *Pinus silvestris* L. and its mutative forms in a region in Georgia (Caucasus). *Bull. Mus. Géorgie (Tiflis),* **3**, 81. Also in *Biol. Abstr.,* **6**, 5081.

LACAILLE, A. D. 1954 *The Stone Age in Scotland.* Oxford.

LAMBERT, A. B. 1832 *A Description of the genus* Pinus, **1** and **2**. London.

LANG, A. (editor) 1898 *The Highlands of Scotland in 1750* (anon.), *from manuscript 104 in the King's Library, British Museum.* Edinburgh.

LANGLET, O. 1937 Om miljö och ärftlighet samt on förutsättningarna för växtförädling av skogsträdt. *Norrlands SkogsvForb. Tidskr.,* 49.

1938 Den svenska tallens raser. *Skogen,* **25**, 156.

1942 Nagra iakttagelser över vinterfargningen hos tall, *P. silvestris* L. *Svensk. bot. Tidskr.,* **36**, 231.

LARSON, C. S. 1937 The employment of species, types and individuals in forestry. *R. vet. agr. Coll. Yearbook.* Copenhagen.

LAUDER, SIR T. D. (editor) 1834 William Gilpin's *"Forest Scenery."* Edinburgh.

LAUDER, SIR T. D. 1873 *Account of the great floods of August 1829 in the province of Moray and adjoining districts.* 3rd edn. Elgin.

LAWRENCE, G. H. M. 1951 *Taxonomy of Vascular Plants.* New York.

LEIBUNDGUT, H. and MARCET, E. 1953 Pollenspektrum und baumartenmischung. *Schweiz. Z. Forstw.,* **104**, 594.

LESLIE, P. 1916 The history of Glenmore forest. *Trans. R. Scot. arb. Soc.,* **30**, 85.

LETHBRIDGE, T. C. 1954 *The Painted Men.* London.

LEWIS, F. J. 1905, 1906, 1907, 1911 Plant remains in Scottish peat mosses. *Trans. Roy. Soc. Edin.,* **41**, 699; **45**, 335; **46**, 33; **47**, 793.

LIBBY, W. F. 1952 *Radiocarbon dating.* University of Chicago.

1954 Radiocarbon dating. *Endeavour,* **13**, 5.

LIESE, J. 1929 Anatomische Unterschiede zwischen den Licht- und Schattennadeln der Kiefer. *Forstarchiv,* **5**, 162.

LIGHTFOOT, J. 1777 *Flora Scotica.* London.

LINDQUIST, B. 1935-8 Studier over skogligt betydelsefulla svenska tallraser, I, II and III. *Norrlands SkogsvFörb. Tidskr.,* 1935, 1; 1937, 126; 1938, 181.

LINDQUIST, B. and RUNDQUIST, — 1943 Krontypvariatonen hos den smalkronige tallen i Norrland. *Skogen,* **30**, 69.

LINDSAY, W. A.,   1903   *Charters, Bulls and other Documents relating to Inchaffray Abbey.*
    DOWDEN, J. and   *Edinburgh.*
    THOMSON, J. M.

LITTLE, E. L. and   1952   Slash pine (*Pinus elliottii*), its nomenclature and varieties. *J. For.*,
    DORMAN, K. W.   **50** (12), 918.

LOUDON, J. C.   1838   *Arboretum et Fruticetum Britannicum*, **1-8**. London.
                     1839   *Magazine of Gardening*, **5** (5), 229.
                     1855   *Encyclopaedia of Plants.* London.
                     1883   *Trees and Shrubs of Great Britain.* London.

LUBBOCK, J.   1892   *Seedlings*, **1** and **2**. London.

MACADAM, W. I.   1887   Notes on the ancient iron industry of Scotland. *Proc. Soc. Antiq.
                               Scot.* New series, **9**, 89.

MACBAIN, A.   1922   *Place names, Highlands and Islands of Scotland*; with notes by W. J.
                               Watson. Stirling.

MACDONALD, SIR   1916   The Roman camps at Raedykes and Glenmailen. *Proc. Soc. Antiq.
    GEORGE   Scot.*, **50**, 317.

                     1919   The Agricolan occupation of North Britain. *J. Roman Studies*,
                               9, III.

                     1934   *The Roman Wall in Scotland.* Oxford.

MACDONALD, J. A. B. 1952   Natural regeneration of Scots pine woods in the Highlands.
                               Forestry Commission, Lond., *Rep. For. Res.*, 26.

MACFARLANE, W.   1908   *Geographical Collections relating to Scotland*, edd. Sir A. Mitchell and
                               J. T. Clark, **1-3**. Edinburgh.

MACGILLIVRAY, W.   1855   *The Natural History of Deeside and Braemar.* London.

MACGREGOR, A.   1955   How Dee's wild life has been transformed. *Press and Journal.* No.
                               31, 443, 11 Oct. Aberdeen.

MACKAY, W.   1914   *Urquhart and Glen Moriston, olden times in a Highland parish.* 2nd
                               edn. Inverness.

MACKENZIE, A.   1891   *The History of the Chisholms.* Inverness.

MACKENZIE, C.   1956   Personal communication.

MACKENZIE, O. H.   1922   *A Hundred Years in the Highlands.* London.

MACMILLAN, H.   1907   *Rothiemurchus.* London.

MALCOLM, D. C.   1957   Site degradation in stands of natural Scots pine in Scotland. *Bulletin
                               of the Forestry Department of the University of Edinburgh, No.* 4.

MALEV, P. I. *et al.* 1955   Carta lesov SSSR. 1:2,500,000. Moscow.

MANLEY, G.   1952   *Climate and the British Scene.* London.

MARCET, E.   1951   Pollenuntersuchungen an Föhren (*Pinus sylvestris* L.) verschiedener
                               Provenienz. *Mitt. schweiz. Anst. forstl. Versuchsw.*, **27**, 348.

MARSHAL, —   1785   In Loudon, J. C., 1838, q.v.

MATTHEWS, L. H.   1952   *British Mammals.* London.

MATTINGLY, H. (trans.) 1948   C. Tacitus, *Agricola.* London.

MCINTOSH, R.   1953   Personal communication.

MCLAREN and   1881   *The supposed deterioration of the Scots pine.* In Elwes, H. J. and Henry,
    MCCORQUODALE   A., 1908, q.v.

McVean, D. N.   1953   Biological flora of the British Isles. *Alnus* Mill. *Alnis glutinosa* (L.) Gaertn. *J. Ecology*, **41** (2), 447.

McVean, D. N.   1955-6   Ecology of *Alnus glutinosa* (L.) Gaertn. *J. Ecology*, **43** (1), 46, 61; **44** (1), 195, 219; **44** (2), 321, 331.

Meyer, J.   1939   Über die Kronenvolbung und Zuwachschwankungen der Kiefer in Norddeutschland. *Z. Forst- u. Jagdw.*, **71**, 369.

    1944   Über spitzkronige Kiefern in Ostpreussen und im Schwarzwald. *Forstarchiv*, **20** (2), 1.

Michie, J. G. (editor)   1901   *The Records of Invercauld, 1547-1828.* New Spalding Club, Aberdeen.

Millar, A. H.   1909   *A Selection of the Scottish Forfeited Estates Papers 1715; 1745.* Scottish History Society, **57.** Edinburgh.

Miller, S. N. (editor)   1952   *The Roman Occupation of South-Western Scotland.* Glasgow University Publication No. 83.

Mitchell, G. F.   1948   Late-glacial deposits in Berwickshire. *New Phytol.*, **47** (2), 262.

    1952   Late-glacial deposits at Garscadder Mains, near Glasgow. *New Phytol.*, **50** (3), 277.

Moiseeva, M.   1941   Über die zentralen Harzgange in den Nadeln der *Pinus sylvestris. Dokl. Akad. Nauk SSSR.* New series, **20** (9), 854.

Mork, E.   1954   In a personal communication from Robak, H.

Mouillefert, P.   1892-8   *Traité des arbres et arbrisseaux,* **1-3** Paris.

Movius, H. L.   1942   *The Irish Stone Age.* Cambridge.

Müller, C.   1883   *Claudii Ptolemaei Geographia.* Paris.

Münch, E.   1924   Beitrage zur Kenntnis der Kiefernrassen Deutschlands, I. *Allg. Forst-u. Jagdztg.*, **100**, 540.

Murray, D.   1883   *The York Building Company, a Chapter in Scottish History.* Glasgow.

Murray, E.   1956   Personal communication.

Murray, J. M.   1920   Variation in Scots pine. *Trans. R. Scot. arb. Soc.*, **34** (1), 87.

    1935   An outline of the history of forestry in Scotland up to the end of the nineteenth century. *Scot. For. J.*, **49** (1), 1.

Nairne, D.   1891   Notes on Highland woods, ancient and modern. *Trans. Gael. Soc. Inverness*, **17**, 170.

New Statistical Account, see Anon.   1845

Nordmark, O.   1950   Om talltypens variation i Sydsverge. *Svenska SkogsvFören. Tidskr.*, **48** (4), 406.

Pardé, L.   1937   *Les Conifères.* Paris.

Paton, H. M. (editor)   1957   *Accounts of the Masters of Works for building and repairing royal palaces and castles. I. 1529-1615.* Edinburgh.

Pavari, A.   1955   Personal communication.

Peach, B. N. and   1917   The bone cave in the valley of Allt nan Uamh. *Proc. Roy. Soc. Edin.*, **37**, 327.

Penck, A. and Brückner, E.   1909   *Die Alpen im Eiszeitalten.* Leipzig. Also in Wright, W. P. 1937, q.v.

Penistan, M. J.   1942   The Caledonian pine forest. *Quart. J. For.*, **36** (2), 59.

PENNANT, T.	1771	*Tour of Scotland 1769.* Chester.
PENNINGTON, W.	1947	Lake sediments: Pollen diagrams from the bottom deposits of the north basin of Windermere. *Trans. Roy. Soc.*, B **233**, 137.
PETER, J.	1876	*The Peat Mosses of Buchan.* Aberdeen.
PHEMISTER, J.	1948	*British Regional Geology, Scotland: The Northern Highlands.* 2nd edn. Edinburgh.
PIGGOTT, S.	1949	*British Prehistory.* London.
	1954	*The Neolithic Cultures of the British Isles.* Cambridge.
POHL, F.	1939	Über eine älljahrlich blühende Waldkiefer. *Forstwiss. Zbl.*, **12** (61st year), 389.
PONT, T.	*c.* 1600	See Blaeu, J., 1654 and Macfarlane, W., 1908.
POSKIN, A.	1949	*Traité de silviculture.* 3rd edn. Paris.
PTOLEMY, —	*c.* A.D. 200	In Blaeu, J. 1654, q.v.
RAFN, J.	1915	*The Testing of Forest Seed during twenty-five years, 1887-1912.* Copenhagen.
RAMSAY, A.	1721	*The Tartana and the Plaid. The Works of Allan Ramsay.* Edinburgh.
READ, H. H.	1948	*British Regional Geology: The Grampian Highlands.* 2nd edn., revised by A. G. MacGregor. Edinburgh.
REHDER, A.	1912	*The Bradley Bibliography.* U.S.A.
	1940	*Manual of Cultivated Trees and Shrubs hardy in North America.* New York.
RICHARDS, P. W. and WALLACE, E. C.	1950	An annotated list of British mosses. *Trans. Brit. bryol. Soc.*, **1** (4). Appendix p. i.
RICHARDSON, H. G.	1921, 1922	Some remarks on British forest history, Parts I and II. *Trans. R. Scot, arb. Soc.*, **35** (2), 157; **36** (2), 174.
RICHENS, R. H.	1945	*Forest tree breeding and genetics.* Imperial Bureau of Plant Breeding and Genetics, Cambridge and Imperial Forestry Bureau, Oxford, joint publication No. 8.
RICHMOND, I.A.	1944	Gnaeus Iulius Agricola. *J. Roman Studies*, **34**, 34.
	1955 (*a*)	*Roman Britain.* London.
RICHMOND, I. A. and McINTYRE, J.	1939	The Agricolan Fort at Fendoch. *Proc. Soc. Antiq. Scot.*, **73**, 110.
RICHMOND, I. A. and ST. JOSEPH, J. R.	1955 (*b*)	In Roman Britain in 1954. *J. Roman Studies*, **45**, 121.
RIGHTER, F. I.	1945	*Pinus*; the relationship of seed size and seedling size to inherent vigour. *J. For.*, **43**, 131.
RINVALL, A.	1914	Ein Beitrag zur Kenntnis der sog. partiellen Variabilitat der Kiefer. *Acta. for. fenn.*, **3**, 1.
RITCHIE, J.	1920	*The Influence of Man on animal life in Scotland.* Cambridge.
RITCHIE, R. L. G.	1954	*The Normans in Scotland.* Edinburgh.
ROBAK, H.	1954	Personal communication.
ROBERTSON, J. (*naturalist*)	1767	MS. of Journal, chiefly for the north-east, covering the counties of Aberdeen, Inverness and Sutherland. National Library of Scotland.
	1771	MS. of Journal for Ross, Argyll, the rest of Inverness, and the hill districts of central Scotland. National Library of Scotland.

ROBERTSON, REV. J.   1794   *General View of the Agriculture in the Southern Districts of the County of Perth.* London.

1799   *General View of the Agriculture of the County of Perth.* Perth.

1808   *General View of the Agriculture of the County of Inverness-shire.* London.

ROBERTSON, W.   1725   Description of the Kincardin-Oneil parish, Aboyn and Glentanar parishes in Aberdeenshire. In Macfarlane, W. 1908, q.v.

ROGERS, C. (editor)   1879, 1880   *Rental Book of the Cistercian Abbey of Cupar-Angus,* 1 and 2. London.

ROSENBOHM, —   1882   *Schr. phys.-ökon. Ges. Königsb.,* **23,** 58.

ROY, W.   c. 1750   Map of Scotland. Sheet 15/2.

1793   *Military Antiquities of Roman Britain.* London.

RUBNER, K.   1934   *Die pflanzengeographischenökologischen Grundlagen des Waldbaus.* Neudamm.

1953   *Die pflanzengeographischen Grundlagen des Waldbaus.* Radebeul and Berlin.

1957   Über Kiefernrassen, insbesonders die nordostbayerische Höhen-kiefer. *Forstarchiv,* **28** (1), 1.

RUBNER, K. and REINHOLD, F.   1953   *Das natürliche Waldbild Europas als Grundlage für einen europäischen Waldbau.* Hamburg.

RUZICKA, —   1929   Ist der norddeutsche Kiefernsamen gegen die Schutte in Bohmen widerstandsfähiger als der einheimische? *Lesn. Pracé.,* **8,** 328.

RYLANDS, T. G.   1893   *The Geography of Ptolemy elucidated.* Dublin.

ST. JOSEPH, J. R.   1951   Air reconnaissance of North Britain. *J. Roman Studies,* **41,** 52.

1955   Air reconnaissance in Britain 1951-5. *J. Roman Studies,* **45,** 82.

SAMUELSSON, G.   1910   Scottish peat mosses. *Bull. Geol. Inst. Univ. Upsala,* **10,** 187.

SANIO, K.   1871   In Beissner, L. and Fitschen, J., 1930, q.v.

SCAMONI, A.   1955   Über den gegenwärtigen Stand unseres Wissens vom Pollenflug der Waldbäume. *Z. Forstgenet. Forstpflanz.,* **4,** 145.

SCHOTT, P. K.   1907   Rassen der gemeinen Kiefer, *Pinus sylvestris* L. *Forstwiss. Zbl.,* 262.

SCHREINER, E. J.   1956   Report on a reconnaissance of *Pinus sylvestris* in Spain. *Proceedings of the third north-eastern forest tree improvement conference, Cornell University, Ithaca, New York, August 30-31, 1955.*

SCHRIEBER, —   (1924)   In Büsgen, M., Münch, E. and Thomson, T., 1929, q.v.

SCHRÖTER, —   1895   *Arch. sc. phys. nat.,* **34,** 70.

SCHWAPPACH, A.   1897   Report on a visit to the forests of Scotland in August 1896. *Trans. R. Scot. arb. Soc.,* **15** (1), 11.

SCHWERIN, F.   1906   Notizen über Coniferen. *Mitt. deutsch. dendrol. Ges.,* **15,** 191.

1926   *Mitt. deutsch. dendrol. Ges.,* **36** (2), 350.

SECOND *Statistical Account* see Anon.   1845

SEITZ, D.   1926   Neue Gehölz- die Plattenkiefer und die Schuppenkiefer. *Mitt deutsch. dendrol. Ges.,* **37** (2), 349.

1929-38   Unsere Edelkiefern, I-VI. *Mitt. deutsch. dendrol. Ges.,* 1929, **41,** 150; 1930, **42,** 56; 1931, **43,** 364; 1933, **45,** 101; 1936, **48,** 146; 1938, **51,** 67.

SEITZ, D.   1937   Die Kiefernrassenzucht in Theorie und Praxis. *Mitt. Forstwirt. Forstwiss.*, **8**, 330 and 557.

SEITZ, W.   1927   *Edelrassen des Waldes.* IV. Berlin.

SELBY, J. G.   1842   *A History of British Forest Trees.* London.

SIMÁK, M.   1953 (a)   Über die Samenmorphologie der gemeinen Kiefer (*Pinus silvestris* L.). *Medd. SkogsforsknInst., Stockh.*, **43** (2), 1.

                      1953 (b)   Beziehungen zwischen Samengrösse und Samenzahl in verschieden grossen Zapfen eines Baumes (*Pinus silvestris* L.) *Medd. Skogsforskn-Inst., Stockh.*, **43** (8), 1.

SIMÁK, M. and   1954   Fröbeshaffenheten hos moderträd och ympar av tall. *Medd. Skogs-*
GUSTAFFSON, A.   *forsknInst., Stockh.*, **44** (2), 1.

SIMPSON, J. B.   1933   The late-glacial re-advance moraines of the Highland Border, west of the River Tay. *Trans. Roy. Soc. Edin.*, **57** 633.

SIMPSON, W. D.   1944   *The Province of Mar.* Aberdeen University Studies No. 121.

                      1949   *The Earldom of Mar.* Aberdeen University Studies No. 124. Aberdeen.

SINCLAIR, SIR JOHN   1791-9   *The Statistical Account of Scotland*, **1-21**. Edinburgh.
(editor)

SINCLAIR, J.   1905   *Schiehallion.* Stirling.

SKENE, W. F. (editor)   1867   *Chronicles of the Picts and Scots.* Edinburgh.

                      1872   *John of Fordun's Chronicle of the Scottish Nation.* Historians of Scotland, **4**. Edinburgh.

                      1876, 1890   *Celtic Scotland*, **1** and **2**. Edinburgh.

SMITH, A.   1874   On Aberdeenshire woods, forests and forestry. *Trans. Highl. agric. Soc. Scot.* 4th series, **6**, 264.

SMITH, A. L.   1918   *A Monograph of the British Lichens.* 2nd edn., **1** and **2**. London.

SMITH, M.   1951   *The British Amphibians and Reptiles.* London.

SORAUER, P.   1909   *Handbuch der Pflanzenkrankheiten*, **1-3**. Berlin.

SOWERBY, J. E.   1868   *English Botany*, **8**. London.

SPEED, J.   1611   *History of Great Britaine.* London.

Statistical Account, see
    Sinclair   1791-9

STECKI, K.   1937   Nowa forma sosny pospolitej. *Roczn. Nauk. rol.*, **41**, 217.

STEVEN, C.   1838   Pines found in the Taurian Caucasus. *Bull. Soc. Imp. Nature. Mosc.* Also in Loudon, J. C., 1839, q.v.

STEVEN, H. M.   1927   The silviculture of conifers in Great Britain. *Forestry*, **1** (1), 6.

STIRLING-MAXWELL, SIR   1910   The annual excursion. *Trans. R. Scot. arb. Soc.*, **24** (1), 73.
JOHN

STRABO   1854   *The Geography.* Trans. H. C. Hamilton and W. Falconer. London.

STRASBURGER, E.   1930   *Textbook of Botany.* London.

STROHMEYER, G.   1938   Über die Zuchterische Bedeutung des Tausendkorngewichts der Kiefer, I. *Forstarchiv*, **14**, 153.

STUART, J. S. and C. E.   1848   *Lays of the Deer-Forest*, **2**. Edinburgh.

SUESS, H. E.   1956   Absolute chronology of the last glaciation. *Science*, **123**, 355.

SUKATCHEV, V. H.	1938	*Dendrologia s osnovamic lesnoi geobotaniki.* Leningrad.
SUSMEL, L.	1954	Pino silvestre. *Monti e Boschi,* 11 and 12, 517.
SUTHERLAND, M.	1934	A microscopical study of the leaves of the genus *Pinus. Trans. N.Z. Inst.,* 63, 517.
SYLVEN, N.	1910	Material for the study of "racc" in forest trees. Some forms of Scots pine found in Sweden. *Medd. SkogsforsknInst., Stockh.,* 7, 175.
	1916	Den nordsvenska tallen. *Medd. f. stat. Skogsförsök.,* 13, 9.
SYNGE, F. M.	1956	The glaciation of the north-east of Scotland. *Scott. geog. Mag.,* 72, 129.
SYREITSCHIKOW, —	1930	In Beissner, L. and Fitschen, J., 1930.
TACITUS, C.	(1922, 1948)	*Agricola.* See Anderson, J. G. C. 1922; Mattingly, H. 1948.
TANSLEY, A. G.	1939, 1949	*The British Islands and their Vegetation.* Cambridge.
TAUBERT, —	1926	In Büsgen, M., Münch, E. and Thomson, T., 1929, q.v.
TAYLOR, —	1618	In Brown, P. H., 1891, q.v.
TETLEY, H.	1939	On the British polecats. *Proc. zool. Soc. Lond.,* 109B, 37.
THALENHORST, W.	1956	Biologischer Forstschutz: Therapie und Hygiene. *Forstarchiv,* 27, 217.
TOLSKY, A. P.	1913	In Wareing, P. F., 1950, q.v.
TROST, R. E.	1926	Eine Kiefernzapfen-Studie. *Deutsche Forstztg.,* Neudamm, 24 (41), 611.
TROUP, R. S.	1928, 1952	*Silvicultural Systems.* Oxford.
TUBEUF, C. F.	(1892)	In Lubbock, J., 1892, q.v.
	1897	*Die Nadelholzer.* Stuttgart.
TUBEUF, K. F. and SMITH, W. G.	1897	*Diseases of Plants.* London.
TURNER, SIR W	1895	On human and animal remains found in caves at Oban, Argyllshire. *Proc. Soc. Antiq. Scot.,* 29, 410.
VAZQUEZ, E. G.	1947	*Silvicultura.* 2nd edn. Dossat, S. A.
VEITCH, J.	1881, 1900	*Manual of the Coniferae.* London.
VICTORIA, QUEEN	1868	*Leaves from the Journal of our Life in the Highlands, from 1848 to 1861.* London.
	1884	*More leaves from the Journal of a Life in the Highlands, from 1862 to 1882.* 2nd edn.
VILMORIN, H. L. DE	1862	Exposé historique et descriptif de l'école forestière des Barres prés de Nogent-sur-Vernisson (Loiret). *Mem. Soc. Imper. Centr. d'Agric. Franç.*
VOYCHAL, P. I.	1946	K voprosu v sortirovanii semyan eli i sosnȳ. *Sborn. nauchno-issledov. Rabot Arkhangel, lesotekh. Inst.,* 8, 77. Also in *For. Abstr.,* 9 (2), 843.
WAGENKNECHT, E.	1939	Untersuchungen über den Speigelrindenanteil verschiedener Kiefernrassen in Zusammenhang mit der Ästigkeit. *Z. Forst- u. Jagdw.,* 71, 505.
WAHLENBERG, G.	1814	*Flora Carpatorum.* Göttingen.
WAINWRIGHT, F. T. (editor)	1955	*The Problem of the Picts.* Edinburgh.

346   BIBLIOGRAPHY

WALKER, J.   1808   *An Economical History of the Hebrides and Highlands of Scotland*, **1** and **2**. Edinburgh.

WALTON, J.   1949, 1956 The vegetation of the Park, in *Glenmore National Forest Park Guide*. Forestry Commission, London.

WANG CHI-WU   1954   Personal communication.

WAREING, P. F.   1949   Photoperiodic control of leaf growth and cambial activity in *Pinus silvestris* L. *Nature*, **163** (4150), 770.

                       1950   Growth studies on woody species, II; the effect of day length on the shoot growth of *Pinus silvestris* after the first year. *Physiol. Plant.*, Copenhagen, **3**, 300.

WATSON, E. V.   1955   *British Mosses and Liverworts*. Cambridge.

WATSON, H. C.   1832   *Outlines of the Distribution of British Plants*. London.

WATT, H. B.   1937   On the wild goat in Scotland. *J. Anim. Ecol.*, **5**, 116.

WHAYMAN, A.   1953   The Black Wood of Rannoch. *Scot. For.*, **7** (4), 112.

WHITE, F. B.   1898   *The Flora of Perthshire*. Edinburgh.

WIEDEMANN, E.   1930   Versuche über den Einfluss der Herkunft des Kiefernsamens. *Z. Forst- u. Jagdw.*, **62**, 498 and 809.

WILLKOMM, M.   1887   *Forstliche Flora von Deutschland und Österreich*. Leipzig.

WILLS, L. J.   1951   *A Palaeographical Atlas of the British Isles and adjacent parts of Europe*, London.

WITTROCK, V. B.   1889   *Hartman's Flora*. Stockholm.
                       1906   In Beissner, L. *Mitt. deutsch. dendrol. Ges.*, **15**, 86.

WODEHOUSE, P. I.   1935   Pollen grains. New York and London.

WOERLEIN, —   1893   *Ber. bayer. bot. Ges.*, **3**.

WOLDSTEDT, P.   1954   *Das Eiszeitalter, Grundlinien einer Geologie des Quartärs*, **1**. Stuttgart.

WRETLIND, J. E.   1936   Om orsakerna till krontypsvaxlingen hos den svenska tallen. *Norrlands SkogsvFörb. Tidskr.*, 44.

WRIGHT, W. B.   1914, 1937 *The Quaternary Ice Age*. London.

ZEDEBAUER, —   1916   In Büsgen, M., Münch, E. and Thomson, T., 1929, q.v.

ZEUNER, F. E.   1946, 1952 *Dating the Past*. London.

INDEX

Aberdeen readvance, 16.

Aberdeenshire, 5, 42, 43, 46, 94, 99, 105.

Abergeldie, 92.

Abernethy, 82, 84–7, 111–2, 114–20, 232–3, 320.
age structure, 119; and Kincardine, parish of, 114; climate, 117; fauna, 119–20; field layer communities, 118–9; geology and soils, 117–8; growth and stocking, 119; history, 115–7; location, 114; natural regeneration, 120; topography, 117; tree species and larger shrubs, 118.

Abies sp., 37.

Ablett, W. H., 229, 231.

Aboyne, 92, 93.
and Glentanar, parish of, 94.
Earl of, 95.

Acanthocinus aedilis, 83.

Accipiter nisus, 81, 124.

Achall, Loch, 212–3.

Achillea millefolium, 226, 321.

— *ptarmica*, 98, 142, 321.

Achnacarry, 165, 169.

Achnashellach, 67, 75, 79, 86, 190, 197, 199–202, 299, 321.
age structure, 201; climate, 200; fauna, 201; field layer communities, 201; geology and soils, 200; growth and stocking, 201; history, 199; location, 199; natural regeneration, 202; topography, 200; tree species and larger shrubs, 201.

Acts of Parliament of Scotland, 54, 56, 125, 192.

adder, see *Vipera berus*.

Adelges, pine, 83.

Aegithalos caudatus, 81, 169.

Aeneas Sylvius, see Pius II.

Affric, see Glen Affric.
Loch, 177–8, 180–1.

age structure (of pinewoods), 76, 98, 104, 109, 119, 123–4, 128, 132–3, 134, 135, 142, 146–7, 154–5, 159, 163, 168–9, 171–2, 175, 181, 184, 186–7, 188–9, 195, 199, 201, 204, 211, 214–16, 221, 224, 226–7.

Agricola, G.I., 45–6.

Agrostis, 72–3, 142, 308, 313, 315.

— *canina*, 321.

— *stolonifera*, 321.

— *tenuis*, 308, 313, 315, 321.

Ahlmann, H. A., 16.

Ajuga reptans, 159, 168, 321.

Alchemilla alpina, 75, 109, 132, 135, 321.

— *vulgaris* agg., 321.

alder, see *Alnus*.

Alexander III, King of Scotland, 51.

Alladale, River, 208–11.

Allerød period, 22, 24, 26, 39.

Alltcailleach Forest, 88–9, 92.

Alnus, 27–38, 43, 48, 52, 69–70, 112.

— *glutinosa*, 69, 70, 93, 97, 103, 108, 118, 123, 128, 132, 135, 138–9, 141, 146, 152–3, 155, 157–8, 163, 167, 170–1, 175, 180, 183, 186, 188, 194, 198, 201, 204, 210, 214–5, 218, 221, 224, 226, 320.

Alps, 2, 55, 234, 280.
Austrian, 2.
Engadine, 236.
glaciation in, 7, 11, 14, 16–7.
Maritime, 2.

Alvie, parish of, 129.

Amat, 74, 87, 206, 207–12.
age structure, 211; climate, 209; fauna, 211; field layer communities, 210–11; geology and soils, 209–10; growth and stocking, 211; history, 208–9; location, 207; natural regeneration, 212; topography, 209; tree species and larger shrubs, 210.

America, North, 23, 51, 296.

Amur, River, 2.

Anas platyrhynchos, 81.

Anatolia, 2.

Ancylus, Lake, 19.

Andersen, K. F., 63.

Anderson, A. O., 51.
J., 40.
J. G. C., 123, 128.
(editor), 45.
M. L. and Fairbairn, W. A., 61, 96, 103, 117, 122, 127, 152, 157, 162, 166, 178, 183, 185, 188, 193, 197, 202, 209, 213, 220, 225.
W. *et al.*, 61.

Anemone nemorosa, 142, 321.

Angles, immigrant, 50.

Anguis fragilis, 82, 99.

Angus, 46.

Anić, M., 1–2.

Anne, Queen, 138.

Antennaria dioica, 312, 321.

Anthoxanthum odoratum, 72–3, 306, 308, 313, 315, 321.

Antitrichia curtipendula, 181, 326.

Antonine Wall, 47.

ants, see *Formica rufa*.

This Book belongs to the Sparsholt College Library.